DATE DUE

May 12 66			
Dec 5 '66			
Feb 8 '67			
Feb 14 '67			
Nov 22 68			
Dec 13, 68			
Feb 18 '69			
Mar 4 '69			
Feb 23 '71			
GAYLORD			PRINTED IN U.S.A.

ALSO BY

CARLETON S. COON

THE ORIGIN OF RACES
(*1962*)

THE STORY OF MAN
(*1954, 1962*)

THE SEVEN CAVES
(*1957*)

These are BORZOI BOOKS,
published by ALFRED A. KNOPF *in New York*

The Living Races of Man

THE
LIVING RACES
OF MAN

by CARLETON S. COON

with EDWARD E. HUNT, Jr.

19  65

NEW YORK: ALFRED · A · KNOPF

L. C. catalog card number: 65–18765

THIS IS A BORZOI BOOK,

PUBLISHED BY ALFRED A. KNOPF, INC.

53350

FIRST EDITION

april '66

La pensée ne doit jamais se soumettre,
ni à un dogme, ni à un parti, ni à une
passion, ni à un intérêt, ni à une idée
préconçue, ni à quoi que ce soit, si ce
n'est aux faits eux-mêmes, parce que,
pour elle, se soumettre, ce serait
cesser d'être

Henri Poincaré

INTRODUCTION
AND ACKNOWLEDGMENTS

In 1956 I began to write this book, but in 1959 it dawned on me that it was really two books and I spent the next three years preparing *The Origin of Races*. Since then the present book has taken shape. It can be read without reference to the first volume, which covers primarily the evolution of the living races of man. In this book the history of each race is briefly reviewed, and most of the pages are devoted to describing the physical attributes of the races and to trying to explain the differences between them.

In the introduction to the first book I stated my intention to discuss in this one racial differences in blood groups and the anatomy of the brain, but only blood groups have been covered. Racial differences in the brain imply differences in intelligence, a subject so laden with emotion that its mere mention evokes unsolicited acclaim and feverish denunciation. Even without reference to the brain or to intelligence, the simple statement that races exist drives a small coterie of vocal critics into a predictable and well-publicized frenzy.

I hope but do not expect that all reviewers will read the whole book and not just this introduction and the final chapter. I also formally request that no one shall quote or cite this book as ammunition for or against any cause or movement whatsoever, because, as any reader can see, I have tried throughout to adhere to the principles clearly stated in the preceding quotation from Henri Poincaré. If anyone quotes, praises, or denounces the book or myself because of some fancied adherence to any dogma, cause, emotion, personal interest, or preconceived idea, I shall conclude that he cannot read simple and beautiful French, or even plain English.

Between 1956 and 1959 and after 1962 Edward E. Hunt, Jr., of Harvard and the Forsyth Dental Infirmary of Boston has cooperated with me at various times in preparing the material for the more technical sections of this book, particularly in Chapters 8 and 9. He has also worked on Chapter 10. Because his skull is packed with a prodigious index file of references to physical anthropology, his ambulant bibliography has saved me much time. It would be inappropriate for me to thank him here as he is a member of the team.

But I feel free to express my gratitude to the geneticist Richard H. Post, of the University of Michigan, who read every word of the manuscript, criticized it constructively, and contributed valuable ideas. My thanks go equally to William C. Boyd of Boston University, a giant in the field of blood groups, who concentrated on Chapter 9. If the hematological umbrella which Boyd has raised over the present treatment of his subject leaks, I inadvertently punched the holes in it.

During the summer of 1964 John L. Pratt, M.D., worked with me here in West Gloucester on racial differences in human skin. Parts of his findings are incorporated in Chapter 8. Some of the weather maps which appear in that chapter were made possible by the kindness of Helmut Landsberg, Chief of Climatology of the United States Weather Bureau.

Although linguistics is a specialized subject remote from physical anthropology, it had to be mentioned in this book because it is used in tracing cultural movements and because many tribes and nations are identified by what they speak. In this field I am indebted to Charles F. Hockett of Cornell, a sample of whose lucid prose appears on pages 40–2; to Thomas A. Sebeok of the University of Indiana; to George L. Trager of the University of Buffalo; and to Joseph L. Greenberg of Stanford University.

The maps were drawn by Vincent Kotschar, who is by training an anthropologist, a geographer, and a cartographer. Lisa D. Coon and he prepared the figures. The photographs, which come from many sources, vary in quality because some of them were taken in the previous century, of people now scattered or extinct, and have been copied from prints.

I am deeply indebted to Mrs. Marjorie D. Jackson and Mrs. Sarah G. Smith for filing, typing, and trying to keep the contents of my study in order. Mrs. Jackson also selected the words to be defined in the glossary.

Miss Cynthia Griffin and Miss Margaret Currier, librarians of the University Museum of the University of Pennsylvania and the Peabody Museum of Harvard, respectively, were as generous of their time and special knowledge in this book as in the last one.

In preparing *The Origin of Races* I was aided by several grants from the Wenner-Gren Foundation, one from the National Science Foundation (NSF 03912), and a contract with the United States Air Force AF33(616) 6306. As the present book terminates the original project, I repeat my expressions of gratitude.

Also, the editor of the New York Academy of Sciences has permitted me to publish a paraphrase on my article "The Taxonomy of Human Variation," which will appear shortly, if it has not already appeared, in their *Proceedings*.

Finally I wish to express my gratitude to my publishers on both sides of the Atlantic and particularly to Harold Strauss and Sophie Wilkins of Alfred A. Knopf, Inc., and to G. Wren Howard and Michael Howard of Jonathan Cape Ltd.

CARLETON S. COON

West Gloucester, Massachusetts
June 9, 1965

CONTENTS

PLATES

Where no credit is given, the photograph is by Carleton S. Coon

FOLLOWING PAGE 320

CIRCUMPOLAR PEOPLES

THE AUSTRALOIDS

THE AFRICANS

FIGURES

MAPS

DRAWN BY VINCENT KOTSCHAR

TABLES

PERIODICALS
AND THEIR ABBREVIATIONS

AA	*American Anthropologist,* Washington
AAE	*Archivio per l'Antropologia e la Etnologia,* Florence
AAnz	*Anthropologischer Anzeiger,* Stuttgart
ActG	*Acta Genetica et Statistica Medica,* Basel
AEASH	*Acta Ethnographica Academiae Scientarum Hungaricae,* Budapest
AfA	*Archiv für Anthropologie,* Brunswick
AFRICA	*Journal of the International Institute of African Languages and Cultures,* London
AfA	*Archiv für Völkerkunde,* Vienna
AGMG	*Acta Geneticae Medicae et Gemellologicae,* Rome
AHG	*Annals of Human Genetics,* London
AHR	*American Historical Review,* Boston
AINA	*Arctic Institute of North America, Anthropology of the North, Translations from Russian Sources,* Toronto
AJHG	*American Journal of Human Genetics,* New York
AJPA	*American Journal of Physical Anthropology,* Philadelphia
AJS	*Australian Journal of Science,* Sydney
AL	*Anthropological Linguistics,* Bloomington, Indiana
AMAAO	*American Medical Association, Archives of Ophthalmology,* New York
AMN	*American Museum Novitates,* New York
AN	*American Naturalist,* Lancaster, Pennsylvania
ANTHROPO-LOGICA	Ottawa
ANTHROPOL-OGIE	Prague
ANTHROPOL-OGIST	(*The Anthropologist*), Delhi
ANTHROPOS	Fribourg, Switzerland
ANTIQUITY	Cambridge, England

ANYA	*Annals of the New York Academy of Science*, New York
AOL	*Acta Otolaryngologica*, Stockholm
AOMA	*Acts of the Ophthalmological Medical Association* (in Japanese), Tokyo
AOS	*Acta Orthopaedica Scandinavica*, Oslo
AOSS	*Acta Orthopaedica Scandinavica, Supplementum*, Oslo
AP	*Asian Perspectives*, Hongkong
APak	*Ancient Pakistan*, Karachi
APAM	*Anthropological Papers of the American Museum of Natural History*, New York
APMA-M	*Anthropological Publications of the Museum of Anthropology, University of Michigan*, Ann Arbor
APUA	*Anthropological Papers of the University of Alaska*, Fairbanks
AR	*Anatomical Record*, Philadelphia
ASAG	*Archives Suisses d'Anthropologie Générale*, Geneva
ASBM	*Annales de la Société Belge de Médicine Tropicale*, Antwerp
AWLM	*Akademie der Wissenschaften und der Literatur in Mainz, Abhandlungen der Mathematisch-Naturwissenschaftlichen Klasse*, Mainz
BAE	*Bureau of American Ethnology, Annual Report*, Washington, D.C.
BASI	*Bulletin of the Archaeological Survey of India*, Calcutta
BBNH	*Bulletin of the British Museum (Natural History)*, London
BDAI	*Bulletin of the Department of Anthropology*, Calcutta
BDGA	*Bericht der deutschen Gesellschaft für Anthropologie*, Berlin
Belleten	*Belleten Türk Tariha Kurumu Basimevi*, Ankara
Biometrika	London
BIRSB	*Bulletin de l'Institut Royal des Sciences naturelles de Belgique*, Brussels
BJSM	*British Journal of Social Medicine*, London
BMJ	*British Medical Journal*, London
BMSA	*Bulletins et Mémoires de la Société d'Anthropologie*, Paris
BPMB	*Berenice P. Bishop Museum Bulletin*, Honolulu
BSGA	*Bulletin der Schweizerischen Gesellschaft für Anthropologie und Ethnologie*, Zurich

BSGI	*Bulletin du Service Geologique de l'Indochine*, Hanoi
BSS	*Bulletin de la Société Suisse d'Anthropologie et d'Ethnologie*, Geneva
CA	*Current Anthropology*, Chicago
CIAO	*Conferencia Internacional dos Africanistas Ocidentais*, Lisbon
CIWP	*Carnegie Institution of Washington Publications*, Washington, D.C.
CMES	*Ceylon Museum Ethnographic Series*, Colombo
CNRS	*Centre National de la Récherche Scientifique*, Paris
CR	*China Reconstructs*, Peiping
CSHS	*Cold Spring Harbor Symposia on Quantitative Biology*, Cold Spring Harbor, N.Y.
CUCA	*Columbia University Contributions to Anthropology*, New York
ELM	*Eugenics Laboratory Memoirs*, London
EQ	*Eugenics Quarterly*, New York
ETHNOLOGY	Pittsburgh, Pennsylvania
FMAS	*Field Museum of Natural History, Anthropological Series*, Chicago
FSAC	*Folia Scientifica Africae Centralis*, Bukavu
GH	*Geographica Helvetica*, Zurich
GR	*Geographical Review*, New York
GS	*Göttinger Studien*, Göttingen
HAS	*Harvard African Studies*, Cambridge, Mass.
HASR	*Herald of the Academy of Science of the USSR*, Moscow
HB	*Human Biology*, Detroit
HG	*Humangenetik, Human Genetics, Génétique Humaine*, Berlin–Heidelberg–New York
HMAB	*Harvard Medical Alumni Bulletin*, Boston
HOMO	Mainz
IIA-ANUS	*Institut Istorii i Arkheologii Akademiia Nauk Uzbekskoi SSSR*, Moscow
IJAL	*International Journal of American Linguistics*, Bloomington, Indiana

IEM-ANG	*Institut Eksperimentalnoĭ Morfologii im. A. N. Natish-vili Akademii Nauk Gruzinskoĭ CCR*, Tiflis
IKO	*Izvestiia Kavkazskikh Otdelenia Russkogo Geografichesko Obschestva*, Tiflis
ISKF	*Institutet for Sammenlingende Kulturforskning, Skrifter, Serie B*, Oslo
JAP	*Journal of Applied Physiology*, Washington
JASC	*Journal of the Asiatic Society*, Calcutta
JCS	*Journal of the College of Science*, Imperial University of Tokyo, Tokyo
JJP	*Japanese Journal of Physiology*, Nagoya
JNCB-RAS	*Journal of the North China Branch of the Royal Asiatic Society*, Shanghai
JNH	*The Journal of Negro History*, Washington
JNS	*Journal of Nutritional Supplement*, Karachi
JOSA	*Journal of the Optical Society of America*, Lancaster, Pennsylvania
JRAI	*Journal of the Royal Anthropological Institute*, London
JSK	*Jinrugaku Senshigaku Koza*, Tokyo
JWAS	*Journal of the Washington Academy of Sciences*, Washington, D.C.
KVII	*Koninklijke Vereeniging Indisch Institut (Afdeling)*, Amsterdam
LANCET	*The Lancet*, London
L'ANTH	*L'Anthropologie*, Paris
MAN	*Royal Anthropological Institute*, London
MBM	*Memoirs of the Berenice P. Bishop Museum*, Honolulu
MIPA	*Materiałow i Prac Antropologiznych, Miscellanea IX*, Wrocław
MIRCB	*Mémoires, Institut Royal du Congo Belge*, Brussels
MIRSN	*Mémoires de l'Institut Royal des Sciences Naturelles de Belgique*, Brussels
MM	*Mankind Monographs*, Edinburgh
MMRH	*Mémoires du Musée Royal d'Histoire Naturelle de Belgique*, Brussels
MMUM	*Museum Monographs*, University Museum, University of Pennsylvania, Philadelphia

MR	*Meteorologische Rundschau,* Berlin
MSAE	*Memorias, Serie Antropologica e Etnologica,* Lisbon
NATURE	London
NG	*National Geographic Magazine,* Washington, D.C.
NH	*Natural History,* New York
NO	*The National Observer,* Silver Springs, Maryland
NYAS-SP	*New York Academy of Sciences, Special Publications,* New York
NYT	*The New York Times,* New York
OCEANIA	Sydney, Australia
PAPS	*Proceedings of the American Philosophical Society,* Philadelphia
PBM	*Perspectives in Biology and Medicine,* Chicago
PMP	*Peabody Museum Papers,* Cambridge, Mass.
PNB	*Psychiatrische en neurologische bladen,* Amsterdam
PNYAS	*Proceedings of the New York Academy of Sciences,* New York
PRGS-SA	*Proceedings of the Royal Geographical Society, South Australian Branch,* Adelaide
PS-D	*Paleontologica Sinica, Series D,* Peking
PSJ	*Polynesian Society Journal,* Auckland
PSRGE	*Publications de la Société Rogale de géographie d'Égypte*
PTPA	*Proceedings of the Third Pan-African Congress on Prehistory,* London
QRB	*Quarterly Review of Biology,* Washington, D.C.
QUATERNARIA	Rome
RA	*Rivista di Antropologia,* Rome
RGA	*Revista Geográfica Americana,* Buenos Aires
RQVM	*Records of the Queen Victoria Museum,* Launcestown, Tasmania
RR	*Radical Review,* New Bedford, Mass.
RSAM	*Records of the South Australia Museum,* Adelaide
RTPM	*Russian Translation Series, Peabody Museum,* Cambridge, Mass.

SA   *Scientific American*, New York

SAAB   *South African Archaeological Bulletin*, Cape Town

SCIENCE   Washington, D.C.

SEP   *Saturday Evening Post*, Philadelphia

SIBA   *Smithsonian Institution, Bureau of American Ethnology, Bulletin*, Washington, D.C.

SMC   *Smithsonian Miscellaneous Collections*, Washington, D.C.

SMU-CPN   *Southern Methodist University, Contributions to the Prehistory of Nubia*, Dallas

SNVA   *Skrifter utgitt av Det Norske Videnskaps-Akademi i Oslo, I, Mat.-Naturv. Klasse*, Oslo

SoA   *Sovietskaya Arkheologiya*, Moscow

SoMJ   *Southern Medical Journal*, Birmingham, Alabama

SSF-CB   *Societas Scientarum Fennica, Commentationes Biologicae*, Helsinki

SWJA   *Southwestern Journal of Anthropology*, Albuquerque

TAPS   *Transactions of the American Philosophical Society*, Philadelphia

TESA   *Trabajos de la Escuela de Sociología y Antropología*, Caracas

TIE   *Trudi Instituta Etnografii SSSR*, Moscow

TMOIP   *Trudi Moscovskogo Obshschestva Ispitateli Prirodi*, Moscow

TRST   *Transactions of the Royal Society of Tropical Medicine and Hygiene*, London

VFPA   *Viking Fund Publications in Anthropology*, New York

WW   *Wen-Wu*, Peiping

YPA   *Yearbook of Physical Anthropology*, Wenner-Gren Foundation, New York

ZZ   *Zinruikagu Zassi*, Tokyo

The Living Races of Man

1

Races Old and New

✕✕✕

We Are Numerous and Variable

At least seasonally or temporarily the human ani-
mal inhabits every continent and almost every island on which it
can find enough to drink, and it can be seen with the naked eye,
with radar, or with some other device on and under both land and
sea, in the air, and occasionally in outer space. It is thus adapted to
survive in all of the major media occupied by other living species
of animals, and is exploring a new one. Its species, *Homo sapiens*
[Linn.], numbers about three billion individuals, probably more
than any other species of land animal of equal or greater body
size. This means that in a biological sense we have so far been a
great success in the struggle for life.

Human beings also vary racially to an unusual degree. In some
entire tribes or nations nearly everyone's skin is chocolate brown.
In others most skins are pale pink. Some races are characterized by
straight hair, whereas the hair of others is tightly coiled. At
least two populations are noted for large deposits of fat held out
in apparent defiance of gravity by an inner network of fibrous
tissue. This fat is on their buttocks. A number of whole tribes and
segments of races are dwarfs. In visible, external, mostly heritable
physical characteristics, human beings vary more from place to
place and race to race than any other mammalian species, except
those that men have altered by domesticating them, most notably
dogs.

Wild animals vary geographically. Populations of warm-blooded animals of a given species that live in cold places tend to have larger bodies than other populations of the same species living in warm places. The opposite is true of cold-blooded animals; the big snakes live in the tropics. Among warm-blooded species that live in cold climates, special adaptations provide insulation, increase peripheral blood flow, or both, thus enabling them to survive the winter. Some groups of people are similarly adapted to a certain extent, although for severe cold we must rely on protection furnished by our hands and our brain.

We Choose Our Mates

LIKE US, domestic animals vary by breed, but without any close correlation with climate because we protect them. And unlike wild animals, which mate mostly at random, the mates of domestic animals are chosen by people, who breed them for some special purpose: to provide abundant milk or eggs; to grow long fine wool; to pull badgers out of holes; or to win prizes at shows.

In human societies that are technologically advanced enough to keep domestic animals other than dogs, usually there is also some kind or degree of division of labor, carrying with it a tendency for selective mating to perpetuate families and communities of specialists. In regions where iron is mined, smelted, and forged by hand—jobs requiring both strength and skill—apprentice smiths are likely to marry their masters' daughters. From these unions special breeds of smiths arise. If these smiths leave home to practice their craft in alien lands, as many of them do, it is easiest and most convenient for them to marry inside their own group, particularly if they are racially different from their customers. Situations like this tend to perpetuate racial differences.

But right in our own society and within our own race (we speak for the moment as Caucasoid Americans), although many young people no longer feel obliged to ask their parents' permission to marry they still tend to wed homogamously; that is, like marry like. Education, income bracket, social class, IQ levels attained in childhood before the couple had met,[1] body size, pigmentation, and of course religion, major racial category, and national origin all influence mating, even today. We do not select our mates as

1 J. N. Spuhler: "Empirical Studies on Quantitative Human Genetics," in *The Use of Vital and Health Statistics for Genetic and Radiation Studies* (New York: United Nations; 1962), pp. 241–50.

purposefully as we do those of our dogs, or for the same reasons, but we select them or are selected by them just the same. And we have every reason to believe that some kind of selection has been taking place as long as the institution of the family has existed, which is a long, long time. Along with geography, homogamy, a product of culture, is responsible for the unusual variability of human races.

The Concept of Race

IN THE PAST there has been much confusion about the meaning of *race* and there still is. In more than one reputable atlas still in circulation, Finland on a racial map of the world is colored yellow for Mongoloid—which Finns are not—simply because they share a linguistic stock with some Asiatic peoples who are partly, and others who are wholly, Mongoloid. No less a scholar than our honorary fellow citizen the late Sir Winston Churchill called the British a race. Because of their religion, Jews have also been called a race. In a sense, linguistic affinity, common residence on an island, and the possession of a family religion tend to impede the flow of genetic material between groups of people, but not necessarily to a race-forming degree. Finns, Britons, and Jews are, in nearly all instances,[2] Caucasoids.

Race is a zoological concept meaning a division of a species. A species is a collection of animals that will breed together when they get a chance and will not breed with other animals—whether they can do so successfully or not—except in desperation or by mistake. All human populations, unless incompatible in certain blood groups, are capable of producing fertile mixed offspring,[3] and this incompatibility can also inhibit reproduction within races. The question of interbreeding with other related species does not arise in our case because we have many genetic differences from our closest kin, the apes, as suggested by the different chromosome counts between us and them.

[2] Except, of course, for some recent Commonwealth immigrants in Britain, and a few exotic remnants of early Jewish expansion and proselytism, like the Falasha of Ethiopia.

[3] As we shall explain in greater detail in Chapter 9, a blood *group* is a system of genetic variables, like the ABO system or the Rhesus system. A blood *type* is a single variable within such a system, such as AB in the ABO group, or *cde* (Rhesus negative) in the Rhesus group.

Naming the Races of Man

EVERY KNOWN SPECIES has a name, as for example *Panthera tigris,* the tiger. The first word in the name indicates the genus, which more often than not has more than one species. *Panthera leo,* the lion, and several other big cats, are genus mates of the tiger. Below the species level is the subspecies, or geographical race, usually indicated by a third word, as in *Panthera tigris virgata,* the Caspian tiger.

The living races of man have been given formal Latin subspecific third names by some scientists. And according to the international rules of zoological nomenclature, the names first designated have priority and should be the ones used. Linnaeus, who started this system, named four—*americanus, europaeus, asiaticus,* and *afer,* the fourth designating Negroes. Other scientists have added a host of new Latin names, creating little but confusion.

There is no general agreement even on the number of races in man, let alone which peoples belong to which. Under the circumstances, many of us feel that in the case of man the rules should be suspended until we can agree on the number and distribution of subspecies. After that, someone can sort out the existing third names, match them for duplications, and select them by order of priority, concocting new ones if there are gaps. Because of current conflicting attitudes toward race in the public mind, however, such an agreement is not likely to be reached very soon.

In this book we shall follow the racial classification proposed in 1962 in *The Origin of Races.* This nomenclature is based both on the living races and on the continuity of racial criteria in the available skeletal remains in each of the major zoogeographical regions of the Old World inhabited during the Pleistocene, without regard for the criteria of evolutionary stages through which each of these regional subspecies passed during that time.

The proposed subspecies are Caucasoid, Mongoloid, Australoid, Congoid, and Capoid.[4] The last two are both African. The Congoids are Negroes and Pygmies. The Capoids are the Bushmen and, in a mixed state, the Hottentots, Korana, and Sandawe (of Tanzania). Like the Congoid, the Australoid subspecies is further divided

[4] The late R. R. Gates in his book *Human Ancestry* (Cambridge, Mass.: Harvard University Press; 1948), on page 367, proposed the same general classification into the same five major groups. But he called *Homo sapiens* not a species, but a superspecies. According to his system, our subspecies are species.

into full-sized Australoids and hereditary dwarfs usually called Negritos. It is possible that both kinds of hereditary dwarfs, Pygmies and Negritos, include two or more populations that became independently dwarfed. Enclaves of short-statured people may be found in other subspecies, particularly the Mongoloid, as for example among the Maya Indians of the Guatemala highlands and in some mountain villages of Colombia. But their small stature is probably comparable to the small stature formerly found in some of the isolated Alpine villages of Switzerland, where this condition has been virtually eliminated by improvements in health and nutrition and by a reduction of inbreeding. Such peoples are not racial dwarfs.

What terms shall we use, then, to designate for the time being the five full-sized subspecies and the two dwarfed subspecies? We propose to call all seven *races*, for the following reasons. In the first place, certain writers, particularly the specialists in blood-groups, refuse to separate the Bushmen from the Negroes, despite many morphological differences, because of a general similarity in blood. Although we do not at present agree with this, we grant that the status of the Bushmen is still open. In the second place, the pygmies and Negritos may really be subspecies themselves and indeed may constitute more than two subspecies; how many we do not know. The pygmy chimpanzee, a comparable primate, is given taxonomic status ranging from genus to subspecies. *Race* is a well-known word notable for its vagueness, but it is precise enough in these instances for our present state of knowledge.

Racial Intermediates in Clines New and Old

N o t e v e r y p e r s o n in the world can be tapped on the shoulder and told: "You belong to such and such a race," and this fact has made some people think that there are no races at all.[5] Ever since man first spread over the earth, interracial contacts have taken place between the populations of neighboring geographical regions, with consequent genetic exchange that has produced racially intermediate, or so-called *clinal*, populations.

Physical anthropologists who have studied the vast sweep of

[5] For two expositions of this point of view, and some refutations thereof, see Frank B. Livingstone: "On the Non-existence of Human Races," CA, Vol. 3, No. 3 (1962), pp. 279–81, including comments by T. Dobzhansky, and the author's reply. See also C. L. Brace: "On the Race Concept," CA, Vol. 5, No. 4 (1964), pp. 313–20, including comments by six other persons, and the author's reply.

human evolution know that such genetic exchanges must have been going on for a very long time. Within some anciently inhabited continental or subcontinental regions the marginal distribution of relatively high frequencies of certain inherited features support this conviction, as indicated by careful studies. In Europe, which is the best example, curly hair, freckling, blood type B, and the so-called "African" Rh blood type *cDe*, are curiously common on the northern and western peripheries, suggesting very ancient contacts across the Strait of Gibraltar or via Suez or both. The marginal distribution of these traits suggests that the genes that control them have in their present location lost their original selective values and are simply retained in low frequencies through a combination of local inbreeding and relaxation of selection.

Other clines within racial homelands may simply reflect the continuous action of environmental selection in special climatic regions. Fair skin, blue eyes, and blond hair are concentrated in northwestern Europe and decrease in frequency quite regularly as one moves southward and eastward. A pigment map of Europe closely resembles a weather map showing the number of cloudy days each year. The simplest explanation of this coincidence is probably that skin color, the key variable, is somehow dependent on the amount of ultraviolet radiation penetrating the atmosphere.

It so happens that the area of greatest blondism, because it was previously covered with ice, was uninhabited until less than 10,000 years ago. This means that blondism in Europe may be less than 10,000 years old, or that the ancestors of the northwestern Europeans formerly lived in a cloudy periglacial region or regions farther south, and that when they moved north they were already as blond as their descendants are now. Until geneticists can establish the rate of selection favoring depigmented skin in cloudy regions, we will not know.

Interracial clines that are for the most part no more than 10,000 years old are the Negro-Caucasoid cline in Africa and the Mongoloid-Australoid one in Southeast Asia, Indonesia, and the Pacific Islands. They differ from intraracial clines in that they involve more genetic variables and also tend to leave telltale pockets of ancient peoples in refuge areas, some of whom have become dwarfs. In the New World a Mongoloid-Caucasoid cline, that of the Mestizos, blankets large areas of Latin America, and Congoid-Caucasoid clinal populations of relatively recent origin are to be seen in several countries in the New World, particularly the United States, where with the northward movement of Negroes to the cities it has become microgeographical.

Thus, if we grant that clinal populations are just as real as populations of nuclear racial regions, we can give everyone a racial name after all. The difference is one of time multiplied by the intensities of numerous forces of natural selection. Given sufficient time and privacy to stew in their own genetic juices, clinal populations will become new races, just as the old races did.

The Numerical Inequality of Races

SOME COUNTRIES do not take a census, and other countries that do, even though they may be racially variable make no accurate racial distinctions. It is therefore impossible to calculate with much accuracy the size of the present populations of the different races. Nevertheless, demographers and cartographers who specialize in this problem have produced some reasonable approximations. In Table 1 the clinal populations have been divided, as if by Solomon, among their parent races; hence the use of the word *predominantly*.

Because the Australoids and Capoids are so few in number, the figures for them include all the putatively mixed-blooded members. Even then they constitute less than one half of one percent, so the special treatment accorded them will not appreciably affect the results. All but the Capoids are given in round millions; the Capoids are in round thousands.

The disparity in numbers seen in these figures does not mean that the races were always unequal in this respect. If we calculate

TABLE 1

THE APPROXIMATE NUMBER OF PERSONS IN EACH RACE*

Predominantly Caucasoid	1,757,000,000	55.7%
Predominantly Mongoloid	1,171,000,000	37.1
Predominantly Congoid	216,000,000	6.8
Australoid	13,000,000	.4
Capoid	126,000	.004
	3,157,126,000	100.004%

* These figures are broadly adapted from the work of Vincent Kotschar, formerly of the Western Printing and Lithographing Company of Poughkeepsie, New York, for use in connection with a map for an atlas entitled *The Odyssey Press World Atlas* (New York: Odyssey Press; 1965).

the area of the cradleland of each race and multiply by a reasonable figure for population density among food-gatherers, it might well be shown that the races were nearly equal during the Pleistocene.

The differences are due to several factors. At the end of the Pleistocene the Caucasoids and Mongoloids expanded their territories. Intensive agriculture followed by industry led to an even greater increase, as did colonization. In Ireland, for example, the introduction of the white potato had far-reaching effects along these lines.[6] After the adoption of this new foodstuff, the population grew from 3,200,000 in 1754 to 8,175,000 in 1846, not counting about 1,750,000 more who had migrated in the meanwhile, a trebling in less than a century. This phenomenon is not confined to man. We cite this example to show that the biological and taxonomic importance of the different races is not a function of their numbers. In this book each will receive equal attention insofar as useful information is available.

Conventional Descriptions of Races

A RACE, let us repeat, is a major segment of a species, originally occupying, since the first dispersal of mankind, a large, geographically unified, and distinct region, and touching on the territories of other races only by relatively narrow corridors. Within such a region each race acquired its distinctive genetic attributes— both its visible physical appearance and its invisible biological properties—through the selective forces of all aspects of the environment, including culture. After having become differentiated in this fashion, each race filled out its space, resisting, because of its superior local adaptation, the encroachment of outsiders with whom it mixed, from time to time if not continuously, along its borders.

Until the emergence of modern genetics, physical appearance was the chief vehicle of racial description. First it took the form of generalizations, as in a Linnaean zoological categorization. Then physical anthropologists made measurements and statistical analyses of racially variable characteristics in significantly large samples of populations. The results of these procedures are summarized in the fairly detailed racial descriptions—with allowances for variations—that follow.

6 W. L. Langer: "Europe's Initial Population Explosion," AHR, Vol. 69, No. 1 (1963), pp. 1–17.

In all of these descriptions we face the problem of allowing for artificial alterations to the human body. Some alterations, like haircuts, body painting, tattooing, scarification, and stretching earlobes, lips, and necks, deceive no one. Others, such as clever hair bleaching and head-flattening through cradling, have deceived certain well-known anthropologists. We shall try not to be fooled.

Caucasoids. Skin is fair in most of Europe, usually darker in Western Asia[7] and India, and becoming almost black in Bengal and southern India. The color of the iris ranges from blue to dark brown. Hair is for the most part straight or wavy. Faces and noses range from narrow and beaked to broad and snubbed. Lips are usually thin and rarely very everted. Teeth are usually small to medium, jaws seldom prognathous, chins usually more or less prominent. In males, beard and body hair is variable but usually well developed. Balding is frequent; graying tends to set in early. Body build is variable, trunks relatively long, and calf muscles usually prominently developed.

Mongoloids. Skin color varies regionally with latitude in both Asia and the Americas from a sallow brunette white to reddish brown. Eyes are brown; hair is black, with red undertones in some populations. Hair is straight and coarse and grows long on the head but is sparse on body and beard. Mongoloids rarely become bald and do not turn gray until an advanced age, if at all. They have "high cheekbones"; that is, the facial bones immediately below and to the side of the eye sockets protrude both forward and laterally. They also have "slant eyes"; that is, the eyeballs are set forward in their sockets and are protected by fat-padded lids that appear slanted because of an internal, or "Mongoloid," eye fold.

When a Mongoloid smiles, his teeth appear large and rounded. The incisors are often, if not usually, "shovel-shaped"; that is, concave behind. Sometimes they project forward. Faces are usually relatively flat-looking, but least so in some American Indians, and noses assume two variants, flat and beaked. Flat noses are commonest in southern China, Southeast Asia, Indonesia, and Siberia, and among the Eskimos and in the Amazon region; the beaked noses, among many tribes of American Indians and some tribal Asiatic peoples like the Nagas of Assam. Lips tend to be thin, with little eversion. There is often considerable alveolar prognathism; that is, a projection of the tooth-bearing portions of both jaws and of the teeth, coupled with a retreating chin.

[7] By Western Asia is meant western Siberia, the Soviet Republics of what was formerly known as Russian Turkestan, Turkey, Iran, Armenia, the Caucasus, Afghanistan, the Arab states in Asia, and Israel.

The body build is variable, tending toward a long trunk and short limbs, with particularly short forearms and lower legs. Wrists are small, and so are, in most populations, hands and feet. Fingernails are usually curved when seen from the side.

Australoids (Full-sized). Among the Australoids are to be seen the most archaic-looking members of mankind, with beetling brows, sloping foreheads, concave temples, deep-set eyes, large, fleshy noses, projecting jaws, and large teeth. Their hair form ranges from tightly curled or "Negroid" to straight, but among the Australian aborigines and most of the Australoids of India it is usually wavy. Their beard and body hair is distributed as in Caucasoids, and like Caucasoids they tend to grow bald and to turn gray quite early in adult life. Their skin color ranges geographically from a sooty near-black that is mat in tone, not shiny, to a medium or even light brown. Their eyes are brown, their hair usually black, except that in some tribes of the central Australian desert it is frequently blond, particularly in women and children. In body build the Australians have struck many observers as closely resembling Caucasoids, although arms and legs may be thinner and longer. In fact, owing to their general appearance, the Australoids have been considered by a number of anthropologists as being archaic survivors of the stock from which Caucasoids also evolved.

Australoids (Dwarfed). In the Philippines, the Malay Peninsula, the Lesser Sunda Islands of Indonesia, the Andaman Islands, and parts of India dwell little pockets of so-called Negritos, refugees from the Mongoloid invasions of the post-Pleistocene period, and until the last century the Andamanese were the sole occupants of their own islands. These diminutive Australoids are not all alike. The Philippine Negritos look the most like shrunken Australian aborigines; the Andamanese are primarily infantile; and the others fit somewhere in between. All of them have black to brown skins, very curly hair, and broad noses. The Andamanese of South Andaman (Önges) are also steatopygous; that is, they have fat buttocks like those of Bushmen.

Congoids (Full-sized). The appearance of African Negroes is well known to Americans and Europeans. Their skin is glossy black or dark brown; their eyes are black with flecks of pigment in the sclera; their hair is tightly curled, and they have moderate to sparse beard and body hair; other characteristics are a tendency to bulbous foreheads and protruding eyeballs; broad, upturned noses with wide nostrils; small, close-set, tightly rolled ears; protruding jaws; large teeth; and thick, everted lips. The skull is rounded in all planes; the occiput (the back of the head) is usually protruding. The body build is very special, with relatively short trunks and long limbs and particularly long forearms and lower legs, shins bowed forward, and large hands and feet. Shoulders are broad and hips narrow. The lumbar spine is incurved (lordosis), and the buttocks protrude without the need of fat padding. So common is a special form of umbilical hernia that it is in effect a racial criterion. Negro muscles have characteristically short, thick bellies (fleshy parts) and long tendons. This is particularly noticeable in the lower leg, and is the opposite of the Mongoloid condition. Negroes have unusually flexible joints; for example, they are able to bend the thumb backward to a marked degree. The African Negroes present a striking physical appearance polar in the races of man, with the Mongoloids at the other pole.

Congoids (Dwarfed). The African Pygmies, found scattered in the forests from the Cameroons to Rwanda and Burundi, are small, with reddish-brown to dark brown skins (mahogany-colored, according to Gates), with tightly curled hair and more abundant beards and body hair than is found in most Negroes. They may also have bulbous foreheads and protruding eyeballs to a greater degree than most Negroes, and broader noses. Some look infantile, other achondroplastic; that is, they have the bulldog syndrome of big head, short face, and short lower legs and forearms seen in comparable dwarfs of all human races and many other animal species. They may represent more than one independent line of dwarfing in noncontiguous populations.

Capoids. Reduced to little more than 100,000 individuals even if one counts the recent mixtures, the Capoids inhabit marginal areas of South and East Africa and were once more numerous and full-sized. They are the atypical remnants of a former major division of mankind. The Bushmen, who constitute the least-mixed relict population, are short, in many cases infantile-looking, with very flat faces and noses and yellowish skins that wrinkle with age. They have the world's most tightly coiled hair, spiraled in tufts with patches of bare scalp between (peppercorn), moderate beard growth, and little body hair. Their head hair is never long because it breaks off. In body proportions they seem more Mongoloid than Congoid, with short limbs, particularly in the lower extremities, and small hands and feet. Their bodies have straight backs, often with little lordosis. However, an appearance of lordosis is given by the development of the fattest buttocks in the world. They have peculiar genitalia, with an infantile penis stance in some of the males, and in the females a reduction of labia majora, and a protrusion of the labia minora which becomes accentuated with age.

Early voyagers familiar with the East Indies and China thought them Mongoloid. Aside from some special features, their resemblance to the Mongoloids is at least as great as that between Caucasoids and Australoids. Whether these resemblances are entirely convergent remains to be explored.

The Contributions of Anatomists

UNLIKE PHYSICAL ANTHROPOLOGISTS, whose subjects are usually standing or seated, the anatomists study subjects that are lying flat. And anatomists can go more than skin deep. They can measure and test various organs and the skeleton, both macroscopically and microscopically. Their subjects having no further appointments, the anatomists can take their time. On the other hand, they have fewer subjects to work with. Most of their studies have been on Caucasoids, Negroes, and Mongoloids, with very little on Australoids and Capoids, and almost nothing at all on Negritos and Pygmies.

They have found considerable differences in human skin, particularly in the thicknesses of the outer layers, in the deposits of melanin, and in vascularization. These differences substantiate the classifications of physical anthropologists. For example, the apocrine glands provide the musky smell of certain races; those of Negroes are supplied with nerve endings that cause the secretion of an enzyme (acetylcholinsterase). This substance is secreted rapidly and vigorously when the nerve endings are stimulated. The apocrine glands of Caucasoids lack acetylcholinsterase, and Mongoloids have hardly any apocrine glands at all.[8]

Both Europeans and Chinese have complicated muscles of facial expression in their cheeks and lips, providing the mechanisms for a variety of subtle looks of hauteur, pain, good humor, and the like, but they are different sets of muscles independently derived from the common undifferentiated subcutaneous mass of thin muscles found in lower mammals and used to elevate hairs or twitch the skin. The differences in belly-to-tendon ratios seen in the muscles of the several races by anthropologists are confirmed and expressed statistically by the work of anatomists, who also find racial differences in the sizes of the endocrine glands. These may be responsible for the differential growth cycles in many other segments and features of the body. The study of racial anatomy

[8] W. Montagna and J. S. Yun: "Skin of Primates. XV. The Skin of the Chimpanzee (*Pan satyrus*)." AJPA, Vol. 21, No. 2 (1963), pp. 189–97.

has gone far to explain many superficial differences, but it has even further to go.

The Contributions of Criminologists

TODAY detectives and laboratory criminologists make extensive use of scientific techniques drawn from many disciplines. Some of these techniques are also useful to physical anthropologists. In 1890 Alphonse Bertillon published his *Photographie judiciaire,* in which he described a system for measuring criminals for the purpose of identification. This system provided a blueprint for the techniques of anthropometry used for almost a quarter of a century before the appearance of the first edition of Rudolf Martin's *Lehrbuch der Anthropologie* in 1914.

But the greatest contribution of criminologists to physical anthropology has been the study of fingerprints.[9] This began in India, where the police first adopted their use for crime detection. In 1900 the police of the British Isles also adopted their use. Fingerprints are uninfluenced by growth or age from the time of their formation during the eighteenth week of pregnancy. They are not subject to selection and are fully hereditary and extremely variable. As we shall presently show, they clearly distinguish between the five living subspecies and also express genetic distance.

The Contributions of Somatotypists

ANATOMISTS of a special kind, called somatotypists, or students of variations in body build, physique, or constitutional type, have already begun to study racial differences in their field of interest. They recognize three main components, each present in various degrees in a number of designated body segments of each human being. The first component is *endomorphy*, characterized by a predominance of volume over surface area, with general softness, roundness, small bones, short distal extremities, and a tendency to obesity. The second component is *mesomorphy*, with heavy bones and heavy musculature, rugged features, and the classic appearance of a heavy athlete. The third component,

9 H. Cummins and C. Midlo: *Finger Prints, Palms, and Soles* (New York: Dover Publications; 1961).

ectomorphy, runs to long lean proportions with an excess of skin surface areas over body mass.

Somatotypists find the Caucasoids, particularly the European ones, more or less in the middle in these categories, probably because the techniques of observation were first designed for studying Europeans. The Mongoloids tend to mesomorphy combined with endomorphy. The Australoids, Negroes, and many of the non-European Caucasoids reach the opposite extreme. Further racially diagnostic differences may be seen in the anatomical location of these components. For example, the Negroes tend to be more mesomorphic in the upper chest and shoulders than the Caucasoids, whose mesomorphy extends all the way to the hands and feet. The dwarfed Australoids and Congoids and the Capoids are harder to study on this basis than the full-sized races, for obvious reasons.

The Contributions of Students of Body Components

A MORE DETAILED WAY of determining variations in body build is to study differences in percentages of body constituents, especially bone, muscle, fat, and viscera. Because these tissues and organs vary in individuals according to age, their study is a useful adjunct to the height and weight constants measured in growing children. Such studies also supplement the work of the anthropometrists in determining physical differences in adults. But the chief applications of both body-component studies and somatotyping are medical, because of correlations with physical and mental disease. From the work of students of constitution in both disciplines we anthropologists garner a free dividend.

The Physiologists' Contributions

ALTHOUGH Johnny-come-latelys in this field, physiologists have already made substantial contributions. By measuring internal and external body temperature, pulse rate, respiration rate, basal metabolism, amount of perspiration lost under certain conditions, and other such variables in terms of work loads, temperature, humidity, altitude, and the like, they have found some basic racial differences. Negroes are superior to whites in keeping cool in wet heat; Australian aborigines and nomadic Lapps have one kind of cold adaptation—heat transfer between blood vessels in the extremities—and Mongoloids have another—a combination of fat insulation and increased peripheral blood flow with high basal metabolism. Other (non-Lapp) Caucasoids do not have any of these. Furthermore, for various reasons, subcutaneous fat protects Negroes less from cold than it does whites. Whites with tanned skins do better on hot deserts than unclothed Negroes of the same height and weight. Only Mongoloids have acquired successful adaptations to the thin air of the Andes and Tibet.[1]

The Doctors' Discoveries

WHILE TRYING to keep everyone alive and healthy, doctors too have discovered some racial differences that help explain why people live where they do. The Mongoloids who can work and reproduce easily at high altitudes catch malaria readily on the lowlands. Some African Negroes who do not thrive at high altitudes do better against malaria because they have the sickle-cell gene in a differentiated state (Ss instead of ss or SS). American Indians died off when the colonists transmitted to them smallpox and other diseases to which the Red Men had hitherto been unexposed and so had developed no immunity. These and other medicoracial discoveries help explain the geographical distribution of races, and why some races outnumber others. In some ancient cemeteries as many as fifty percent of the skeletons were of children who had been born alive but had died before the age of two.[2] Selection for immunity to disease has been a factor in the evolution of races for a very long time.

The Independent Taxonomies of the Geneticists

GENETICISTS, an independent lot who now hold the center of the stage in the study of race, have been behind the anthropological

---

[1]Documentation for these statements may be found in Carleton S. Coon: *The Origin of Races* (New York: Alfred A. Knopf; 1962), Chapter 2.

[2] See, for example, D. Ferembach: *La Nécropole Épipaléolithique de Taforalt* (Maroc oriental) (Rabat, 1962).

footlights during only the last forty years. Concerned at first primarily with the inheritance of congenital diseases, in the 1920's
some of them shifted their interest to blood groups—first to trans-
fusion groups, then to many others—and more than any other
investigators they have obtained masses of detailed information
concerning human variation. That their information deals exclusively with clearly inherited characters gives their work a unique
value in the study of human evolution.

Geneticists have made two principal contributions to racial
studies. They have made us realize that races must be studied as
populations, and they have mapped, over a substantial portion of
the earth's surface, the global gene frequencies for over twenty
traits inherited as alleles (alternative genes on single chromosomal
sites). Such traits can be traced more accurately in a genetic sense
than the usual anthropometric criteria, which are inherited through
the interaction of several independently variable gene sites, and
which are influenced by changes in age and by environmental
factors, including nutrition.

W. C. Boyd, a leader in the application of this discipline to racial
classification, has most recently proposed a list of some thirteen
races within seven main geographical groups, as follows.[3]

TABLE 2

BOYD'S 1963 CLASSIFICATION OF RACES

European	African	Asian
1 Early European (C)	i N. African (C)	7 Asian (M)
2 Lapps (C)	ii 6 African	8 Indo-Dravidian (C)
3 N.W. Europeans (C)	(Cong + Cap)	
4 E. & Cent. Europeans (C)		
5 Mediterraneans (C)		

American	Pacific	
9 American Indian (M)	10 Indonesian (M > A)	
	11 Melanesian (A > M)	
	12 Polynesian (M > A)	
	13 Australian (A)	

This table is reproduced as it appeared in *Science*. The seven geographical groups
are European, African, Asian, Indo-Dravidian, American, Pacific, and Australian.
The "North African" race is not numbered among the thirteen, being apparently
included among the Mediterraneans. The capitals in parentheses indicate our
designations of these "races."

[3] W. C. Boyd: "Genetics and the Human Race," *Science*, Vol. 140, No. 3571
(1963), pp. 1057–65.

This classification is in many ways extremely interesting to nonserological physical anthropologists. Boyd places the North Africans in the European camp, as do we. He separates the American Indians from the Asians, and states further that if subsequent studies confirm his tentative findings he will subdivide the American Indians by continents. We agree that the American Indians and the Mongoloids have been separated long enough to be called races in his sense, but not necessarily subspecies in ours, a designation which he has not claimed.

Boyd recognizes the Australians as a separate group and race. His Indonesian, Melanesian, and Polynesian "races" are patently intermediate between Mongoloids and Australoids, in blood as in other respects, as their histories indicate. Their anatomical characteristics, however, incline them to different sides of the interparental fence without equally close distinctions in serology. This observation has interesting genetic and adaptive indications, of use in a general theory of race formation.

In formulating his classification, Boyd did not mention that certain serological factors such as the sickle-cell trait and substances in blood groups A and B have been shown to protect people who possess them against certain diseases. Because of racial differences in blood factors, malaria, smallpox, plague, and other wholesale killers find more victims in some races than in others, and an epidemic can change the blood-group frequencies of a population at least as rapidly as can interracial gene flow. From one point of view this knowledge, to be reviewed in Chapter 9, is of great importance because it helps explain the geographical distributions of races.

Even without this added dimension, Boyd's efforts have helped greatly to bring together the contributions of workers in different disciplines in the interest of racial classification. We are, we hope, approaching the path to a general agreement, after which we may be able to attach valid racial third names to *Homo sapiens*.

2

Geography, Culture, and Racial Diversity

❊❊❊

The Problem of Racial Diversity

So far, we have presented a fivefold classification of the living races based on the continuity of their physical differences on the scale of time; a rough racial census showing great numerical disparities, and a brief statement of the reasons for it; descriptions of the races based on several independent disciplines, all of which point to the same conclusions; and a rather "busy" map (pages 24–5) showing present racial distributions over the world. Before proceeding to a more detailed regional survey, we shall briefly explore the problem of why the races of man differ as much as they do.

The Great Variability of Higher Primates

One reason for our great variability is that we are higher primates. Zoologists have observed that among highly evolved species individual animals tend to vary considerably among themselves, and this is particularly true of our nearest relatives, the higher primates. Chimpanzees of a single population vary almost as much in skin color as do the races of man. They also vary tremendously in body size, temperament, and behavior, as shown particularly in the works of Adolph Schultz and Jane Goodall.[1]

[1] A. H. Schultz: "Characters common to higher primates and characters specific for man," QRB, Vol. 11 (1936), pp. 259–83, 425–55; "Age Changes, Sex Differ-

Of all the primates, chimpanzees are closest to man in anatomy, serology, and behavior. It is very likely that at the remote time when the ancestors of the living races expanded from their place of origin into the cradlelands where they became racially differentiated they were just as variable as chimpanzees are now. Each local set of ancestors thus probably carried with it a wide range of genetic possibilities, some of which were more favorable for survival in one environment and others in another.

Initial adaptations to variations in climate must have been rapid. Once the descendants of a set of ancestors had multiplied to the point of filling in their living space, they had probably already become genetically differentiated in some respects from the others.[2]

Up to this point in the history of human evolution, man's racial differentiation may have followed a pattern normal for other large mammals, but once the races were established in their homelands, if not before, a specifically human behavior pattern set in. In each region the human population came to be broken up into small breeding isolates between which genetic exchanges took place infrequently. Gene flow between major racial areas over interracial frontiers was also slow. The reason for this behavioral peculiarity is man's acquisition of what anthropologists (not members of ladies' clubs) call *culture*.

Language the Key to Culture

THE ESSENTIAL TOOL of culture is, of course, language.[3] With a means of communication superior to that of other mammals, man finds himself able to organize people into coherent, self-contained groups of several families that share food, and to teach his offspring considerably more, say, than a lioness can teach her cubs, or a porpoise parent its exotically aquatic young.

---

ences, and Variability in the Classification of Primates," in S. L. Washburn, ed.: *Classification and Human Evolution* (Chicago: Aldine Publishing Co.; 1963), pp. 85–115. J. Goodall and H. van Lawick: "My Life among Wild Chimpanzees," NG, Vol. 124, No. 2 (1963), pp. 272–308.

2 A recent study of English sparrows taken in seventeen places in North America and the Hawaiian Islands, with series of 100 to 250 specimens each, shows that racial differentiation had taken place in no more than fifty years in a number of characteristics. Some of the changes are phenotypical, such as increased size and weight in colder regions, but there are also differences in bill size and form and in plumage color. We must remember that birds move about more rapidly than terrestrial mammals. R. F. Johnstone and R. K. Selander: "House Sparrows: Rapid Evolution of Races in North America," *Science*, Vol. 144, No. 3618 (1964), pp. 548–50.

3 C. F. Hockett and R. Ascher: "The Human Revolution," CA, Vol 5, No. 3 (1964), pp. 135–70.

As new inventions are made, some of them are added to the body of learning that in every viable culture accumulates geometrically, more in the postulated manner of Lamarckian inheritance of acquired characteristics than in the Darwinian manner, in which happenstance and coincidence play larger roles. By building culture into his environment, man gave himself something new to be selected for. We do not mean that he is the only animal to do this, only that he does it so much more than the others do, through his fluidity of communication, that he has unintentionally made himself unique.

Culture Affects Physiology

AS STATED in Chapter 1, physiologists have demonstrated that geographical variations are related to some of the physical differences among human races. That man can withstand even major variations in his environment is due to the technology of environmental protection, one department of culture. Fire, housing, and body covering permit people to live in marginal regions otherwise uninhabitable for most primates. Thus certain races have been selected in certain ways by extremes of climate which, without culture, they might not otherwise have survived.

An excellent example is provided by the Alakaluf Indians of southern Chile who before coming in contact with Europeans used the crudest of cutting tools, made fire, and built warm, skin-covered huts and bark canoes. In weather hovering around the frost line, through rain, sleet, snow, and high winds, they went about naked or nearly naked throughout the year. Their physiological cold adaptation, which involves a high basal-metabolism rate, would probably not have been adequate for survival in that environment, however, without fire and shelter.

It is possible that this capacity of some Mongoloids for cold adaptation—with the help of fire and shelter—may go back to the first appearance of this subspecies in China. The climate of the Choukoutien site, the home of Sinanthropus, probably imposed as much cold stress then as it does now, and this would be considerable for naked hunters—even with fire, which they had, and the shelter of caves.[4]

---

[4] B. Kurtén and Y. Vasari: "On the Date of Peking Man," SSFCB, Vol. 23, No. 7 (1960), pp. 3–10. Kurtén and Vasari assign this site to a cool oscillation, comparable to Elster II in Europe, with cooler summers but winters no colder than

Another example is the melanotic moth *Biston betularia*.[5] It is either gray or black, and the black form is a recessive mutant. These moths normally perch on light-hued lichens growing on dark tree bark. Under natural conditions the gray type is protected by its color from predators. But in English woods affected by industrial air pollution the lichens have been killed and the moths are obliged to perch on the bare bark. There the black moths have 50 percent more chance of survival than the gray ones and the species is rapidly changing its color. There is nothing unusual about the mechanism that is changing the moth's color. What is unusual is that the principal variable in this high selection rate is culture itself.

The object of this digression is neither to discourse on moths and cold adaptation nor to confuse the reader, but to point out three possibilities, or propositions. The problem of genetic selection in man in response to culture is not a simple one to which pat answers can be given. Rather it calls for the best skill of several disciplines. Some of our peculiarities may have been acquired more rapidly than they would have been had we been cultureless animals. Moreover culture, which has affected other free-living animals too, has probably affected us more profoundly than it has any others because we created it, we cannot escape it, we have been constantly exposed to it as long as there have been men on earth, and we could not live without it.

Racial Geography

TO THESE THOUGHTS it may be added that throughout most of man's existence the races have largely lived apart, exposed to their private cultures, in their original homes. This would be hard to believe from a quick inspection of Map 1, a cartographic jungle showing a distribution of races and racial intermediates that have been thrown together in many parts of the world too recently for assimilation.

---

at present. We come to the same conclusion with regard to the winters, among other reasons because macaque monkeys were present in Choukoutien at that time. Today they are found as far north as Peking, and over all of Honshu in Japan. It is doubtful that they could have survived winter temperatures lower than those existing in these places today. See W. Fielder: "Übersicht über das System der Primates," in *Primatologia*, Vol. 1 (Basel: S. Karger; 1956), 1. 173, Fig. 47.

5 J. B. S. Haldane: "A Defense of Beanbag Genetics," PBM, Vol. 7, No. 3 (1964), pp. 343–59. See particularly page 348.

Much of the complexity seen on the map is obviously the product of the movements of peoples since the discovery of the New World and other remote regions by Europeans. It is patently due to innovations in transportation and to the excessive use of natural resources by Europeans. In countries like India and China, and those of North Africa and the Arab states, where the natives were already efficiently exploiting the land when it was discovered or invaded, the Europeans have come and gone, leaving technical

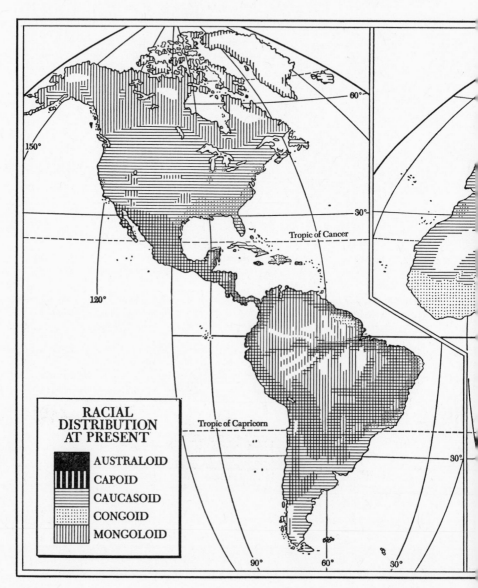

RACIAL
DISTRIBUTION
AT PRESENT

AUSTRALOID
CAPOID
CAUCASOID
CONGOID
MONGOLOID

improvements and overpopulation in their wake. In countries like the United States, Canada, and Australia, the Europeans came to stay, having met no substantial opposition or population problem, but they brought members of other races with them, to complicate the map still further.

Even if we draw another map, this time showing the racial distribution of the world around A.D. 1492 (see Map 2), some incongruities still remain. Madagascar is already inhabited by a mixture

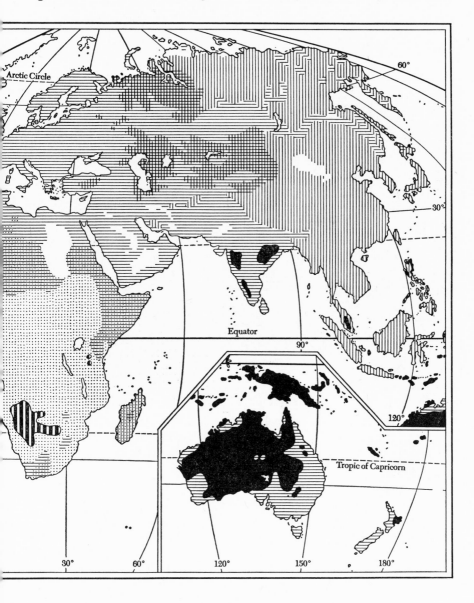

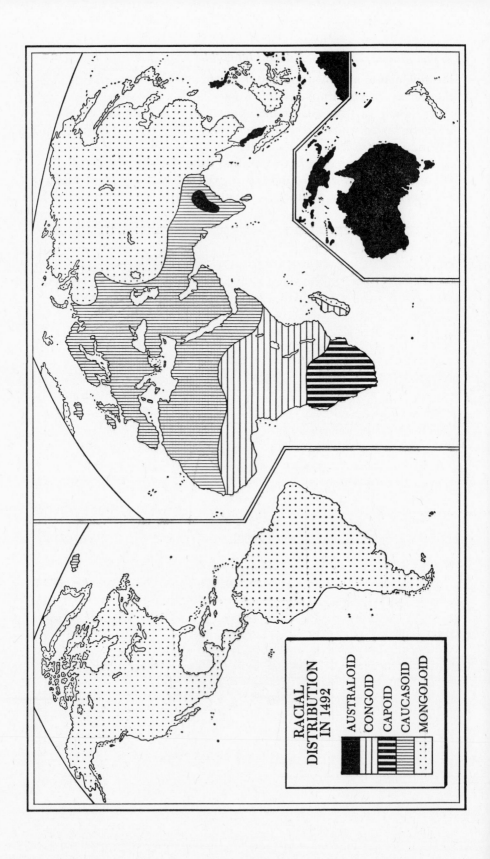

RACIAL
DISTRIBUTION
IN 1492

AUSTRALOID
CONGOID
CAPOID
CAUCASOID
MONGOLOID

of Mongoloids and Negroes, and pockets of Australoid dwarfs dot Southeast Asia and Indonesia.

We must go back still more, almost to the end of the last ice age (the Würm or Wisconsin), to at least 13,000 years ago (11,000 B.C.). Then our map (Map 3) looks simpler. The Caucasoids are confined to the then inhabited parts of Europe and to Western Asia, the Mongoloids to China, and the Australoids to Southeast Asia and its adjacent islands. Africa is the home of Africans only, for the Berbers had not yet arrived from their Caucasoid home, and the Mongoloids had not yet invaded Southeast Asia and the islands. Map 3 looks for all the world like the distribution of the subspecies of a cultureless animal—which makes zoological sense. This does not mean that man was without culture then, only that no people had grown efficient enough to allow the expansion of one race into the territory of another.

Geographical Barriers to Gene Flow during the Pleistocene

IN ADDITION to locating the five cradles of mankind, Map 3 shows the northern limits of human habitation in the Old World during nearly all of the Pleistocene. We can draw these limits with varying degrees of accuracy on the basis of archaeological sites, particularly those containing remains of fossil man. Most of these sites fall roughly on the warm side of the present winter frost line, in regions where unfrozen drinking water can be obtained nearly every day from natural sources.

This frost line reaches about 63° N. latitude in Western Europe because of the tempering effect of the Gulf Stream and the westerly winds. In China and Japan it touches the Pacific at 37° and 39° N. latitude. In between its route is irregular, dipping south to a low of about 27° N. latitude in Nepal because of the chilly wastes of the Tibetan plateau.

Several lines of evidence suggest that during both the glacial and the interglacial episodes of the Ice Age (roughly 30 percent and 70 percent respectively of the 1,500,000 years of the so-called Middle and Upper Pleistocene)[6] the frost line stood more or less where it is now. According to J. K. Charlesworth, west of the

6 L. S. B. Leakey: "Age of Bed I, Olduvai Gorge, Tanganyika," *Nature*, Vol. 191, No. 4787 (1961), pp. 478–9. D. Ericson and G. Wollin: *The Deep and the Past* (New York: Alfred A. Knopf; 1964). K. P. Oakley: *The Problem of Man's Antiquity*, BBMNH, Vol. 9, No. 5 (1964).

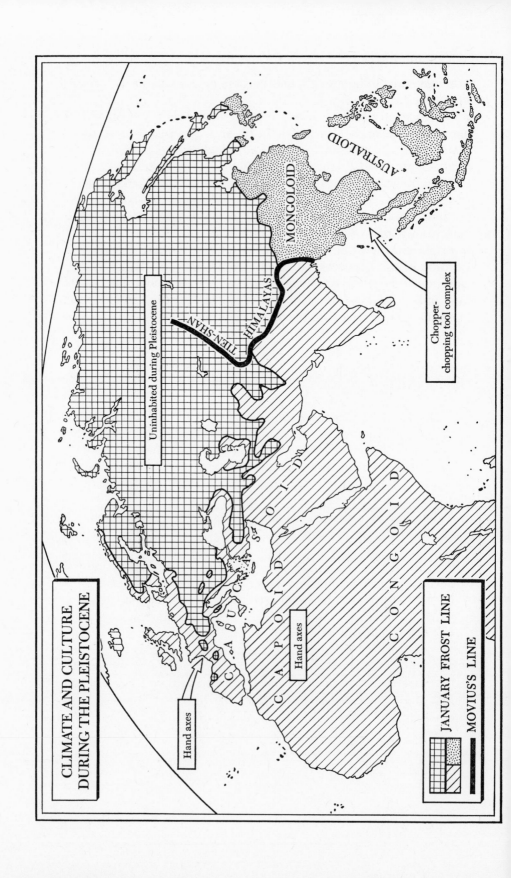

CLIMATE AND CULTURE DURING THE PLEISTOCENE

Uninhabited during Pleistocene

Chopper-chopping tool complex

Hand axes

Hand axes

MONGOLOID

AUSTRALOID

HIMALAYAS

TIEN-SHAN

CAUCASOID

CAPOID

CONGOID

JANUARY FROST LINE

MOVIUS'S LINE

frost line in the critical maritime section of Western Europe, where the frost line reaches its most northerly point, during glacial advances winter temperatures may have been even a little milder than they are now. Summer temperatures, however, were much cooler then and the cloud cover was intense. During interglacials, on the contrary, the summers may have been warmer than today, and east of the frost line the winters were probably some 6.3° F. (3.5° C.) colder than at present.[7]

These conclusions, with which not all Pleistocene geologists agree, may help explain some otherwise puzzling facts. Fossil hippopotamus are found west of the present winter frost line in Europe as far north as Scotland, and nearly all archaeological sites, from the Atlantic to the Pacific, lie on the warm side of the line. Sites found on the cold side of it either are in small islands of warm climate, as in Hungary, or are of glacial rather than inter-glacial date, as in Markkleeberg, near Leipzig. In Markkleeberg, Lower Paleolithic hunters slaughtered mammoths that they ambushed as the animals passed through a narrow migration corridor during the third or Riss glacial period.[8]

The Five Cradles

DURING THE PLEISTOCENE the Caucasoid homeland extended from Norway down to the Riviera and from Portugal to Baluchistan. It was separated from northwest Africa by the Strait of Gibraltar and from the Horn of Africa by the Bab el Mandeb, both narrow bodies of water, and it had a dry-land all-weather gate to Africa over Suez. There we may be certain that Caucasoids and Africans faced each other.

The Baluchistan coast, where Caucasoid territory joined India, is today almost as barren as the face of the moon. What it was like at different stages of the Pleistocene we do not know. Caucasoid territory reached up into modern Uzbekistan, where during the winter, when the climate was like that of today, it was separated by 2,000 miles of frost from the nearest inhabited part of the Mongoloid territory. During the summer a corridor running

[7] J. K. Charlesworth: *The Quaternary Era* (London: Edward Arnold; 1957), pp. 640–3.

[8] R. Grahmann: *The Lower Paleolithic Site of Markkleeberg and Other Comparable Localities near Leipzig*, ed. H. L. Movius, Jr., TAPS, NS Vol. 45, Pt. 6 (1955).

through the Zungarian Gates was frost-free for only four months, and even then it passed through some very dry desert country on the Chinese side of the mountains.

Thus during both glacials and interglacials some contact was possible between Caucasoids and Africans, between both kinds of Africans, between Caucasoids and Australoids, and between Australoids and Mongoloids. Inside Africa barriers of water and desert alternated. During pluvials, more or less equivalent to glacials, there was no Nile, and the Sahara was well watered because of large lakes and swamps which then existed to the south of it. During interpluvials the lakes and swamps shrank but the desert returned. The zone of contact between Australoids and Mongoloids, in southern China, was always a broad one. The greatest interracial barrier during the Pleistocene was that parting the Caucasoids from the Mongoloids, but even it may have been breached at least once before the Ice Age was over.

Cultural Barriers to Gene Flow during the Pleistocene

EXCEPT for the Caucasoid-Mongoloid barrier, geography did not offer any serious impediment to gene flow between the five cradles of man during the Pleistocene, but impediments existed, or the living races would not still be as different as they are. We know that culture is the key factor; cultural barriers are still effective today and operate at all levels of cultural complexity. Some of these levels can be little different from those which obtained during much of the Pleistocene.

Cultures vary in many ways, but the aspect of culture that affects gene flow the most is the systems of mating. In man, mating is not just a matter of sex. In many cultures sex is taken for granted and mating is based largely on economics. It involves who shall feed whom and who shall do what kind of work in the family and in the community.

As explained in *The Origin of Races*, living hunters and gatherers are organized into breeding isolates, averaging about 350 individuals and rarely exceeding twice that number. Each isolate usually contains several bands that come together at least once a year for ceremonies. At these times marriages are also arranged. All the people in the isolate are ordinarily related to each other and everyone knows everyone else and what all the relationships are. In many cases the systems of kinship are elaborate, from our point of view, as kinship means more to them than to us. Rules of kinship determine who may or may not marry whom.

Except for the sanctioned incest of royalty as in Pharaonic Egypt and Incaic Peru, as far as we know all peoples forbid brother-sister, father-daughter, and mother-son matings. Beyond this, different systems permit marriages between classes of kin, each of which may include a variety of biological relationships ranging from first, second, and even third cousin outward to the periphery of the extended kin. The number of women potentially available to a man at any one time is usually small and if no proper partner is ready for marriage a man may have to wait until one is born, grows up, or becomes a widow. A woman is less likely to face such a problem in most societies, particularly among hunters, because of the prevalence of polygyny. Women can double up in marriage whereas man cannot.[9]

Another feature common to many societies is that persons of different generations and age grades may marry, providing their membership in the proper kinship categories permit it. An elderly man may have a harem of wives ranging from puberty to senility, particularly if he is a great hunter, leader, or both. All of these conventional marital arrangements make good sense because they fill an immediate and permanent need, to help preserve equilibrium in the major social unit concerned.

Because this social unit is also a breeding isolate to a large extent if not almost exclusively, these rules have several less conspicuous but equally essential functions.[1] They keep inbreeding within the extended kinship group at a minimum, and this is vital in small isolates. Polygyny, the continued fertility of the older men, and the fact that clever women may connive to become plural wives tend to weight the gene pool in favor of the qualities that make for success, along with other unrelated genes that the leader and his wives may happen to possess. In such a situation, polygamy intensifies natural selection, and contributes to the survival of small populations and to genetic differentiation between them.

These populations are kept small because of the amount of food available within a territory small enough to permit bands to meet. They are kept apart because everyone needs to know his territory as intimately as a farmer knows his fields or a postman

---

[9] Except of course in the world's few polyandrous societies, which seem to be limited to India, Nepal, and the Marquesas.

[1] For one of the most lucid and thorough studies of such an isolate, see J. V. Neel, F. M. Salzano, P. C. Junqueira, F. Keiter, and D. Maybury-Lewis: "Studies on the Xavante Indians of the Brazilian Mato Grosso," AJHG, Vol. 16, No. 1 (1964), pp. 52–140. The kinship study was the work of Maybury-Lewis.

his route. The people and their land are inseparably bound by emotional ties rationalized in ancestral myths. Encroachment on the territory of another group would lead to mysterious dangers and warfare.

Living in such mutual isolation, each group builds up over many generations its own sets of cultural symbols: dialects, even languages, religious practices, food tabus, and such conspicuous labels as patterns of body painting, hairdos, and other art forms. Even today the Scots keep their tartans, and the villages of Maya Indians circling Lake Atitlán in Guatemala have separate costumes. All these symbols reinforce the separate identities of peoples and interfere with gene flow.

On theoretical grounds, it is apparent that this tendency has existed for a long time. The archaeological record provides evidence of it. In France, where Paleolithic archaeology has been pursued more intensively than anywhere else, four different Mousterian industries, each with its own sets of tools, existed during the first part of the Würm Glaciation. F. Bordes has interpreted this evidence to mean that bands of Neanderthals using these four "kits" alternately moved in and out of the same caves. If he is right, each of them kept its own kit over a period of nearly eighty thousand years, and only one of these kits seems to have evolved into an Upper Paleolithic industry.[2] During the next twenty-odd thousand years, in the same region of France four different Upper Paleolithic industries apparently did the same thing, and only one of them, the Magdalenian, evolved into local Mesolithic industries.[3]

If we grant most isolates of hunters a territory of 1,000 to 3,000 square miles, and we know that a Pleistocene racial cradle covers several million square miles, it is not difficult to calculate that each such racial breeding ground must have contained several thousand isolates at any one time. If one of a hundred matings in each isolate was exogamous in each generation, it would take thousands of years for a mutation arising in one isolate to reach all the others, and even longer for it to spread from one racial cradle into another.

This does not mean that each isolate persisted as a separate unit throughout the Pleistocene. As we know from studies of modern food-gatherers, some isolates become so reduced in numbers that their remaining members are absorbed by their neigh-

2 F. Bordes: "Mousterian Cultures in France," *Science,* Vol. 134, No. 3482 (1961), pp. 803–10.
3 D. de Sonneville-Bordes: "Upper Paleolithic Cultures in Western Europe," *Science,* Vol. 142, No. 3590 (1963), pp. 347–55.

bors. Others expand and divide, some segments seeking new territories. Individuals forced to leave because of antisocial actions, such as murder, may live to join other isolates.

Direct evidence for the longevity and degree of genetic isolation of a Pleistocene population is rare. Only one population sample, a series of 122 skeletons, is large enough to give us much information. That is the carefully studied[4] Mouillian population buried in the cave of Taforalt in northeastern Morocco, between about 10,000 B.C. and 8,500 B.C., according to Carbon-14 figures. This isolate, composed of Caucasoid ancestors of the living Berbers, endured for at least fifty generations, during which there is no evidence of cultural change. No morphological changes may have taken place either; the series shows little variability. There is indication of an incidence of sacral anomalies, including *spina bifida,* of 75 percent, and an infant mortality of 56 percent below the age of two. To what extent the anomalies and the infant mortality were progressive we do not know, but the first, at least, suggests inbreeding. There are now, and probably were then, no geographical barriers in that region to prevent gene flow.

In sum, what evidence we have from the present and the past serves to explain why the races of man came to be as different as they are. As one would expect, their differences are particularly marked in characteristics that adapt people to special stress and trial in climate and in disease. New mutations favorable in any climate could always be passed on, but the process was slow because of the genetic disadvantages of their bearers in other traits. Since the end of the Pleistocene, geographical barriers between major races have been overcome by innovations in transportation, but culture has continued to retard the assimilation of races through such mechanisms as social classes, ethnic castes, and occupational elites. Despite this reduction of barriers to communication, the races of man are still with us, although interracial clines have grown.

Cultural Parallelism and Genetic Contacts

TODAY, as everyone knows, there is much unrest in the world. Part of it is caused by rivalries between peoples who have risen to comparable levels of cultural complexity in different regions and who now face each other with growing irritability because of

4 Ferembach: op. cit.

the increasing ease of global transportation and communication. Huge nations are as hostile now as small tribes were in the past. For present purposes we are interested in only one aspect of this dangerous problem—that is, to determine whether cultures that are today equally complex reached their present levels independently or as a result of contact permitting gene flow, or both.

Whenever a group of people possessing a common culture obtains technological means of increasing its production of food and consumer goods, the division of labor increases. As it increases, specialization tends to follow the same lines everywhere and to produce the same kinds of social institutions above the family level. The reason for this is clear. Human needs, or instincts if you like, are the same the world over. All peoples need government, solace when disturbed by private or public crises, an exchange of goods, and privacy to consort with their peers.[5] Thus it requires no Atlantis, no Lost Continent of Mu, no unrecorded transatlantic or transpacific voyages, to explain why Aztecs, Incas, Chinese, Sumerians, Egyptians, and other civilized peoples had priests, kings, scribes, or other record-keepers, soldiers, or companies of craftsmen. Such categories and groups of specialists arose when the social situation required them, with or without genetic contact.

Another supposed indication of genetic contact is the similarity of cultural details. The Mayas and Egyptians built pyramids. Blowguns were used both in the New World and in the Old. Some of the Australian aborigines made blade tools and microliths, just as the Europeans and Western Asians had done millennia earlier. To claim without evidence that each of these instances of parallelism must have been due to contact is to discredit the inventive capacity of the different races of man.

For example, the Mixtec Indians of Mexico squeeze royal purple dye out of a snail, *Purpura patula*, found in the Pacific Ocean. The Phoenicians did the same with two other snails, *Murex truncatus* and *Murex brandaris*, found in the Mediterranean.[6] This does not mean that Phoenician navigators colonized, or even reached, America, and least of all that the Indians of the Middle American highlands got their aquiline noses from Semitic ancestors.

Yet in a few instances such contacts now seem possible. Pottery resembling the Middle Jomon ware of Japan has been found on

5 See C. S. Coon: "Growth and Development of Social Groups," in G. Wolstenholme, ed.: *Man and His Future* (London: J. & A. Churchill; 1963), pp. 120–31. Also R. Fletcher: *Instinct in Man* (New York: International Universities Press; 1957).

6 P. Gerhard: "Emperors' Dye of the Mixtecs," NH, Vol. 73, No. 1 (1964), pp. 26–31.

the coast of Ecuador, with a comparable Carbon-14 date of between 2,000 B.C. and 3,000 B.C.[7] If chemical analysis of the sherds from both places shall prove the Ecuadorean pieces to have been made in Japan, this of course means that a few early Japanese navigators could have reached the coast of South America. It need not mean that they had much to do with the peopling of that continent, which is the limit of our present interest. In any case, both were Mongoloid.

Selection in Migration

LET US NOW CONSIDER what happens to peoples who we know have moved. Many modern studies have indicated that people who migrate voluntarily tend to seek environments as similar to those of their ancestral homes as they can find. The distribution of Scandinavians and Finns in the United States and Canada shows this clearly. The same may be true also of involuntary migrants, such as Negroes in the New World, who were brought to warm, humid places where it was believed, and on the whole correctly, that they could work more efficiently, more cheaply, or both, than either Europeans or American Indians.

Other migrants choose their new homes not because of geography but for opportunities to trade. Greeks and Lebanese, inveterate traders, have gone to places in the New World and Africa where they could become rich, as many have. Chinese have gone where they could trade, cook, and wash clothing without much concern for location as long as they could succeed. In these instances, the selection was not so much concerned with the environment in which the people settled as it was with their points of origin. The Chinese who came to America to work were almost exclusively Cantonese and all came from the same few places in Kwangtung province. The Lebanese from one village all tend to go to the same place, just as people from Essex, England, founded and populated Essex, Massachusetts. The Italians living in some of the western suburbs of Philadelphia almost all came from a few villages in the Abruzzi Mountains, and on the Main Line the same families intermarry, or refuse to intermarry, as they did in Italy.

In addition to geographical selection at home and abroad, individual selection has been observed in the instances studied.

[7] B. J. Meggers, E. Estrada, and C. Evans: "Possible Transpacific Contact on the Coast of Ecuador," *Science*, Vol. 135, No. 3501 (1962), pp. 371–2.

Japanese who emigrated to the United States (including Hawaii) are physically different from their siblings who stayed in Japan.[8] Italian Swiss in California differ from their siblings in Switzerland.[9] The Basques of Argentina are super-Basques in that they have a higher frequency of Rh-negative (r or cde) than Basques at home.[1] If genetic selection in migration operates today, there is no reason to suppose that it failed to do so in the past.

It may also have been important in the initial peopling of uninhabited regions such as Australia and the New World. The first migrants to both these continental land masses were obviously inhabitants of the peripheries of their racial cradlelands. Peripheral populations facing uninhabited land masses are less likely to possess exotic genes received from zones of interracial contact than others are. They are also less likely to have been influenced by new mutations concerned with general evolution (anagenesis). We cannot therefore consider the Australian aborigines to be exactly the same as their fellow Australoids of Southeast Asia at the time of the Mongoloid invasions. By the same token some of the differences between American Indians and Asiatic Mongoloids may be explained.

The Rise and Fall of Elites

SELECTION in migration may take place even if no one moves any great distance or into a new environment. The migration may be simply from the farm to the city or from one part of a city to another. What is involved is homogamy based on occupation, rank, or both. Rare or impossible among food-gatherers, this phenomenon characteristically appears with the increased specialization of trades and professions accompanying the rise of cities.

Many European studies have shown that lumberjacks, blacksmiths, tailors, and the like differ in physique, and that champions in various sports and events are naturally selected for size, shape, and physiological capacities appropriate to the kind of exertion needed in each. Occupational and athletic selection, however, is not what we are talking about here. Our subject is brain, not brawn.

8 H. L. Shapiro: *Migration and Environment* (New York: Oxford University Press; 1939).

9 F. S. Hulse: "Exogamie et Heterosis", ASAG, Vol. 22, No 2 (1957), pp. 103–25.

1 A. E. Mourant: *The Distribution of the Human Blood Groups* (Springfield, Ill.: Charles C. Thomas; 1954). After M. A. Etcheverry, 1947.

Here we turn naturally to the history of the Jews, who have preserved their ethnic identity, religion, and language (at least for ritual use) for over 3,000 years. Since the Diaspora they have lived in more or less self-contained communities up to the present century. Blood-group studies show a certain continuity, most marked in the more conservative isolates, as in the ghetto of Rome.[2] To what extent the various branches of the world's Jews exhibit an anatomical continuity is beside the point here. So is the extent to which they may or may not have mixed with Gentiles, or been subjected to different climatic influences.[3]

The point is that, whatever their origin or genetic history, the Jews have for a long time constituted a community of more or less endogamous isolates engaged principally in trades and professions requiring high intelligence, for which they have been pruned. It requires no statistics here, for they are easily available elsewhere, to state that the Jews have contributed far more than their numerical share of the world's geniuses in many fields. N. Weyl has found that Jews bearing priestly names exceed the others in excellence of achievement. This is in part explained, he states, by the fact that it has long been a practice to marry bright young men destined for the rabbinate to rich merchants' daughters and to encourage them to have large families.[4]

Many other examples may be cited, such as that of the Parsis who left Iran for India in the eighth century A.D. to escape forcible conversion to Islam. Ever since, they have practiced strict endogamy. They also have a hereditary caste of priests who marry, but only those sons who show aptitude follow in their father's profession. Like the Jews, they have produced more than their share of outstanding individuals in industry, government, and science.

A third example is provided by a caste of Negro blacksmiths who serve the less Negroid tribesmen of Tibesti in the central Sahara. These smiths, an endogamous group, not only work iron but also act as advisers to tribal chiefs and as messengers between them. Without high intelligence, they would be unable to perform these functions.[5]

2 L. C. and S. P. Dunn: "The Jewish Community of Rome," SA, Vol. 196, No.3 (1957), pp. 118–32.

3 C. C. Seltzer: "The Jew; his racial status; an anthropological appraisal," HMAB, April 1939, pp. 3–11. Coon: *The Races of Europe* (New York: The Macmillan Co.; 1939); and "Have the Jews a Racial Identity?" in I. Graeber, ed.: *Jews in a Gentile World* (New York: The Macmillan Co.; 1942), pp. 20–37.

4 N. Weyl and S. T. Possony: *The Geography of Intellect* (Chicago: Henry Regnery & Co.; 1964). See especially pp. 97–9.

5 P. Fuchs: *Die Völker der Südost-Sahara* (Vienna: Wm. Braumüller; 1961), pp. 184–8.

The rise of elites speeds up anagenetic evolution in populations that have reached a certain level of cultural complexity, but the coin has two sides. Like selection in migration, this process drains those left behind, the so-called *sedentes*. An elaborate study of rural communities in Tasmania has shown that with the movement of settlers from farm to city the rural population has declined in measurable intelligence.[6] The same thing has happened in parts of the United States.

In Western Asia elites had grown up over several thousands of years when in the thirteenth century A.D. Hulagu Khan killed off the populations of entire cities where the elites were concentrated. Since then there has not been enough time to replace them from the already drained countryside.[7]

The conclusion is that since the urban revolution some five thousand years ago, if not before, culture has speeded up anagenetic evolution among elites while retarding it among those left behind. Because this has happened in all races that have achieved the necessary degree of cultural complexity, we must be careful, in making interracial comparisons, to define the segments of the races that we are talking about.

How Races and Cultures Can Change Places

FINALLY, to add to the complexity of the interplay of race, geography, and culture, it may be noted that race and culture can change places. Two fairly recent, well-documented examples are the Black Caribs and the Ottoman Turks.

The Black Caribs are people who look like Negroes, speak an American Indian language and are culturally Indians, yet serologically they are between 90 percent, and 94 percent Negro.[8] During the seventeenth century one or more slave ships were wrecked on the shores of St. Vincent, an island in the Lesser Antilles 18 by 12 miles in size. The island was inhabited by Carib Indians, who were at war with the Europeans. In order to escape recapture, the Negroes adopted Carib culture, even to the point

6 P. Scott: "An Isonoetic Map of Tasmania," GR, Vol. 47, No. 3 (1957), pp. 311–29.

7 Weyl and Possony: op. cit., pp. 145–6. Also Coon: *Caravan* (New York: Henry Holt; 1958).

8 I. L. Firschein: "Population Dynamics of the Sickle-Cell Trait in the Black Caribs of British Honduras, Central America," AJHG, Vol. 13, No. 2 (1962), pp. 233–54.

of flattening their children's heads with boards. At first they helped the Caribs resist the whites, but when the Caribs refused to intermarry with them they fought the Caribs, who were reduced to a few families in the early 1700's. In 1796 the English subdued the Black Caribs, as they were now called, and moved them to Roatán Island off the coast of Spanish Honduras. At this time they numbered 5,080. By 1802 they had begun to appear in British Honduras, and now they have increased to a figure variously given as 20,000 to 50,000 and have settled in Roatán and along the Atlantic coast from British Honduras to Nicaragua.

I. L. Firschein, who studied their blood groups, suggests that originally they may have been more Indian than they are now because of the superiority of one or more of the Negro genes in resisting malaria. He has produced extensive documentary evidence from family histories to support this conclusion. How much more Indian they may once have been is not known.

The Ottoman Turks arrived in Asia Minor in the thirteenth century, a small band of horsemen numbering between 400 and 2,000, the remnants of a nomadic tribe expelled from Central Asia by the Mongols. The Seljuk Turks, who ruled the land and had themselves arrived only two centuries earlier, gave the Ottomans land to settle in near Ankara. From this small beginning, the Ottoman Turks quickly rose to power. In 1453 they captured Constantinople (Istanbul) and then swept over the Balkans. They had found Asia Minor well populated with Caucasoid Greeks, Armenians, and Kurds, and a few Seljuk Turks and Turkomans. During the next five centuries the Ottomans, who had come without women, intermarried with the native peoples of Anatolia and of the Balkans. They particularly admired the beauty of the Circassians, whom they converted to Islam. They also adopted many Christian youths, captured in childhood, who served their sultans as Janissaries in positions of authority. The Turks made themselves Caucasoid partly because they admired the Caucasoid features and partly because of their zeal in spreading Islam.[9]

We do not know exactly how Mongoloid the Ottoman Turks were when they left Central Asia, or how Mongoloid the Seljuks were either. The Turkomans today are primarily Caucasoid. In body measurements,[1] physical appearance, and in the ABO blood groups, the living Turks of Turkey show little visible trace of their

[9] H. A. R. Gibb and H. Bowen: *Islamic Society and the West: Islamic in the Eighteenth Century*, Vol. 1, Part 1 (London; Oxford University Press; 1950).

[1] H. T. E. Hertzberg et al.: *Anthropometric Survey of Turkey, Greece, and Italy* (New York: Pergamon Press; 1963).

Mongoloid origin. But they have appreciably less subcutaneous body fat, in the males, than Greeks and Italians, and in this respect, for what it is worth, they resemble the Chinese.[2] Yet linguistically they are still Turks.

On Race and Language, by Charles F. Hockett

TO THESE TWO EXAMPLES of the interplay between race and culture we add a section on race and language, written specifically for use in this book by the distinguished linguist, Charles F. Hockett.

"I suppose that we could view the racial history of mankind as the history of human gene pools: a community splits, so that a single gene pool becomes the (initially identical) gene pools of the two daughter communities; communities meet and interchange genes as well as other things; population expands and spreads and the genes go with the people. If we had full information about gene pools themselves, then in trying to reconstruct the racial history of mankind we should hardly need any other sort of information. But, of course, we don't, and never shall. Accordingly, we must make the best use we can of any and all information that is susceptible of genetic and racial interpretation.

"One type of indirect information is our information about human languages. There is, of course, no direct tie of necessity between genes and language—as was once suspected. But there is this basis for indirect inference: if two communities, speaking different languages, have been in sufficiently close and prolonged contact for one to borrow a sizable number of words from the other, then we can be sure—and this seems to be a generalization valid for all our species and all past time—not just one for Western civilization—that the communities have exchanged genes too. There is also another basis for indirect inference, which we can take up after discussing this one a little.

"Let us take an example. English and French are clearly distinct languages, and our records of the two show this distinctness. Yet English carries an enormous load of loan words from French, showing by their shape a thorough adaptation to English; and French currently is acquiring a considerable load of loans from contemporary English. If we had no other information, we would infer that Englishment has genes as well as words, imported from

2 K. P. Chen, A. Damon, and O. Eliot: "Body Form, Composition, and Some Physiological Functions of the Chinese on Taiwan," ANYA, Vol. 110, Part III (1963), pp. 760–77.

France, and that Frenchmen are now acquiring genes, as well as words, from England and America. The historical evidence shows that both inferences are right. Our load of French words in English was brought about by the Norman Conquest, The Normans who invaded England were, at that time, Germanic-speaking invaders of France: but they picked up plenty of French genes (as well as abandoning their earlier language and learning French) when they conquered Normandy; and they passed plenty of French genes on to the Englishmen they subjugated. The current fashion for borrowing English words into French is sociologically of a somewhat different sort, what with printing and radio and television; but at least some genes from England and America are obviously invading France along with the words.

"Now let us consider a somewhat different situation. Suppose we find two communities that speak *the same language*. This is not a matter of borrowing words: the *linguistic* ancestors of the people in the two communities must, not long ago, have been a single community. Perhaps the community split into two (or more) daughter communities, each inheriting language habits and genes from the parent community. If so, the genetic inference is obvious. But the situation may be more complicated than this—and still permit a racial inference.

"Suppose we note that the Gullah Negroes of the Sea Islands of Georgia speak what can only be called a variety of English, and that the present inhabitants of the islands of Kauai in Hawaii, largely Japanese but to some extent Hawaiian in ancestry, also speak what can only be called a variety of English. Here we would be quite wrong if we inferred that one of the communities acquired its present language, through long and intimate contact, from the other. The actual story is that the antecedents of each community acquired its present language through long and intimate contact with two other communities—Southern Caucasoids in the first case, American and British 'Haoles' in the second. The genes of these two donor groups were surely in part the same; hence we could be safe in assuming that the Gullah Negroes had some ultimately English (or 'Caucasian') genes in their pool, and that the Kauaians do also. In both cases, since a former language was lost and a new one taken on, the contact had to be sufficiently thoroughgoing to ensure gene flow too.

"This example leads us to the second type of situation in which some inference can be made, a situation sharply different from the first one we described above, although, superficially, it may seem similar. Suppose we find two communities which speak different languages, perhaps with no obvious load of loan words in either from the other; but that the distinct languages prove, on examination, to be related. That is: we are forced to conclude from the way that language works that at some time in the past, perhaps even several thousand years ago, they were the same language, and that they are now different only because in the intervening period they have undergone various independent developments. Here, again, some indirect racial inference is possible.

"For example, Bengali (a language of India) and English are the current results of different lines of development of what was, perhaps five to seven thousand years ago, a single language. That Bengali and English are related is beyond all doubt; that the relationship is of the sort just described, rather than merely a similarity due to borrowing from one to the other or by both from some common source, is also beyond all doubt. Now this is an extreme case. Yet we can at least be sure that, whatever other sources there may be for the gene pools of Bengali-speaking and English-speaking communities, *some* of the genes are held in common, and have been passed down in both lines of descent from the speakers of the ancient parent language. It may be that this inference is too vague to be of much value when one's aim is to reconstruct racial history, and it would not be proper to place too much faith in it as long as there are various other types of evidence that can be interpreted more directly and easily and less vaguely. Yet the inference is surely correct as far as it goes.

"It is for the reasons set forth above that, in our attempt to find out all we can about the racial history of Man, we find it worth while to collate what is known as the 'genetic' relationships of the languages of the world. It should be pointed out that it is sometimes not easy, and occasionally perhaps impossible, to determine whether the similarities between two languages are due to their common linguistic ancestry or to borrowing of forms of one from the other or of both from some third; or, indeed, to both of these possible reasons (as in the case of English and French). Such decisions have to be made by the specialists in linguistics, and are sometimes very long in being made with any sureness. But it is at least worth while to tabulate what is currently known or strongly (and conservatively) suspected by the experts."

The Classification of Languages

THE PRECEDING SECTION is valuable to us not only because of its intrinsic interest, but also because it serves as an introduction to a brief explanation of the classification of languages. In the next five chapters linguistic classification will be used as a means of identifying the peoples who speak related languages, such as the Berbers or the Polynesians.

As Hockett has explained, race is inherited, a language is learned. Just as races differ because of mixture, natural selection, social selection, and random drift, so languages come to change through borrowing, analogy, and changes in sounds.[3] The word *language* itself is an example of borrowing. When people say a *deck* of cigarettes instead of a *pack* of cigarettes, they are substituting one word for another through an analogy between cigarettes and playing cards.

Sounds change because of fashion, imitation of dominant personalities, or to a much greater degree simply because of the innumerable tiny imperfections of pronunciation in the speech of each of us—all of which can lead to drift. While sounds are changing in a language, people who speak it can still understand each other because in every sentence we use more sounds than we need to convey our meaning. But after populations who originally spoke the same language have parted company and become isolated from each other for a length of time, the change is more critical. If they later meet again, they will be unable to understand each other. They will be talking different languages.

It is the task of the linguistic scientist to determine whether or not languages are related. He does this to a large extent by comparing lists of cognate words that have or once had the same meaning. He must of course consider at the same time the effects of borrowing, analogy, and changes in sounds. If he finds that two languages have more cognates in common than could be explained by the law of chance, he concludes that they are genetically related—and he is using the word *genetically* in a different sense from a biologist. Biologists need not sneer at this: linguists used the word first.

Languages found to be related are said to belong to a common family. But because degrees of relationship vary, some linguists expand the classification to include the categories of phylum, superfamily, family, subfamily, and linguistic group. Other linguists do not like to express linguistic relationships in so elaborate a framework. In the next five chapters we shall follow both methods, depending on whose work we are quoting, but in the main we shall rely on the classification of the languages of the world by G. L. Trager, in the 1965 edition of *Collier's Encyclopedia*.

3 C. F. Hockett: "Sound Change," presidential address given at the annual meeting of the Linguistic Society of America, Dec. 28, 1964, New York.

Cultural Selection in the Formation of Races

THE EXAMPLES of the Black Caribs and the Ottoman Turks, which we cited before discussing linguistics, point up another factor in the interplay between culture and race. It is that some people wish to be incorporated with others and for more than one reason. We see this every day. Japanese women with a light skin and a narrow nose are preferred in the cities as mates over darker, more moon-faced ones. Syrian Christians have a practice of sending lighter-skinned girls to the United States to be married, and darker ones to Brazil. Selection for light-skinned brides among successful American Negro males is too common an ocurrence to require documentation.

Cultural selection in the formation of the races of man is, as always, a complicated matter and follows more than one direction. As in the remote past, it continues to play a decisive part in the paired facets of amalgamation and selection which influence human racial differentiation. V. Gordon Childe entitled a book *Man Makes Himself*. He might have added a fourth word, *Variable*.

3

Europe and West Asia

✵✵✵

The Divisions of the Caucasoid Region, Past and Present

As stated in Chapter 2, the Pleistocene homeland of the Caucasoids was an irregularly shaped area extending from the Atlantic coast of Europe to Baluchistan, bounded on the north by uninhabited lands and on the south, except for the Isthmus of Suez, by salt water. During the Pleistocene, therefore, from the standpoint of human habitation Europe really was a separate continent, and not merely a peninsula of Asia. Like two triangles meeting at their points, these two halves of the Caucasoid homeland faced each other at the Bosporus, the chief avenue of cultural and genetic communication.

At the end of the Pleistocene, Caucasoid hunters from both Europe and West Asia moved north into the previously uninhabited areas of Scandinavia and of European and Asiatic Russia. At that time began the uninterrupted contacts between Caucasoids and Mongoloids which created the clinal populations of Central and Northern Asia.

Geographic and Climatic Peculiarities of Europe and West Asia

THE PARTS of Europe and West Asia inhabited during the Pleistocene differ from the homelands of the other races in several respects. Extending from 55° to 36° N. latitude, the European cradleland lies north of all the others. It overlaps by only two degrees the Mongoloid and Capoid homes, each of which runs from 38° N. latitude to about the Tropic of Cancer. But West Asia, between 44° and 13° N. latitude, spans both the Mongoloid and the Capoid ranges.

Climatically Europe and West Asia resemble each other, and in combination they are unique. According to the Köppen system —used by many geographers because it is based on exact definitions[1]—Europe and West Asia hold a near monopoly of the so-called *Cfb* and *Csa* climates, the maritime and the Mediterranean.[2] Both have mild winters with the temperature of the coldest month above 26.6° F. (-3° C.). The maritime climate has cool, wet summers; the Mediterranean has hot, dry ones. The former is concentrated in Western Europe and central Anatolia; the latter along the shores of inland seas and on the western slopes of Zagros Mountains. A variant of the Mediterranean climate, *Csb*—with cool, dry summers—is found in Portugal and on the mountains of Iran. During the unglaciated portions of the Ice Age—72 percent of it—the climates of these regions were probably more or less as they are today. During the glaciated portions—28 percent—part of what is now Mediterranean was maritime, and what is now maritime was wet and foggy. The cave country of southern France was heath or moorland covered with low, thorny scrub. To the north was tundra. Both made prime browsing and grazing for the large animals that the Upper Paleolithic people hunted.

The prevalence of maritime and Mediterranean climates in Europe and Western Asia depends on a combination of unusual geographical features. Europe has the longest coastline, in proportion to its surface area, of all continents, even though it is the second smallest and has a long land frontier with Asia. The Gulf Stream bathes its North Atlantic coast with warm water. Its principal mountain ranges run east and west, permitting the prevailing westerly winds to carry moisture far inland, especially during the summer. The Mediterranean basin also forms an unimpeded course for rain-bearing winds during the winter, watering Western Asia, which also derives some moisture from the Black and Caspian seas.

Living in the maritime climate for millennia, and in the periglacial one before it, Northern and Western Europeans have been

---

[1] See P. E. James: *An Outline of Geography* (Boston: Ginn & Co.; 1935), pp. 370–9.
[2] W. Köppen does not use these terms.

exposed to the selective influences of dim light, chilly but not very cold winters, cool summers, and great extremes of seasonal variation in the length of daylight. No more invigorating or stimulating climate could be found. A similar climate at a higher altitude and a lower latitude is found in the central plateau of Anatolia, and narrow strips of it flank the peaks of the Caucasus Mountains. This Anatolian-Caucasian region is the heart of the part of the world in which agriculture and animal husbandry began. When these inventions spread into Europe, they needed little alteration or selection because of the similarity of climates. That is one reason why food production spread into Europe rapidly and helped unify the original Caucasoid homelands even more than before.

Other types of climate extend to the north and east and to the south and east. To the north and east are, successively, dry lands (B climates), cold damp lands (D climates), and polar deserts (E climates). To the south and east, mostly dry climates prevail, with a few exceptions. The Yemen Plateau has a *Cw* climate, cool with dry winters and summer rain. Small portions of Tadzhikistan and Uzbekistan, flanking the Tien Shan Mountains, have Mediterranean-like climates.

From the point of view of adaptation, the cold climates can Pleistocene, and we see such adaptations mainly in the body proportions of such people as the Russians, Lapps, and far Northern Norwegians. But the dry climates of the south and east, particularly Arabia, are found in regions that have been inhabited as have influenced Caucasoid people only since the end of the long as Caucasoids have existed. Therefore adaptation to dry air, and particularly to dry summer heat, may have been an important factor in the evolution of some Caucasoid populations, just as adaptation to cool damp weather and dim light was to others. In the climatic extremes of northwestern Europe and Arabia divergent Caucasoid racial types evolved.

The Archaeological Evidence of Caucasoid Unity and Diversity

APART FROM LANGUAGE, the most basic element of culture is toolmaking, believed to have been invented at about the same time as language, and at the same evolutionary level. But only tools have survived as imperishable evidence of culture. They indicate that during the Pleistocene the inhabited parts of the Old

World were divided into two major archaeological regions, a western and an eastern one, by a geographical frontier that we shall call Movius's Line, after its discoverer.[3] (See Map 3, p. 28.) It runs down the spine of Asia to the Pamirs, east along the southern flank of the Himalayas, then south along the frontier of India and Burma into the Indian Ocean. Although it may have been breached a few times and in more than one place before the end of the Pleistocene, on the whole a self-contained archaeological tradition evolved on either side of it.[4]

In each region toolmaking began with the same common simple techniques of splitting pebbles and shaping crude cores of quartzite, flint, or in some cases fossil wood into choppers (tools shaped on one edge) and chopping tools (shaped on both), but the industries of the two regions had begun to diverge as early as the First Interglacial Period, 1,375,000 to 1,205,000 years ago. During at least the next million years, each followed its own evolutionary course.[5]

TABLE 3

CHRONOLOGY OF THE PLEISTOCENE
(AFTER D. B. ERICSON AND G. WOLLIN)

	Began	Ended (years before present)
Würm-Wisconsin, Main	65,000	11,000
Interstadial	95,000	65,000
Early	115,000	95,000
Third Interglacial	340,000	115,000
Riss-Illinoian	420,000	340,000
Second Interglacial	1,060,000	420,000
Mindel-Kansan	1,205,000	1,060,000
First Interglacial	1,375,000	1,205,000
Günz-Nebraskan	1,500,000	1,375,000
Villafranchian	?	1,500,000

Although the paleolithic archaeology of Europe and West Asia is extremely complex and impossible to summarize adequately in a few pages, we may, for present purposes, make a few generalizations. The principal mineral materials were quartzite and flint, in the later periods almost exclusively flint. Obsidian came in late, and was particularly abundant in Armenia. Bone, antler, and

[3] H. L. Movius, Jr.: *Early Man and Pleistocene Stratigraphy in Southeast Asia*, PMP, Vol. 19, No. 3 (1944).
[4] Movius: "Old World Prehistory: Paleolithic," in A. L. Kroeber et al.: *Anthropology Today* (Chicago: University of Chicago Press; 1953), pp. 163–92.
[5] Our chronology is based on Ericson and Wollin: op. cit.

ivory were fashioned into tools mostly toward the end of the Pleistocene.

Stone tools may be divided into those made by producing cores, by producing flakes, and by producing blades. Some tools of all three categories are also retouched. The earliest were core tools and simple flakes. The core tools were gradually replaced by flake tools during the Third Interglacial and Early Würm. During the latter part of the Second Interglacial a new invention in flake production appeared. Instead of striking flakes off a core without previous preparation, the toolmaker preshaped his core to enable him to strike off with a single, well-directed blow a flake of preconceived form. This was the so-called Levallois technique. Blade tools were made by a further refinement of this technique, in which the craftsman placed a punch of horn, bone, or some other elastic material between the core and the hammer. Such blades began to appear in Early Würm and gradually outnumbered flake tools in Late Würm.

The tools found in a single level of a site form an integral whole known as an industry. Each industry so far recognized has been found in more than one site in regions adequately explored by archaeologists. The geographical ranges of these industries vary greatly in size.

At all periods of the Pleistocene different industries coexisted, as indicated by examples cited in Chapter 2. Some contemporaneous industries borrowed techniques from each other; some died out; and others merged. The sequences of broad categories of industries in West Asia and Europe followed similar courses, and some industries were the same in each, except for minor local differences. No general category of industries seems to have been unique in either Europe or West Asia, but individual industries were, particularly during the Late Würm and especially in Europe.

From the First through the Third Interglacial periods, two industrial traditions coexisted, one with flakes only, the other with both flake and core tools. The first began with the Clactonian and evolved into the Tayacian. The second began with the Abbevillian (formerly called Chellean) and evolved into the Acheulean. The Abbevillian-Acheulean industry was characterized by hand axes and by flakes technically different from those of the Clactonian-Tayacian sequence. Toward the end of the Third Interglacial these two sequences converged into a complex of closely related cultures, some of which are known as Mousterian and others as Levalloiso-Mousterian, depending on the percentage in each of flakes struck off by the Levalloisian technique.

In Europe four such industries are recognized. Three of them became extinct. The fourth, the so-called Mousterian of Acheulean tradition, not only carried over a modified form of hand axe from the Acheulean but also evolved into a local Upper Paleolithic culture, the Perigordian, found in southern France and northern Spain.

In Western Asia also, a local Levalloisian-Mousterian culture containing the so-called Emireh points, which are retouched on the bulb side of the base, evolved into an Upper Paleolithic culture. This was the well-known Aurignacian, which spread into Europe. In France and northern Spain it coexisted with the Perigordian for a while and later replaced it. During the late Würm, a North African industry penetrated Spain by way of Gibraltar. We know this because tanged, bifacially retouched flakes of the so-called Aterian industry of Morocco and elsewhere have been found in several sites in southern Spain. This suggests the introduction of African, presumably proto-Bushman, genes into Western Europe at that time. The Solutrean, a distinctive industry with large, bifacially retouched blades, appeared and disappeared. The Magdalenian arose alongside the others and gradually replaced them. This was the culture which produced most of the cave art and made the greatest use of bone, antler, and ivory. In Southern Europe and Western Asia variants of the Aurignacian culture lasted to the end of the Pleistocene, as did the Magdalenian in Western Europe.

Toward the end of the Pleistocene, both the Magdalenian in Europe and the Aurignacian in Western Asia evolved into Mesolithic industries that were carried convergently into the erstwhile unpopulated lands of Northern Europe, Eastern Europe, and western Siberia. But some sites in Siberia may be older. Habitation sites in the Upper Yenisei Valley at Malta, 80 kilometers northwest of Irkutsk, and at Buret, 50 kilometers farther north, contain remains of semisubterranean houses similar to those occupied by Ugrian-speaking tribes farther north in modern times. The industry at these sites is a local Upper Paleolithic one which contains some implements of Mousterian aspect and others which are Solutrean. The excavators also found many female figurines.

C. S. Chard places these sites, which have not been dated by Carbon-14, at the end of the Würm, at about 10,000 B.C.[6] G. Bushnell and C. McBurney would have them earlier.[7] A. P. Okladnikov,

[6] C. S. Chard: "New World Origins: A Reappraisal," *Antiquity*, Vol. 33, No. 129 (1959), pp. 44–9.

[7] G. Bushnell and C. McBurney: "New World Origins Seen from the Old," *Antiquity*, Vol. 33, No. 130 (1959), pp. 93–101.

the Russian archaeologist in charge, does not give them definite dates, only cultural associations with the West.[8] At any rate, these cultures evolved through several stages into a Neolithic of long duration. The interior of northeastern Siberia, now known through many sites, was probably unoccupied before 2500 B.C., a point of interest to specialists concerned with the origin of the American Indians.

The evidence summarized in this section indicates that in a general way during the Pleistocene the inhabitants of Europe and West Asia maintained a balance between local cultural isolation, parallel cultural evolution with an exchange of basic techniques if not of tool types, and broad cultural diffusions from time to time. Toward the end of the Pleistocene the Western Asian cultures spread eastward and northward into southern Siberia. This implies the possibility of a combination of local genetic differentiation in the Caucasoid homeland with enough gene flow between individual regions to maintain the broad unity of the subspecies, and enough between the Caucasoid homeland as a whole and other regions, in Asia and Africa, to serve the same purpose for the entire human species.

A Summary of Caucasoid Racial History

THE PHYSICAL EVOLUTION of Caucasoids in Europe has been traced with varying degrees of certainty from the First Interglacial—the time of the Heidelberg jaw or the Mauer mandible—to the end of the Pleistocene. In Western Asia the record is briefer; it starts with the Third Interglacial. More work, however, promises to extend this record backward in time. In Europe we find a threefold succession of early Caucasoids, Neanderthals, and Upper Paleolithic people. In Western Asia only the last two have been found.

Because this subject is covered at length in *The Origin of Races*, Chapter 11, there is no need to repeat it in detail here. But certain additions and changes based on new discoveries need be recorded, and also we must make a closer identification of specific skeletons with special industries.

A new fossil cranium has been found in a cave in Greece,[9]

8 A. P. Okladnikov: *Ancient Population of Siberia and Its Cultures*, RTPM, Vol. 1, No. 1 (1959).

9 P. Kokkoros and A. Kanellis: "Découverte d'un crâne d'homme paléolithique dans la péninsule chalcidique," *L'Anth*, Vol. 64, No. 5–6 (1961), pp. 438–46.

accompanied by animal bones but without tools. It has tentatively been assigned to Würm I. It has heavy, continuous browridges, a flattish orbitonasal region, and a flat occipital base. It resembles most closely Monte Circeo and to a lesser extent Jebel Ighoud (Morocco) and Broken Hill. E. Bostanci considers it a very primitive member of the Mediterranean branch of Neanderthals.

Another change is that the Krapina finds from Yugoslavia, formerly assigned to the Third Interglacial, have been reassigned to the Göttweig Interstadial of the Upper Würm Glaciation.[1] This makes them part of the Upper Paleolithic cranial assemblage, which makes excellent sense, because in certain respects they resemble closely the modern population of their region. Like the living Croats, they are mostly brachycephalic.

The old idea that Upper Paleolithic Caucasoids evolved directly from Neanderthals in Europe, West Asia, or both, is currently being revived[2] for three reasons. The search for a homeland in which Caucasoids could have evolved directly from Lower to Upper Paleolithic man without an intervening Neanderthal stage becomes more hopeless every time a new region is explored archaeologically. More and more evidence is being found of cultural continuity between Mousterian and Upper Paleolithic industries in various places. Neanderthal skulls, teeth, and bones are very variable, and some of them are far less deviant from the Upper Paleolithic remains than was once thought. And some of the Upper Paleolithic skulls show certain Neanderthaloid features.[3]

In France, where the Mousterian of Acheulean tradition seems to have evolved into the Lower Perigordian,[4] we have trouble testing this hypothesis anatomically because only one skeleton can be identified with certainty with each culture. The Neanderthal specimen is the adolescent cranium of Pech de l'Azé; the Perigordian one is the Combe Capelle skeleton. The "classic" Neanderthals whose remains have been described at length belonged to the

E. Bostanci: "An Examination of a Neanderthal-type Fossil Skull Found in the Chalcidique Peninsula," *Belleten*, Vol. 28, No. 3 (1964), pp. 373–81. A. Kanellē and A. Sabba: *Kraniometrikē Meletē tou Homo Neanderthalensis tōn Petralēnōn* (Thessalonikē; Aristoteleion Panepistēmion Thessalonikēs, Physikomathematike Scholē; 1964).

1 E. W. Guenther; "Zur Altersdatierung der diluvialen Fundstelle von Krapina in Kroatien," BDGA, 6 Tagung (1959), pp. 202–9.

2 C. L. Brace: "The Fate of the 'Classic' Neanderthals: A Consideration of Hominid Catastrophism," CA, Vol. 5, No. 1 (1964), pp. 3–43.

3 This has been observed particularly in the endocranial cast of Cro-Magnon 3. V. I. Kochetkova: "Muliaj Mozgovoi Polosti Iskopaemovo Cheloveka Kro-Magnon III," TMOIP, Vol. 14 (1964), pp. 111–35.

4 Bordes: op. cit., pp. 803–10.

La Quina–La Ferrassie tradition, which died out. The rest of the European Upper Paleolithic specimens that can be positively identified with cultures are all Aurignacian or Magdalenian. Nevertheless, Pech de l'Azé and Combe Capelle are enough alike to support the hypothesis that one evolved into the other.

In West Asia the transition from Mousterian to Aurignacian is shown in a site in Ksar Akil in Lebanon, the description of which is still waiting publication, and probably in another in Yabrud, Syria, which is being dug again. The physical evidence, mostly from Mt. Carmel, is more abundant and much clearer.[5] By emphasizing the importance of these two instances of evolution from Neanderthal to Upper Paleolithic Caucasoid we do not mean to imply that this transition could not have happened elsewhere. It not only could have but probably did occur in more than one place. The Magdalenian people of Europe, whose industry began later than the Aurignacian, were probably descendants of earlier Upper Paleolithic peoples, just as the Mesolithic peoples of Northern Europe were descended from Magdalenians.

In West Asia from the Bosporus to the upper waters of the Amu Darya it is more than likely that epipaleolithic people, like those whose skeletons were found in Hotu Cave,[6] evolved into the Mesolithic populations of the same regions. Thus, when the erstwhile empty lands of Northern and Eastern Europe and Western Siberia were opened for settlement by the retreat of the ice cap, hunters, fowlers, and fresh-water fishermen moved in from both sources and met. The available skeletal material, such as it is, supports this view. Other skeletal material shows that as the northwest Europeans were moving northward and eastward, Mediterranean people were moving northward into France.

The principal Mesolithic culture of Palestine was the Natufian. The skeletons of Natufians excavated at several sites indicate that they were rather short, lightly built, Gracile Mediterraneans with long heads and narrow faces, like many Arabs, Spaniards, and Portuguese today.[7] They also resemble some of the living Dravidian peoples of southern India.

The Mesolithic people of the northern borders of the Caucasoid country of Western Asia were heavier-boned and larger-toothed,

[5] T. D. McCown and Sir A. Keith: *The Stone Age of Mount Carmel,* Vol. 2 (Oxford: Clarendon Press; 1939).

[6] J. L. Angel: "The Human Skeletal Remains from Hotu Cave, Iran," PAPS, Vol. 96, No. 3 (1952), pp. 258–69.

[7] T. D. McCown: "Natufian Crania from Mt. Carmel," Ph.D. Thesis, University of California, Berkeley, 1940. Ferembach: "Squelettes du Natoufien d'Israël étude anthropologique," *L'Anth,* Vol. 65, No. 1–2, (1961), pp. 46–66.

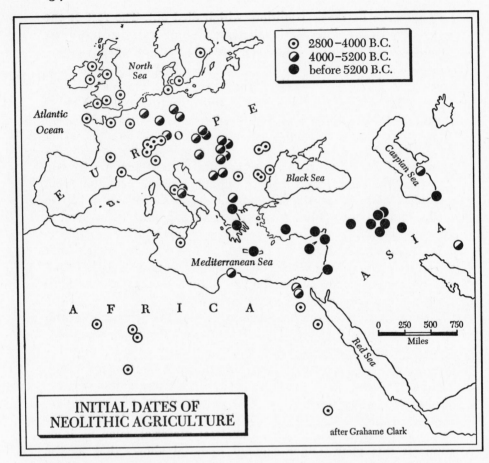

Legend:
- ⊙ 2800–4000 B.C.
- ◑ 4000–5200 B.C.
- ● before 5200 B.C.

INITIAL DATES OF
NEOLITHIC AGRICULTURE

after Grahame Clark

judging by those so far excavated, particularly at Belt and Hotu caves. Thus Mediterranean and Nordic populations may be distinguished both in Europe and in West Asia during the span of the Mesolithic. It is a moot point whether the Nordic skeletal type of Neolithic Northern Europe came from the West or the East, or from both.[8]

The racial history of Europe and Western Asia from the beginning of agriculture around 7,000 B.C. to modern times was covered in detail in *The Races of Europe*.[9] During the twenty-six years since the appearance of that work, Europeans in several countries have published extensive studies of local populations of

[8] K. Bröste and J. P. Jørgensen: *Prehistoric Man in Denmark*, 2 vols. (Copenhagen: Einar Munksgaard Publishers; 1956). See also Coon's review of same in *Antiquity*, Vol. 32, No. 127 (1958), pp. 207–8.

[9] Coon: *The Races of Europe*.

various periods from the Neolithic to medieval times. These provide useful documentation, but contain few if any surprises.

When agriculture was introduced into Central and Western Europe it followed two routes, up the Danube and across to the Rhine, and along the Mediterranean coasts into France, and from there over the English Channel into the British Isles. Along both routes the local climates were suitable for the introduction of West Asian plants and domestic animals (if indeed some of them did not originate in Eastern Europe). There was no need to substitute local species, as had to be done when the same agricultural complex was carried into China and the Sudan, regions of summer rain. For this reason agriculture moved rapidly, taking no more than 1,700 years to go from the Black Sea (6,220 ± 150 B.C. in Macedonia) to the North Sea (4,500 ± 100 B.C. in the Netherlands).[1]

It followed two routes, one north and the other south of the Alps, meeting at what had been the Pleistocene boundary between heath and tundra and is now the boundary between Germanic and Romance languages. The Mediterranean Neolithic cultures were the first to reach the British Isles. To what extent these were population movements and to what extent diffusions among earlier populations it is difficult if not impossible to tell. In Germany at any rate there were several Neolithic cultures and considerable anatomical variation, with no particular correlation between culture and cranial type.[2]

During the later history of Europe, climatic changes played a predominant role in influencing the movements of peoples. During episodes of mild winter weather, Germanic and Celtic tribesmen browsed their cattle out of doors at all seasons. At times of continental climate, life became hazardous. Entire tribes and nations, which had become populous in the meantime, moved southward, invading France, Spain, Portugal, Italy, Greece, and even Asia Minor and Palestine, as every student of European history knows. Northern peoples also settled in the British Isles in several waves, some prehistoric, others historic.

In the drier lands of Eastern Europe and west-central Asia the critical variable was not so much temperature as drought. There nomadic peoples who had built up large herds were forced to move as the grass failed. They invaded Iran, Iraq, Afghanistan, Greater

1 C. C. Lamberg-Karloski: "Concerning Gimbutas' 'The Indo-Europeans: Archaeological Problems,'" AA, Vol. 66, No. 4, Part 1 (1964), pp. 887–9.

2 H. Grimm: "Neue Ergebnisse zur Anthropologie des Mitteldeutschen Neolithikums," paper read at 7th International Congress for Anthropological and Ethnological Sciences, Moscow, August 3-10, 1964.

India, and China, as well as Western Europe. The principle of this discussion is that the lands too cold for human habitation during the Pleistocene became climatically unstable after the last ice had melted, and the period of readjustment to an interglacial climate produced far-reaching population movements. These movements unified the Caucasoid peoples to the extent we see today; the repeated invasion of Mediterranean lands from the north were especially influential.

Language Studies and Racial Movements

THESE MOVEMENTS and invasions can be traced by several means besides the examination of skeletons and archaeology. One of these is the comparison of languages living and extinct, as outlined in Chapter 2. In the following linguistic survey we must remember that language is, from our point of view, only a tracer. It cannot account for the biological processes by which races are formed, but it can indicate who moved where.

Following G. L. Trager's recent classification of the languages of the world,[3] we may assign the languages spoken today in the Caucasoid homeland to three major units or phyla: Indo-Hittite, Ural-Altaic, and Afro-Asiatic. In addition there are a number of lesser units, including Basque, South Caucasic, and North Caucasic. Basque is an isolated language. South Caucasic is a family, and North Caucasic may be a family, a superfamily, or simply a collection of neighboring languages.

Of Indo-Hittite, only the superfamily Indo-European survives. Ural-Altaic includes one superfamily, Uralic, divided into two families, Finno-Ugric and Samoyed, and three other families, Turkic, Mongolic, and Tungusic. Only one of the five Afro-Asiatic families, Semitic, is spoken outside of Africa, where the phylum presumably originated.

We have no knowledge of Semitic before around 2500 B.C., when the Akkadians took over writing on tablets from the Sumerians. Indo-Hittite appears about 1,300 years later, when the

3 G. L. Trager: "Languages of the World," in *Collier's Encyclopedia*, 1964 edition, Vol. 14, pp. 299–304. For the sake of consistency, and in order to be both conservative and up to date, we are following Trager's classification in this and the next four chapters. We have also extensively used A. Meillet and M. Cohen: *Les Langues du Monde*, CNRS, Paris, 1952; and the table in *Atlas Narodov Miri*, Moscow, 1964. Where other studies have been consulted, pertinent references will be given.

Hittites invaded Asia Minor from Europe. Ural-Altaic is not known with any certainty before the Christian era. Between the beginning of Sumerian writing and the introduction of the Phoenician and Greek alphabets, many languages of Asia Minor and Mesopotamia were written in cuneiform, and all of them are extinct. Sumerian has no demonstrable linguistic affiliation, which is not surprising since there is no other written language of the same age. Equally isolated are Elamite, spoken in southwestern Iran, and Hurrian, spoken in the northern Zagros. Hatti and Halde, which were mutually related, influenced Hittite and Armenian, respectively. The Greek alphabet was later adopted by several peoples of western Asia Minor, including the Lycians, Lydians, Carians, and Pisidians, whose inscriptions are too fragmentary for linguistic analysis, but which were not in Greek.

Other presumably non-Indo-Hittite languages of antiquity include early Cretan (Linear A; not B, which was Greek); some local language of Cyprus represented by a single bilingual inscription paired with Greek; and, according to most scholars who have worked on it, Etruscan, spoken in northern Italy.[4] Traditionally one or more pre-Hellenic languages were spoken in Greece before Greek; a non-Indo-Hittite element may have been incorporated in the essentially Celtic Pictish of Scotland;[5] and finally, one such language survives—Basque. These languages, all extending from Cyprus to Scotland, and all but one extinct, have been tentatively assigned to a phylum called Mediterranean.

Basque, the extinct Mediterranean languages, the extinct so-called "Asianic" languages, the languages of the Caucasus, and a morphologically similar language, Burushaski, spoken in a remote valley of northwestern Pakistan, constitute a recognizable wedge between the Semitic languages on the southwest and the Indo-European and Ural-Altaic languages to the north. They outline an ancient geographical continuity uniting the highlands of Western Asia with Europe south and west of the winter frost line, and north of the Arabian peninsula.

The Semitic languages, which probably became differentiated in Arabia, are very much alike, whether living or extinct. This fact denies them much antiquity in Asia. The family is divided into an

4 Z. Mayani has recently derived Etruscan from the Indo-Hittite Illyrian, represented today by Albanian. He agrees that the Etruscans came from Asia Minor. Z. Mayani: *Les Étrusques Commencent à Parler* (Paris: Arthaud; 1961). R. Bloch has rejected this identification in a review of Mayani's book in *Antiquity*, Vol. 37, No. 147 (1963), p. 238.

5 K. H. Jackson: "The Pictish Language," Chapter 6 and Appendix in F. T. Wainwright, ed.: *The Problem of the Picts* (New York: Philosophical Library; 1956), pp. 129–66.

eastern and a western subfamily. The eastern subfamily consists only of Akkadian and its closely derived Babylonian and Assyrian. The western subfamily is split into a northern and a southern language group. The northern consists of Canaanite and Ara-maean. Canaanite consists of Hebrew and Phoenician.[6] The southern division has only one language, Aramaean. Hebrew has been revived as a spoken language in Israel; modern Aramaean, in two forms, is still spoken in two villages of northern Syria and among the Nestorian Christians living in the Rizaiyeh region of northwestern Iran and adjacent parts of Iraq. Southwestern Se-mitic consists of Arabic and three southern Arabian languages spoken in Dhofar and on the island of Socotra. (See Map 7, p. 73.)

As linguists have been studying Indo-Hittite for well over a century, many theories about its origins and spread have been proposed. One, reported by Trager, is that the speakers of the earliest Indo-Hittite lived in south-central Russia sometime after 3500 B.C.—during Neolithic times. Before 2500 B.C. a group left for the southeast, eventually reached Asia Minor, and produced Hittite and several related languages of the Anatolian family. The superfamily that was left was Indo-European, which is what some linguists call the whole phylum.

According to this reconstruction, the ancestors of the speakers of Armenian, Indo-Iranian, and Hellenic between 2300 B.C. and 2000 B.C. departed from south-central Russia in close succession. What may be called the European superfamily was left. Italic and Celtic languages were taken west and south, leaving Germanic and Balto-Slavic. The Germanic speakers migrated west and north, and then Baltic speakers left the Slavs, who remained alone in their homeland.

Another theory, based on the identification of the words for plant and animal species in the reconstructed old Indo-European, places the homeland of that family in Northern Europe in the region drained by the Elbe, the Oder, and the Rhine.[7] The key words in this geographical exercise are "beech," "salmon," and "turtle." Beech does not grow east of a line from Königsberg (now Kaliningrad) to Odessa. Salmon runs only in these three rivers. Turtles do not occur north of Germany. The same study indicates that the combined Indo-European speakers had gold, hoes, pigs, cattle, sheep, goats, wagons and wagon wheels, and possibly horses.

---

6 Plus Ugaritic, known only from a single site.

7 P. Thieme: "The Indo-European Language," SA, Vol. 199 No. 4 (1958), pp. 63–74.

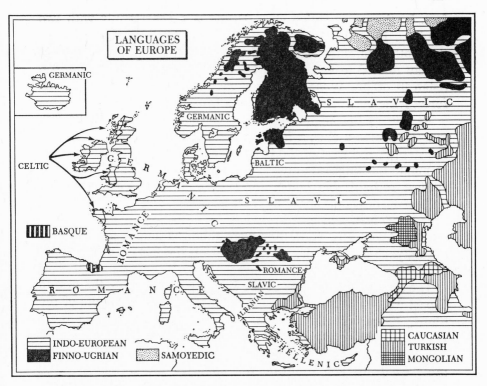

LANGUAGES
OF EUROPE

GERMANIC

CELTIC

BASQUE

INDO-EUROPEAN
FINNO-UGRIAN
SAMOYEDIC

CAUCASIAN
TURKISH
MONGOLIAN

GERMANIC

BALTIC

SLAVIC

ROMANCE

ROMANCE
SLAVIC

ALBANIAN

HELLENIC

These words indicate a late Neolithic or an early Bronze Age date, in that region probably no earlier than 2500 B.C. If this interpretation is correct, however, it does not mean that Indo-European is no more than 2,500 years old, or that these people invented agriculture, the wheel, or metallurgy; only that the vast expansions of Indo-European-speaking peoples, whose languages have been carried to many parts of the world, did not begin until after they had acquired agriculture from a center farther east. They even reached Chinese Turkestan, where Indo-European speech persisted through the Buddhist period—to be replaced by Turkish—and some of them drove their wagons over the Hindu Kush to India.

Ural-Altaic Languages

VERY CONSERVATIVE LINGUISTS are not satisfied that the Uralic and so-called Altaic languages have so far been shown to constitute a phylum. Other scholars consider this an established fact. In the conservative view, Uralic is a superfamily with two families, Finno-Ugric and Samoyed. The Altaic part consists of three other families, Turkic, Mongolic, and Tungusic, which are closely related to each other. Uralic is European, Altaic Central Asian in origin. What languages were spoken in antiquity in the forest lying between the two centers is unknown.

As late as the beginning of the Christian era the Uralic languages formed a cluster in the forests of eastern Russia north of the steppes and west of the Urals. Because this is still their region of maximum linguistic diversity, it is believed to have been their earliest recognizable home. Among the first to leave were the Samoyeds, or people speaking their language, and today the Samoyeds hunt, fish, and breed reindeer in a vast segment of western Siberia. About A.D. 1000 they were followed across the Urals by the Ostyaks and Voguls, who camped on the banks of the Upper Ob River.

The linguistic ancestors of the Lapps were probably the first to depart westward and northward, followed by the ancestors of the Finns, Esths, Livs, Karelians, and the Finnish tribes around Leningrad. These movements probably did not begin much before A.D. 500, when after the Hunnish incursions the Slavs began to press eastward and infiltrate the home of the Ugrian-speaking peoples. Some of the latter, the Cheremisses and Mordvins, are still there, living in enclaves among Russians and Turkish-speaking Tatars.

Before the fifth century A.D., under Hunnish influence, the Ugrian-speaking Bulgars moved southward, eventually to Bulgaria, where they adopted Slavic speech. In the ninth century A.D. the Ugrian-speaking Magyars migrated to Hungary under Turkish leaders. By the time Leif Ericson discovered North America, the Uralic-speaking peoples had arrived in their present locations in Siberia and Europe.

Of the other three Ural-Altaic families, Tungusic does not concern us in this chapter, nor does Mongolic except in the sense that Genghis Khan's hordes left a colony of Mongolian-speaking Buddhist Kalmucks on the west bank of the Lower Volga in Russia, where some are still to be found. Others have migrated back to the Altai, to Paraguay, to Philadelphia, Pennsylvania, and to Medford, New Jersey. Mongolian is also spoken in a few relict villages of northeastern Iran and northwestern Afghanistan by people called the Chahar Aimak.

But Turkish does concern us because it is spoken in many parts of Eastern Europe from Bosnia to the Crimea and up into the

Tatar settlements of eastern Russia; in the republic of Turkey; among many nomadic and seminomadic tribes of Iraq and Iran; and across the whole sweep of Central Asia from the Caspian to China.

TABLE 4

SOME NAMES OF FINNO-UGRIAN PEOPLES OF EUROPE AND WESTERN SIBERIA, IN RUSSIAN AND ENGLISH

Russian	English	Russian	English
I FINNIC GROUP		**II UGRIAN GROUP**	
Finni	Finns	Vengri	Magyars
Kareli	Karelians	Khanti	Ostyaks
Estontsi	Esths	Mansi	Voguls
Livi	Livs		
Ijortsi	Ijores	**III SAMOYED GROUP**	
Vepsi	Veps	Nentsi	Samoyeds of area from Kanin Peninsula to Yenisei
Saami	Lapps*		
Komi	Zyrians		
Udmurti	Votyaks	Entsi	Samoyeds of Lower Yenisei
Mariitsi	Cheremisses		
Mordva	Mordvins	Ngansani	Samoyeds of Taimyr Peninsula
		Selkupi	Ostyak-Samoyeds of Upper Ob-Yenisei

* Although the Lapp language contains many Finnish words, some authors consider it to belong to the Ugrian group.

Turkish is first known from inscriptions of the eighth century A.D. in the Altai Mountains athwart the spine of Asia, in a cold forested region connecting the Siberian taiga with the chilly Tibetan plateau. As far as we know, this is the Turkish homeland, whence the historic Turks, converted to Islam by the Arabs and Persians in Russian Turkestan, enthusiastically spread their new faith almost as widely as had their teachers. In fact, they conquered the Arabs in their holiest lands, whence they were evicted with British help in World War I.

The Living Europeans

DESPITE their linguistic differentiation, which is a product of history, the living Europeans are to a large extent unified racially. If we discount clothing, mannerisms, treatment of the hair, and other artifacts of culture, it is not often easy to tell by looking at a person exactly what country or ethnic group he or she comes from. If we turn to third- or fourth-generation Americans of unmixed European descent, say English or Greek, our chances of success are even smaller. If we examine most of the genetic attributes invisible to the naked eye, such as blood groups or the ability to taste the bitter chemical compound phenylthiocarbamide (PTC), we are still on insecure ground. Only in a few such disease-thwarting traits such as the sickle-cell gene or that governing a group of anemias known as thalassemias can we narrow our identification down to one or two countries that have endemic malaria.

This difficulty is not due to lack of information. More has been written about the physical characteristics of Europeans than about those of the inhabitants of any other region of equal area. Germans, Scandinavians, Swiss, Poles, and Russians have been especially active in studying the racial variations of the inhabitants of their countries, county by county, village by village, and even occupation by occupation. In 1899 W. Z. Ripley,[8] one of the first to classify Europeans on the basis of multiple traits, named three races: Nordic, Alpine, and Mediterranean—labels used ever since. Within a year J. Deniker produced a list of six.[9] His Nordic race is the same as Ripley's. In place of Alpine he proposed Western European, Eastern European, and Dinaric, and divided Mediterranean into Atlanto-Mediterranean and Ibero-Insular. Other classifications that followed were mostly elaborations of these two systems.[1]

Most modern physical anthropologists have discarded these subracial designations, partly because they are reminiscent of Hitler's activities (which is not a valid reason), and partly because they have been used to designate selected individuals of extreme types rather than populations. But one can legitimately speak of the peoples of northwestern Europe, for example, as a group with an elevated mean stature and the world's highest frequency of blondism, without implying that everyone living there is either tall or blond or both. The peoples of Central Europe can also be designated as groups in which brachycephaly is common, without im-

8 W. Z. Ripley: *The Races of Europe* (New York: Appleton; 1899).

9 J. Deniker: *The Races of Man* (New York: Charles Scribner; 1900).

1 The interested reader may find them listed and described in the following works: E. von Eickstedt: *Rassenkunde und Rassengeschichte der Menschheit* (Stuttgart: Gustav Fischer Verlag; 1934). Coon: *The Races of Europe*. E. W. Count: *This is Race* (New York: Henry Schuman; 1950). R. Biasutti: *Razze e Popoli della Terra*, 2nd ed. (Torino: VTET; 1959), 4 vols. J. Comas: *Manual of Physical Anthropology* (Springfield, Ill.: Charles Thomas & Co.; 1960).

plying that everyone living there is an Alpine in Ripley's sense. Actually the only thing the various "Alpine" populations have in common is brachycephaly, which appears and disappears within populations from time to time for reasons still unknown.[2] In sum, there is no scientific reason to prevent anyone who so wishes from naming geographically distinct populations within a subspecific region as long as he makes it clear that he is referring to mean or central tendencies rather than to rigidly defined types, and if he also indicates whether or not such a population merges gradually with its neighbors.

In attempting to describe the physical variations found among living Europeans in brief compass, it is feasible to proceed trait by trait, rather than group by group, because of the essential racial unity of Europeans and the infrequency of ethnic mosaics found in many other parts of the world. In mean stature, for example, we find the tallest people in Scotland, Iceland, Scandinavia, the eastern Baltic region, and the Balkans, particularly Montenegro and Albania. In general the crest of tallest stature runs on the cold side of the winter frost line, more or less coinciding with the 15° F. January isotherm. To the south and west, stature decreases until one reaches Portugal, southern Spain, and southern Italy. North and east of this crest, stature also decreases as one approaches northern Norway and the Urals. In body build the slenderest people are also found in the Mediterranean regions, whereas east of the line of tallest stature, body build becomes stockier. As we shall show later, the variations in stature and body build may be explained to a certain extent on the basis of climate.

Compared to the inhabitants of most other parts of the world, the Europeans are relatively hairy, and the greatest amount of body hair is found in the populations of the Alpine region, the least in Eastern Europe among those thought to have some Mongoloid ancestry. The hair form of Europeans ranges from curly to wavy to straight, but the majority are straight-haired. Curly hair is commonest in the Mediterranean countries and Western Europe and rarest in the east, but these differences are not great.

Most Europeans have light skins; the fairest are found in northwestern Europe in the region east of the Baltic. The darkest skins occur in Portugal, southern Spain, southern Italy, and Rumania. A distinction may be made between depigmented skin which tans

[2] G. Billy: "Race Alpine et Type Alpin," paper read at the 7th International Congress of Anthropological and Ethnological Sciences, Moscow, August 3–10, 1964.

readily and that which only burns and blisters or becomes coarse and ruddy under conditions of bright sunlight. The latter type of skin is found mostly in northwestern Europe.

One of the most distinctive attributes of Europeans is the high percentage of blondism. No population, however, is 100 percent blond, and the hair of many people who are blond as children darkens later. There are dark-haired Swedes, and light-haired individuals in all of the countries of the Mediterranean. The difference is simply one of frequency. Blond hair may be divided into golden blond, which contains a reddish element, and ash blond, which verges on gray. Golden-blond hair is concentrated in Scandinavia, northwestern Germany, the Netherlands, and the British Isles, and ash-blond hair is commonest among the Finns and northern Slavs. A similar dichotomy is evident in eye color. Pure or mixed light eyes that are predominantly blue have the same geographic distribution as golden-blond hair; grayish eyes follow the distribution of ash-blond hair. It would seem that de-pigmentation in response to reduced sunlight has taken two different forms each in skin, hair, and eyes, and that the distributions of these forms overlap. The center of blond hair is concentrated farther east in Sweden, Finland, the Baltic states, and Poland. As a result, one frequently sees Irishmen with dark hair and blue eyes, and Poles with brown eyes and blond hair.

The most fully documented morphological attribute in the European literature is the cephalic index, the ratio between head length and head breadth. Among most European populations the mean figure—ranging from about 78 to 85—is relatively high when compared with the figures for most of the world. In other words, most Europeans are mesocephalic, subbrachycephalic, or brachycephalic. Dolichocephalic populations are confined to parts of Sweden, Norway, Great Britain, and Spain, and to all of Portugal, Sardinia, and Corsica. In other words, some of the blondest and darkest and some of the tallest and shortest peoples of Europe are the longest-headed. There is no linkage, other than geographical coincidence, between pigmentation, stature, and head form.

Among the brachycephalic populations, high indices, from 85 upward, are in many cases not entirely genetic in origin. In Albania and Montenegro babies are carried in horizontal cradles strapped to the mother's backs. In this cradle the baby's body is bound down at the shoulder and waist. Although the head is not attached, it is difficult for the child to move it from side to side and the occipital region becomes flattened. This flattening remains throughout life, giving the individual the appearance of a pointed head, which the older classifiers of race included among their biological criteria. I. Deniker's so-called Dinaric race, described as tall, hooked-nosed, and planoccipitally brachycephalic, owes part of these specifications to artifice. We know this because children born of planoccipital parents in the United States, where cradling is not practiced, lack this feature.[3]

In Europe the phenomenon of brachycephaly goes back at least 30,000 years, as shown by the crania found at Krapina in Croatia. Several carefully studied collections of skulls from successive cemeteries in Central Europe have shown alternations of long-headed and round-headed populations. These changes have been interpreted as a record of successive invasions and replacements, but this is not necessarily true. In Poland, between the Carpathians and the Baltic, in a region of great ethnic stability and continuity, the mean cranial index has increased from about 74 to 84 since A.D. 1300, in about thirty generations. T. Bielicki and Z. Welon have shown that this change is due to a selective advantage for cephalic indices in the 80.5 to 83.5 segment of the range. Individuals with these intermediate indices have significantly more living brothers and sisters than the more brachycephalic group (83.5 and over), and the latter have significantly more living siblings than the longer-headed group (under 80.5).[4] Why in Poland natural selection favors brachycephaly over dolichocephaly has not been determined.

The face forms of these Central Europeans, however, have not kept pace with the head form. As far as we can tell, the faces have not changed. Europeans in general have moderately long and relatively narrow faces, and noses of varying shape. Facial flatness is rarer and less extreme than in most other populations of the world. Broad faces and low-bridged noses with uptilted tips occur in all populations, but they are commoner in Eastern Europe than in the Mediterranean countries, and in colder and damper regions than in warmer and drier areas. The presence of relatively low-bridged noses in colder, damper lands may be due more to a selective response to climate, or even to a relaxation of selection, than to an ancient Mongoloid admixture, although the latter is not excluded. We shall see more about the relationship between the form of the nose and climate when we consider Arabia.

3 Coon: *The Mountains of Giants*, PMP, Vol. 23, No. 3 (1950).
4 T. Bielicki and Z. Welon: "The Operations of Natural Selection on Human Head Form in an East European Population," *Homo*, Vol. 15, No. 1 (1964), pp. 22–30.

Negroid Influences in Europe

MUCH HAS BEEN WRITTEN about the influences of Negroid infiltration into Mediterranean countries and about Mongoloid genetic penetration in Eastern and Central Europe. Both have been exaggerated. In fact, the shoe is on the other foot. Europeans and West Asians have penetrated Africa and East Asia far more.

The Moors— that is, the Arabs and Berbers—occupied much of Spain and Portugal for seven centuries, and Arabs also held Sicily for a while. Arabs and Berbers are themselves Caucasoid, but they brought a number of Negro slaves with them. The Romans had some Negro slaves, and the Portuguese introduced plantation slavery with African labor after the expulsion of the Moors. Undoubtedly there is a Negro element in the Mediterranean countries and even in lands bordering the Black Sea. Otherwise it would be difficult to explain the presence of the sickle-cell gene in Greece and Italy, or the African Rh gene in Eastern Europe. But this gene does not show up notably in most of the blood-group distributions, nor are Negroid features very often seen in individual Europeans.

Mongoloid Influences in Europe

A NUMBER OF PEOPLES living on European soil whose ancestors came out of East and Central Asia during the last millennium may still be identified as separate ethnic units. They are characterized by a special language, religion, and other cultural features. These include principally the Buddhist Kalmucks, who are no different physically from their kin in Mongolia, and various groups of Muslim Tatars who speak Turkish and are Turks.

But other invaders out of Asia, principally the Huns and Avars, may have contributed genes to Europe without leaving any culturally or linguistically identifiable descendants. Several cemeteries containing the skeletons of Hun and Avar invaders and their followers have been excavated in Hungary, and the crania in them carefully studied.[5] They were patently a heterogeneous lot, with several kinds of East Asiatic Mongoloids, Turks, and

[5] This subject has been covered in detail in Coon: *The Races of Europe*, pp. 226–36.

Caucasoids, and had much less influence on the racial composition of modern Hungary than the ancestors of the Magyars, who arrived early in the tenth century A.D.

Over twenty years ago P. B. Candella attributed the relatively high frequency of blood group B in Eastern Europe to a gradual seepage of Mongoloid genes out of Asia between the fifth and fifteenth centuries A.D.[6] At the time Candella wrote, neither the relationship between the ABO groups and selection for resistance to disease, nor the low frequencies of blood group B in Siberia, were known.

The So-called Ural Subrace

BEFORE THE INVASIONS of the Huns, Turks, and Mongols, there were probably few if any proper Mongoloids in Eastern Europe. But the country on both sides of the Urals was inhabited by peoples whom Russian anthropologists designate as the Ural type or subrace. This subrace still survives in the Ostyaks and Voguls as well as among Finno-Ugrian-speaking peoples of the Volga-Kama region. According to M. G. Levin, all these people tend to have straight soft hair, comparatively light skin, a high percentage of light and mixed eye color, few if any epicanthic eye folds, moderately thick beards, a mean stature of about 160 centimeters (5 feet 3 inches) for adult males, comparatively short and moderately wide faces, concave or turned-up noses, thin lips, and mesocephalic heads with a mean index of 79 to 80. Levin considered these peoples to represent a chain of intermediate Mongoloid-Europoid populations dating to the time of the first settlement of the western Siberian forest belt,[7] but they are more nearly European than East Asian both morphologically and in blood-group frequencies. This Uralic component undoubtedly played a part in the formation of the present-day Hungarians, Esths, and Finns, all of whom absorbed other populations as they moved westward.

6 P. B. Candella; "The Introduction of Blood Group B into Europe," HB, Vol. 14, No. 3 (1942), pp. 413–44.
7 M. G. Levin: "The Anthropological Types of Siberia," in M. G. Levin and L. P. Popatov, eds.: *The Peoples of Siberia*, translated by S. P. Dunn (Chicago: University of Chicago Press; 1964), pp. 99–104.

The Basques and the Lapps

IN CHAPTER I we reproduced Boyd's classification of the peoples
of Europe into races on the basis of blood-group frequencies. Boyd
finds polar extremes in these characteristics between the Basques
and the Lapps. Other Europeans fall for the most part into intermediate categories. The Basques are characterized by a high frequency of Rh-negative blood and a low one of type B. The Lapps,
on the other hand, are high in type A, particularly A^2, which is
primarily a European form, and have a moderate incidence of
type B.

As for the Basques, they are not distinct morphologically and
indeed those living in Spain have a different mean cephalic index
than those living in France.[8] They are not the only Europeans
with a high incidence of Rh-negative blood; and low incidences
of type B are common in France, as a recent survey has shown.[9]
The genetic polarity of the Basques among European peoples is
thus less pronounced than it has been made to seem. The Basques
are notably ethnocentric and speak an odd language, two factors
which have attracted much attention and which may have limited
the influx of new genes from their neighbors.

The Basques have lived on the shores of the Bay of Biscay and
on the flanks of the western Pyrenees as long as we know, but the
Lapps are relative newcomers to their present home.[1] The first
known inhabitants of that chilly outpost were a Mesolithic people
who flaked implements similar to those found in Denmark and
Sweden. No one could have preceded them there because of the
ice cap. This Mesolithic industry was followed by a Neolithic
one utilizing slate implements. Then during the first few centuries
of the Christian era the country was visited by seafaring Iron Age
Norwegians. After A.D. 400 the visitors settled the coast, but not
the present Lappish country of Finnmark, which has a continental
climate.

No Mesolithic or Neolithic skeletons have been found, and the
Iron Age remains show no evidence of mixture. We do not know

8 P. Marquer: "Contribution a l'Étude Anthropologique du Peuple Basque et
au Problème de ses Origines Raciales," BMSA, Vol. 4, No. 1, 9th series (1963),
pp. 1–240.

9 H. V. Vallois and P. Marquer: "La Répartition en France des Groupes
Sanguins A B O," BMSA, Vol. 6, No. 1 (1964), pp. 1–200.

1 T. Sjövold: *The Iron Age Settlement of Arctic Norway* (Tromsö, Oslo: Norwegian University Press; 1964).

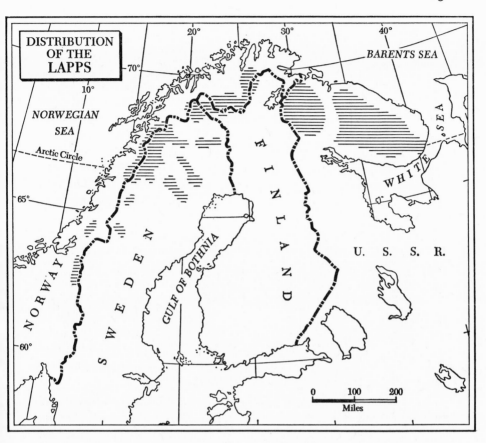

exactly when the ancestors of the Lapps arrived, but there is no indication that they were there before A.D. 600. Nor do we know whether they absorbed any earlier, pre-Norwegian population. In recent centuries they have been mixing with both Norwegians and Finns.

A number of specialists have tried to classify the Lapps racially, with conflicting results.[2] The confusion has been caused by certain local, Lappish peculiarities that do not fit into preconceived racial frameworks. As their language and probable ethnic origin would suggest, they resemble the Ugrian-speaking Ural peoples in stature, facial form, hair texture, beard growth, and general pigmentation. Fewer than half have dark hair or eyes, and more than half have various shades of ash-blond hair, and mixed or light eyes.[3] But the Lapps differ notably from the Ostyaks in the form of the head;

[2] R. T. Anderson: "Lapp Racial Classifications as Scientific Myths," APUA, Vol. 11, No. 1 (1962), pp. 15–31.
[3] R. R. Gjessing: *Die Kautokeinolappen* (Oslo: ISKF; 1934).

their cranial vaults are long, wide, and low-vaulted, whereas the Ostyaks have narrower and higher heads.[4]

Lapp skulls tend to be flat on top, so that if one is placed on a table upside down it may not roll over.[5] A possible explanation of this peculiarity may be suggested by their method of cradling. The Lapp cradle is made of a hollow tree trunk with a concave surface facing the back of the baby's head, and with a flat headboard.[6] This may account for the fact that Lapps exhibit vault flattening instead of the occipital flattening found in Albanians and other Balkan peoples. Lapp teeth have very small crowns, comparable to those of Hungarians and Bushmen, but the crowns are high and their roots are long, slender, and spiky. Also, the incisors and canines are relatively large and long in relation to the premolars and molars. The third molars are the smallest of the three.[7]

A study of the long bones reveals that whereas the ratio of upper-arm to forearm length is normal for Europeans, the tibia and fibula are relatively short, as in other Arctic peoples and in the Japanese.[8] Furthermore, a congenital dislocation of the head of the femur is relatively common among Lapps, particularly among women. This is explained partly by the angle of torsion of that bone and partly by a shallow acetabulum with a defective upper rim. The heredity of this condition has been studied.[9]

All in all, these studies suggest that the Lapps are descendants of ordinary Ural people mixed with Norwegians, Finns, and possibly earlier inhabitants of the Far North, strongly influenced by their Arctic environment, subjected to an unusual type of cradling, and inbred. As for their blood groups, as far as we know they do not differ greatly from those of the Ostyaks, but we are not sure. The A group among the latter has not yet been broken down into A-1 and A-2.[1] Even if the Lapps turn out to be more deviant from the Ural peoples than would now appear, this should cause no surprise in view of their history and experiences.

[4] K. E. Schreiner: *Zur Osteologie der Lappen,* 2 vols. (Oslo: ISKF; 1935). P. Liptak: "Materiali Po Kraniologii Khantov," AEASH, Vol 1, Nos. 1–4 (1950), pp. 197–230.

[5] R. Selmer-Olsen: *An Odontometrical Study on the Norwegian Lapps* (Oslo: SNVA; 1949), No. 3.

[6] B. Collinder: *The Lapps* (Princeton: Princeton University Press; 1949), pp. 67–8.

[7] Selmer-Olsen: op. cit.

[8] Schreiner: op. cit.

[9] B. Getz: *The Hip Joint in Lapps and Its Bearing on the Problem of Congenital Dislocation,* AOSS, No. 18 (1955). The rim anomaly has an incidence of 20 percent, as revealed by X-ray. There is a 5 percent incidence of actual dislocation resulting from it.

[1] Mourant: "Gruppi Krovi Narodov Severnoi Evropi i Azii," TMOIP, Vol. 14 (1964), pp. 46–53.

The deduction, from studies of blood groups, that the Lapps constitute one of the poles in the racial composition of the European population opposite to that represented by the Basques cannot be literally supported by other evidence, but such a polarity nevertheless exists. It involves not the Lapps alone, but the peoples whose ancestors inhabited forests in the lee of the Urals before agriculture began, including the forebears of the Lapps. The other pole includes not the Basques alone, but the marginal inhabitants of the Atlantic fringe of Western Europe.

The Primary Racial Characteristics of the Living Europeans

AS A FIRST STEP in analyzing the living Europeans as a racial unit, let us momentarily disregard three variables; pigmentation, stature, and the cephalic index. The first is influenced by light, the second by temperature, and the third by artifice or some unknown selective factor or both. What remains then is a continent of people who are much alike in most respects but who are differentiated into three zones lacking sharp borders.

In the north and northeast, in the regions first occupied after the retreat of the ice, there is a tendency to stocky build, relatively broad faces with deep jaws and straight or concave nasal profiles. In the west and along the northern fringes of the Mediterranean lands, and in the Balkans, the body build is still powerful, but rangier. Faces are narrower and noses more often straight or convex, and beards and body hair more abundant. In the far south particularly in Spain, Portugal, and the islands of the Mediterranean from the Balearics to Crete, the body build is more slender, faces are narrower and more chiseled, noses more often straight, jaws more delicate, and beards and body hair less heavy than in the intermediate zone.

Let us take this half-finished sketch into a magic darkroom and leave on only a dim green light. We put our print into a pan of developer concocted of pigmentation, stature, and the cephalic index. Now we see emerging before our eyes the "races" of Europe as specified by the classifiers of the old happy days of simple morphological description: the Nordics, the Alpines, the Dinarics, the Gracile Mediterraneans, and the rest. Then we fix the print in a bath of blood-group solution and turn on the white lights. Boyd's polarity is added, sharpening the image as if by a third dimension.

The "races" of Europe now make sense both as a pattern of human geography and in terms of the past. But something is still lacking. Our picture is not properly bordered or framed. To the north, west, and south it has sharp boundaries where the land meets the water, but the eastern edge cuts through dry land. Europe is only the western half of a major homeland. We must now cross the Aegean and move around the shores of the Black Sea.

The Living West Asians

ALTHOUGH physical anthropologists have not spanned Western Asia in as great detail geographically as they have Europe, they have amassed enough regional data to permit several generalizations. One is that, like Europe, West Asia is roughly divisible into several, more or less horizontal zones. In the far north, Ugrian-speaking peoples who came from west of the Urals occupy the Ob River basin. We have already described them. In race essentially northeastern European, they grade into the northern Siberian tribes that become more Mongoloid as one moves eastward to the Bering Sea and the Pacific Ocean. South of the western Siberian swamps and forests lies a belt of arable land now occupied by the descendants of Russian settlers. South of that runs a string of deserts, and between the deserts and the mountain escarpment is a strip of grasslands, oases, and foothills ending in the mountain spine of Central Asia. On that strip, in those oases, and in the foothills lives a population of partly Mongoloid origin that was almost entirely Caucasoid before being overrun by the westward expansion of Turks and Mongols.

In the West Asian highlands south of this zone, from the Aegean to Pakistan down to the Indian Ocean, and including the Caucasus, nearly all the people are Caucasoid and essentially similar to the people of Europe from Greece to France. The exceptions are a few Mongoloid enclaves such as the Hazara and Chahar Aimak of west-central Afghanistan and northeastern Iran.

The Arabian Peninsula and the desert fringes north of it are inhabited by Mediterraneans like those on the fringes of southwest Europe, but they occupy a much larger and a more unified territory. Along the coasts of southern Arabia, Negroids and Negroes live among the Arabs. Some are the product of the African slave trade; others may have been there longer. Even an ancient Australoid element may be seen dimly.

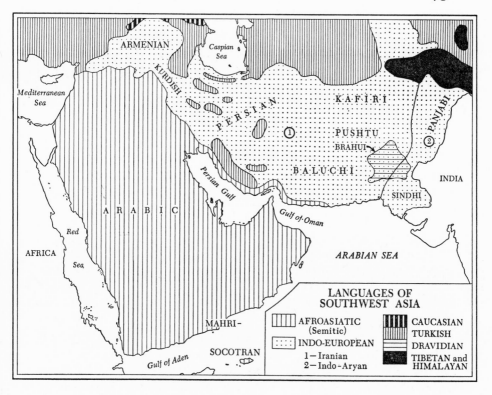

LANGUAGES OF
SOUTHWEST ASIA

|||| AFROASIATIC (Semitic) |||| CAUCASIAN
:::: INDO-EUROPEAN   ==== TURKISH
1—Iranian   ==== DRAVIDIAN
2—Indo-Aryan   ■ TIBETAN and HIMALAYAN

The West Asian Highlanders[2]

BECAUSE the highlanders of West Asia are the most numerous of
the various groups mentioned and are most comparable racially
to the majority of Europeans, we shall describe them first. In their
geographical zone no large area of blondism like that of Northern
Europe is to be found, which is not surprising as this zone contains

[2] TURKS OF TURKEY. Hertzberg et al.: op. cit. Mlle Afet: "Recherches Anthropologiques sur 59,728 Turcs des Deux Sexes," ASAG, Vol. 9 (1941), pp. 79–192.

ARMENIANS. Seltzer: *The Racial Characteristics of Syrians and Armenians*,
PMP, Vol. 13, No. 3 (1936). R. Kherumian: *Les Arméniens* (Paris: Librairie
Orientaliste Paul Geuthner; 1943).

THE PEOPLES OF THE CAUCASUS AND TRANSCAUCASIA. R. von Erckert: *Antro-
pologicheskaiia izmereniia nekotorykh Kavkazakh narodov*, IKO, Vols. 7–8 (1882–
1883); "Kopfmessungen Kaukasischer Völker," AFA, Vol. 18 (1889), pp. 263–81,
297–335; Vol. 19 (1890), pp. 55–84, 211–29, 331–56. Field: *Contributions to the
Anthropology of the Caucasus*, PMP, Vol. 48, No. 1 (1952). V. V. Bunak, G. F.
Debetz, and M. G. Levin, eds.: *Contributions to the Physical Anthropology of the
Soviet Union*, RTS-PM, Vol. 1, No. 2 (1960). M. G. Abdushelishvili: *Antropologiia
Drevnevo i Sovremennevo Naseleniia Gruzii*, IEM-ANG (1964).

IRAN AND AFGHANISTAN. Field: *Contributions to the Anthropology of Iran*,

no comparable area of heavy cloud cover combined with high humidity.

Most Western Asian highlanders have brunette-white or light brown skins and black or dark brown hair. Although brown eyes are in the majority nearly everywhere, the percentage of light-mixed and light eyes rarely falls below 25 percent. Compared to most Europeans they have hairy bodies—most of all the Armenians—abundant beard growth, and bushy eyebrows that characteristically meet in a tuft over the root of the nose. The hair on the head is straight or wavy; the beard sometimes curly.

Their bodies range from slender to thickset, tending particularly toward the latter, and the combined length of trunk, neck, and head usually constitutes about 53 percent of the stature, as among most Europeans. Stature itself is not very variable. It runs to about 166 centimeters or 5 foot 5 inches. Regional means vary about two inches on either side. Their faces are characteristically parallel-sided, with foreheads and jaws relatively broad in comparison to midfacial breadth. They are rarely prognathous. Their noses are high at root and bridge, and mostly narrow. The nasal profile is straight or convex, more often the latter, but some of this convexity is no doubt due to occipital flattening caused by cradling.[3]

Cradling is prevalent in the western and northern parts of this region, particularly in Turkey, northwestern Syria, Lebanon, Armenia, the Caucasus, Kurdistan, and among the Tajiks. The children of the highly brachycephalic Lebanese and Armenians are mesocephalic when born in the United States and reared without cradling.[4] Among such brachycephalic peoples as Ossetes and Georgians,[5] and Kurds,[6] uncradled individuals are dolichocephalic

---

FMAS, Vol. 29, No. 1 (1939), Pub. 458; "Mountain Peoples of Iraq and Iran," AJPA, Vol. 9, No. 4 (1951), pp. 1–3; *The Anthropology of Iraq. Part II, No. 2. Kurdistan and Part II, No. 3. Conclusions*, PMP, Vol. 46, No. 2 & 3 (1952); *An Anthropological Reconnaisance in West Pakistan, 1955*, PMP, Vol. 52 (1959). B. S. Guha: *Racial Affinities of the Peoples of India*, Part A of *Census of India, 1931*, Vol. 1, Part 3 (for Pathans and Nuristanis). G. T. Bowles's unpublished data on 168 Pashto-speakers.

Bibliography on Turkomans, Tajiks, and Uzbeks will be found in the next section. Various small unpublished series measured in Iran and Afghanistan by Carleton S. Coon and not yet described in print will be cited as they are mentioned.

[3] Among Albanian mountaineers, those with deformed heads had 16 percent more convex profiles than the undeformed. Coon: *The Mountains of Giants*, p. 97.

[4] J. F. Ewing: *Hyperbrachycephaly as Influenced by Cultural Conditioning*, PMP, Vol. 23, No. 2 (1950).

[5] Field: *Contributions to the Anthropology of the Soviet Union*.

[6] Coon, in an unpublished series of measurements of Shikak Kurds.

or mesocephalic. Pending further study, it seems possible that there is less brachycephaly of genetic origin in the West Asian highlands than in Europe.

In the distribution of pigmentation certain clinal tendencies appear. The lightest skins are seen along the Aegean coast of Turkey, the darkest on the Persian Gulf, particularly in Baluchistan. Eye color also gets darker from west to east. The percentage of mixed and light eyes ranges from 85 percent among the western Turks and 80 to 70 percent among the peoples of the Caucasus down to 35 percent among the Sayyads, a group of Persian fishermen and fowlers who live on the marshes of the lower Helmand River; to 15 percent among the Pathans; and to less than 5 percent among the Baluchis.

The Baluchis are descended from Persian tribesmen transported in the tenth century A.D. from northwestern to southeastern Iran. In their new home the exiles conquered the indigenous Dravidian-speaking Brahuis, but they, as often happens, have since absorbed their overlords.

In the most inaccessible mountains of northeastern Afghanistan lives a culturally archaic people formerly called Kafiris and now known as Nuristanis. Until the 1890's they practiced an ancient Indo-European pagan religion, after which they were forcibly converted to Islam by the Afghan government. In their foggy refuge they still preserve a considerable amount of blondism, the exact amount of which remains to be determined.

A Comparison Between West Asian Highlanders and West Europeans

BLOOD-GROUP STUDIES made on most of the West Asian highlanders show an essentially European pattern, with group A more numerous than B, and A_2 present as well as A_1. But only in remote tribes of the Caucasus do the frequencies of A and B fall as low as among the Basques. The fingerprint patterns of the Caucasian mountaineers are also within the ranges of those of several Basque series.[7] Except for artificially flattened heads in

[7] Marquer: "Contribution à l'Étude du Peuple Basque et au Problème de ses Origines Raciales," BMSA, Vol. 4, No. 1 (1964), pp. 1–240. V. V. Bunak: "Anthropological Composition of the Population of the Caucasus," in Bunak, G. F. Debetz, and M. G. Levin: *Contributions to the Physical Anthropology of the Soviet Union*, RTS-PM, Vol. 1, No. 2 (1960), pp. 1–23.

Fig. 1.– FINGERPRINTS OF BASQUES AND CAUCASIANS.

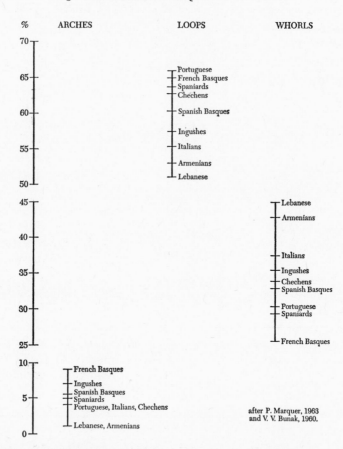

the Caucasus, the only demonstrable genetic difference between the two peoples is that the Basques are less hirsute.[8]

Whether or not the Basque and Caucasian languages are related, both are geographically marginal. So are the peoples who speak them. Under these circumstances, the physical resemblances between these peoples which we have detected do not fully solve the riddle of the origin of the Basques. They serve to accentuate the general racial continuity of West Asian highlanders and the Europeans of the comparable highland zone from Greece to the Atlantic.

Even the Turks, whose Ottoman ancestors were absorbed by the previous inhabitants of Asia Minor, are virtually indistinguish-

[8] Figure 1, "Dermatoglyphics of Basques and Caucasians," from Marquer: *Contribution à l'Étude du Peuple Basque et au Problème de ses Origines Raciales,* p. 205.

able from the Greeks in nearly all dimensions unaffected by cradling, which most Greeks do not practice.[9] Otherwise the only consistent differences are that the Turks have less body fat than the Greeks and slightly larger faces. In these respects the Anatolian Turks tend to resemble their relatives the Turkomans, who live nearer the Turkish homeland.

Peoples of the Northern Borderlands

THIS AREA comprises the Soviet republics of Turkmenistan, Uzbekistan, and Tadzhikistan, and also the strip of Afghanistan between the south bank of the Oxus River and the northern slopes of the Hindu Kush. This is the ancient Turan, long inhabited by Persian-speaking peoples and until recently a center of Islamic culture and learning—a busy and populous land of deserts, grasslands, oases, and highland villages. Today it is occupied by several kinds of peoples; Persian-speakers and Turkish-speakers; nomads, cultivators, urban traders, and craftsmen; Sunni and Shi'a Muslims; and even a few Arabs and Jews. The principal groups are Tajiks, Sarts, Uzbeks, and Turkomans. The Tajiks are Persian-speaking Shi'a who live in the Soviet republic of that name, in adjoining parts of Afghanistan, and even across the Tien Shan in China. The Sarts are oasis cultivators and city dwellers of Persian descent who now speak Turkish. The Uzbeks are Turkish-speaking, upland cultivators who live in their own republic and in northern Afghanistan. The Turkomans are nomads ranging from the eastern shore of the Caspian to Uzbekistan, and scattered elsewhere, as in Iraq and on the flanks of the Caucasus. Because of detailed studies by Russian anthropologists, we are able to summarize the physical attributes of the principal peoples of this region.[1]

The Tajiks are northeastern representatives of the Western Asian Highland group, with heads deformed by cradling, brunette

[9] H. T. R. Hertzberg and his associates took 213 measurements each on 915 male Turks, 1,084 male Greeks, and 1,357 male Italians, all NATO personnel. When Turks and Greeks were compared, interservice differences were found to exceed international differences. In both forces pilots and student pilots are taller and heavier than Air Force ground crews and soldiers. Both social and nutritional selection may be reflected here. Hertzberg, et al.: op. cit.

[1] Field: *Contributions to the Anthropology of the Soviet Union*, SMC, Vol. 110, No. 13 (1948), Pub. 3947. I. Schwidetzky: "Turaniden-Studien," AWLM, No. 9 (1950), pp. 235–91. L. V. Oshanin and V. Ia. Zezenkova: *Voprosi Etnogeneza Narodov Srednei Azii v Svete Dannikh Antropologii* (Tashkent: IIA-ANUS; 1953).

pigmentation, and a proportion of as much as 45 percent of mixed and light eyes. They are not as hairy as most Western Asians, being in this respect more like Europeans. Some of those who live in Soviet territory show a Mongoloid admixture, with as much as an 11 percent incidence of epicanthic eye folds. Other Tajiks, particularly in Afghanistan, show no visible evidence of such mixture, although their blood-group frequencies suggest it—even more than in most of the series studied in Soviet territory. This condition may well be due to gene flow between these southern Tajiks and their Mongoloid neighbors the Hazara, who are also Persian-speaking Shi'as.

The Sarts are essentially like the Tajiks, but the Uzbeks are more Mongoloid than either of those two, with a greater propor-tion of concave nasal profiles, a weaker beard growth, as much as a 30 percent incidence of epicanthic folds, and fewer mixed and light eyes. Like the Tajiks of Afghanistan, they show a greater proportion of blood group B than of A.

The Turkomans are also Caucasoid-Mongoloid hybrids, but of a different kind, possibly owing to desert adaptation. They are taller than most of the others, and rangy, lean, and characteristically dolichocephalic.[2] They have long broad bony faces, with the breadth across the cheekbones notably exceeding that of the fore-head and jaws. Some have hawk-like profiles, others the concavity of the Mongol. Few show any trace of blondism, or much body hair. Their hair is coarse. Their beards are scanty and in some cases grow quite long. Unlike other Caucasoid-Mongoloid hybrid groups, they show no evidence of Mongol origin in their ABO blood groups, which are low in B. When added to the morphologi-cal distinctiveness of the Turkomans, this blood-group peculiarity suggests, as we shall discuss later, that the Mongoloid element in their ancestry was Siberian. This possibility is important histori-cally because the Turkish-speaking peoples who invaded Europe and the West Asian highlands from time to time were essentially the same as the living Turkomans.

Russian Turkestan contains several other Turkish-speaking peoples who, except for their language, are essentially Mongols. They will be discussed in Chapter 5. Chief among them are the Kirghiz and Kazak, who are centered on both sides of the Altai and range from Iran to Manchuria. Compared to the Turkomans and the Tatars, they have had minimal impact on Europe and West Asia.

2 It has been suggested but not demonstrated that this form of head is due to deformation by annular binding.

The Arabs

THE DESERTS, mountains, and oases of Southwest Asia form the home of a relatively homogenous, nuclear population of Caucasoids of the variety known as Gracile Mediterraneans, comparable to the Andalusians, Corsicans, and Sardinians. Until after Muhammad's death in A.D. 632, the Arabs were simply the native inhabitants of the Arabian peninsula. Then the Prophet's followers began to swarm in all directions until, in an almost incredibly short time, their conquering and proselyting armies and their companies of missionaries and traders had reached the Atlantic, Central Asia, and the Pacific.

Sedentary Arabs of the Northern Fringe of the Desert[3]

TODAY many peoples of Western Asia are inaccurately called Arabs, among them the sedentary Palestinian Arabs, who now live mostly in Jordan, the Druses, the Lebanese, the Alawiya of northwestern Syria, and the sedentary Arabic-speakers of Iraq. Many are still Christians, and a few still speak other Semitic languages, notably Syriac.

The mountaineers of Syria and Lebanon, whatever their religion or speech, form a southwestern extension of the Central Highland population of West Asia, which they resemble in every essential respect. The sedentary Arabs of the desert border of Syria, from Damascus to Aleppo, are physically intermediate between the mountaineers and the Bedawin. They are more slender

3 Seltzer: *The Racial Characteristics of Syrians and Armenians.* W. M. Shanklin and N. Izzeddin: *Anthropology of the Near East Female,* AJPA, Vol. 22, No. 3 (1937), pp. 381–415. Shanklin: "Anthropometry of Syrian Males," JRAI, Vol. 68 (1938), pp. 379–414. Field: *The Anthropology of Iraq. Part I, No. 1. The Upper Euphrates,* FMAS, Vol. 30, Part I, No. 1 (1940), Pub. 469; *Part I, No. 2. The Lower Euphrates-Tigris Region,* FMAS, Vol. 30, Part 1, No. 2 (1949), Pub. 631; *Part II, No. 1. The Northern Jazira,* PMP, Vol. 46, No. 1 (1951); *Part II, No. 2. Kurdistan;* and *Part II, No. 3. Conclusions.* M.-R. Sauter: "Les Races brachycephales du Proche-Orient, des origines à nos jours," ASAG, Vol. 11, No. 1 (1945), pp. 68–131; "Recherches anthropologiques en Palestine méridionale," ASAG, Vol. 15, No. 2 (1950); Ewing: op. cit.; P.-A. Gloor: "Recherches anthropologiques en Palestine méridionale I. Enquête sur les Arabes (série masculine)," ASAG, Vol. 15, No. 2 (1950), pp. 107–42.

than the former, longer-headed, less hairy, and a little lighter in skin and eye color.

Northeastern Syria and northern Iraq contain few sedentary Arabs because the Bedawin graze their flocks right up to the villages of Kurds, Turks, and Turkomans. But sedentary Arabs occupy the entire alluvial plain of southeastern Iraq, the marshes at the head of the Persian Gulf, and the land along the coast of Iran, where they cultivate wheat and rice, breed water buffalos, and catch fish and waterfowl in the marshes. Many of them harbor traditions of a noble Bedawin origin, but physically they are more like the ancient inhabitants of this region whose bones have been unearthed by archaeologists. They are a little bigger and more robust than the Bedawin, and a little hairier, and darker-skinned. A few are perceptibly Negroid in hair, skin, and facial features, yet do not belong to the Negroid castes of blacksmiths and other specialists, and indeed intermarriage with these castes is forbidden to them.

The Arabs of the Desert

THE REQUIREMENTS of desert living based on pastoralism, the intensive cultivation of the oases, and the need of importing metal implements have created a division of labor that is expressed in a code of chivalry, and have brought about a balance of political power and the immunity of technological outcastes from warfare. At the top of the social pyramid stand such noble camel breeders as the Rwala and the Shammar. Under their protection are the shepherd tribes, whose flocks prevent them from moving as fast as the camel breeders. Then come the villagers of the oases. The blacksmiths, the Sulubba, and gypsies compete for the bottom of the scale. At the very bottom, theoretically, are the slaves, but in actuality they enjoy positions of greater comfort and prestige than all but the nobles whose chiefs they serve.

These groups interbreed little. Among noble Arabs the preferred mating is a marriage between parallel cousins—that is, between a man and his paternal uncle's daughter. This system fits in well with the whole complex of loyalties, mobility, and the protection of dependents, because it does not overextend the number of persons whom an honorable man must avenge. This endogamy is reflected in the physical attributes of Bedawin, who have been extensively measured from the Turkish border to the

Hijaz,[4] and in the considerable variation found in the blood-group percentages for different camps of a single tribe.[5]

The physical type of the Bedawin, which is a distinct one, can best be described by comparison with the Western Asian highlanders. Both have the same range of stature, but the Bedawin are more lightly built and have longer legs, smaller chests, and finer extremities. Their heads are dolichocephalic and are smaller than those of any of the mountain people except the Baluchis. Their faces are narrower, their nasal profiles more often straight than convex, and they have little body hair and characteristically sparse beards. Their head hair is black or dark brown, fine-textured and straight or wavy, often forming ringlets when allowed to grow long. Their skin, which tans deeply, is usually brunette white or light brown if it is unexposed and well washed.

The Sulubba, who serve the Bedawin as tinkers and guides, are also (or were) noted hunters, living on gazelle and oryx in the summer when the Bedawin have retired to their wells. Perceptive students of the Arabian scene believe them to be survivors of the preagricultural, prepastoral Neolithic hunters, whose artifacts are scattered over the desert.

The Sulubba differ physically from the Bedawin in the very ways that the Bedawin differ from the settled people of the northern desert fringe, and they in turn from the Western Asian mountaineers. The Sulubba's skin is a little lighter; their faces are even smaller and narrower, particularly their jaws. These differences support the theory that they are the relicts of ancient hunters, and that the Bedawin are derived from cultivators, particularly of the Yemen Highlands, who at one time or another left their drying fields for the more profitable life of herding.

The gypsies are new and few. For the smiths who walk unharmed from camp to camp, plying their necessary trade, we have no measurements, only the observation that most of them are not true Negroes, like many of the slaves, but something else, or

4 Available are thirteen series of measurements, six published by H. Field, five by W. M. Shanklin, one each by H. V. Vallois and L. Cipriani. Field: *The Anthropology of Iraq.* W. Dostal: "Die Sulubba und ihre Bedeutung für die Kulturgeschichte Arabiens," AfV, Vol. 11 (1956), pp. 15–42. Shanklin: "The Anthropology of Transjordan Arabs," PNB, No. 3 & 4 (1935), pp. 3–12; "The Anthropology of the Rwala Bedouins," JRAI, Vol. 45 (1935), pp. 375–90; "Anthropology of the Akeydat and the Maualay Bedouin," AJPA, Vol. 21 (1936), pp. 217–52; "Anthropometry of Syrian Males"; "Anthropology of Transjordan Bedouin with a discussion of their racial affinities," AJPA, Vol. 4, No. 3 (1946), pp. 323–76. Vallois: "Les Bédouins Taamré du Désert de Judée: Étude Anthropologique," *L'Anth,* Vol. 63, No. 1–2 (1959), pp. 62–92. F. S. Vidal: *Anthropometry of al-Hasa Oasis,* Ms.

5 Shanklin: "The Anthropology of the Rwala Bedouins."

something in between. Oasis people have been measured in Hofuf, al-Hasa Province, Saudi Arabia. As they live in a moist, palm-shaded microenvironment, they differ from the Bedawin physically in that they have rounder faces, their noses are more concave, and their appearance is generally softer for they do not face the selective pressures of desiccation and windborne dust.

The Southern Periphery

AROUND THE SOUTHERN RIM of Arabia and beyond the Empty Quarter, or Sea of Sand, stretches a rim of kingdoms, protectorates, petty sheikhdoms, and warring tribes all the way from Yemen to Lahaj-Aden, the Hadhramaut, Dhofar, and Socotra Island, Muscat and Oman, and the Trucial Sheikhdoms. In the southern part of this region rain falls in summer, permitting agriculture in the highlands, particularly in Yemen, the most populous nation of Arabia. There the bulk of the population is concentrated on the fertile plateau reaching from the rim of the escarpment to the desert, and centered about San'a.

The tribesmen of this central-plateau region do not differ appreciably from the Bedawin north of the desert.[6] To the south, but still in the highlands, from San'a to Ibb, Taiz, Lahaj, and finally Aden, the people grow shorter, and rounder-headed, with a drop in mean stature from 164.5 to 161 centimeters (5 feet 5 inches to 5 feet 3 inches) and a rise in cephalic index of from 76 to 81. But if we go directly west from San'a, climbing down the escarpment to the coastal plain—the Tihama—which borders the Red Sea, the change is more rapid. Mean stature drops abruptly with altitude to 160 centimeters (5 feet 3 inches) and the cephalic index jumps to 84. Whereas most of the Plateau tribesmen have a brunette white or light brown skin color, the coastal people have an incidence of 75 percent medium brown or dark brown skin. Only 4 percent have mixed or light eyes, whereas 25 percent do on the plateau.

The Tihama is a strange, little-known place. It is mostly desert,

6 Metrical constants of the series of Yemenis, Hadhramis, and other southern Arabians, including local Negroes and Negroids, measured by Carleton Coon in 1933–4 are included by L. Oschinsky in Appendix D of his *The Racial Affinities of the Baganda and Other Bantu Tribes of British East Africa* (Cambridge: W. Heffer & Sons; 1954). The measurements of twenty-one Arab sailors from Bandar Linjeh on the southeast Persian coast, and the tables for the morphological observations of all series, are still unpublished.

with little rainfall, high humidity, and stifling heat. Water for agriculture flows from the escarpment, and malaria is rife among the Arabs, who leave most of the heavy work to the Negroes and to a caste of Negroid serfs and sweepers known as Hojeris, a people of unknown and probably complex origin.

Moving around the coast out of this cloying heat, past the Bab al Mandeb to the shore of the Indian Ocean, we come to the drier Hadhramaut (in Arabic, The Presence of Death) whence migrated the ancestors of the Ethiopians and, more recently, thousands of merchants and missionaries to Malaya and Indonesia. Some of the latter have returned with Mongoloid wives and half-Mongoloid children, who, with the local Negroes, give the Hadhramaut Valley towns an international look. Here as on the Tihama the Negroes do most of the agricultural work.

The tribal Hadhramis, mostly pastoral people, resemble the southern Yemeni highlanders and the people of the Aden region in being short, subbrachycephalic, and small-faced, with sharply chiseled features. Their hair falls in ringlets to their shoulders, but their beard and body hair is scanty.

Farther east, the tribesmen of the Dhofar country, rich in grass because it catches the rain of the southwest monsoon, are cattle herders who speak some of the ancient southern Arabian languages replaced by Arabic elsewhere in southern Arabia. Although essentially similar to the Hadhramis physically, they are divided into endogamous castes, among which some individuals of somewhat Australoid appearance may be found.

In surveying the climate, the cattle complex, the social structure, and the racial characteristics of the whole fringe of Southwest Asia from the Tihama to Baluchistan, we find that we have begun to leave the strictly Caucasoid part of the world and stand in a narrow corridor connecting Africa and India. Southern Arabia is not an easy place to work in, and much remains to be discovered. When it is, the rewards will be worth the effort.

4

Africa

❊❊❊

Racial Distribution in Africa

Throughout historic times Africa has been the home of members of three races two of which, the Congoid and Capoid, evolved in it and until the modern period lived nowhere else. The third, the Caucasoid element, includes the mixed and unmixed descendants of peoples who invaded Africa from Western Asia and possibly also from Europe at various times between 12,000 B.C. and about A.D. 1200. These are Arabs, Berbers, the Cushites of the Horn of Africa, and in more attenuated form, some of the peoples of the highlands of East Africa and the Sudan.

During the Pleistocene we have reason to believe that the ancestors of the living Capoids dwelt north of and in the Sahara and the Congoids south of it. According to this hypothesis, presented in *The Origin of Races*, the Capoids moved to South Africa along the East African highlands under Caucasoid pressure, displacing or absorbing Congoid populations more primitive than themselves. During the last few years much new information has been coming out of Africa and if this trend continues we may soon be in a position not only to test this theory but also to document the racial history of Africa as a whole.

Today the indigenous population of Africa is mostly clinal. In the Sudan and East Africa, Caucasoids shade into Negroes; and telltale pockets of partly Capoid peoples survive in the Sahara and along its northern fringes. The South African Bantu have patently absorbed some earlier, full-sized Capoid populations, and there are even, on the northern fringes of the Kalahari, some food-gathering Negroes who speak Bushman languages. Africa is racially the most confusing of all continents. Part of this confusion, however, can be dissipated by recounting what little is known of African prehistory and history and by considering its geography.

African Geography and Climates

A F R I C A is the second largest continent. It is more nearly circular in shape than any other save Australia and Antarctica and has the shortest coastline in proportion to its area, a little more than a fourth as much as Europe. Over three fourths of its surface lies within the tropics, much more than in the case of any other continent. Its essential unity is reflected in the fact that almost to the end of the Pleistocene it contained only a single mammalian fauna, the Ethiopian. Elephants, giraffes, rhinoceroses, gnus, and other typically African animals grazed and roamed from Tangier to Capetown. Much of the Sahara, now as at other times a desert barrier, was intermittently well-watered and teeming with vast herds of countless game animals, like those now rapidly vanishing from Kenya, Tanzania, and Bechuanaland. This was true during the pluvial periods of the Pleistocene—more or less corresponding to the glacial advances in Europe. Until about 25,000 B.C. there was no Nile River north of Batn al Hajar, some fifty miles southwest of Wadi Halfa in the Sudan.[1] The water that now flows into the Mediterranean from the great lakes of East Africa and from Lake Tana in Ethiopia then flooded a series of shallow lakes. (The Sudd Swamp and Lake Chad are remains of these.) This provided a water barrier between the Capoid and Congoid regions and tempered the climate of the southern Sahara.

Between the Sahara Desert and Cape Province, the whole eastern side of Africa is a huge plateau. It begins in the Ethiopian highlands and passes through Kenya, Uganda, Rwanda, Burundi, Tanzania, the Rhodesias, and most of the Union of South Africa, swinging westward also into Katanga and Angola. This plateau

1 T. Monod: "Late Tertiary of Pleistocene in the Sahara," VFPA, No. 36 (1963), pp. 117–229. P. Said and B. Issawi: *Preliminary Results of a Geological Expedition to Lower Nubia and to Kurkur and Dungal Oases, Egypt,* SMU-CPN, No. 1 (1964). J. de Heinzelin and R. Paepe: *The Geological History of the Nile Valley in Sudanese Nubia: Preliminary Results,* SMU-CPN, No. 2 (1964).

was created by the buckling of the earth's granite-covered shield of basalt, and most of the soil in the plateau was formed by the decay of the granite, which is full of quartz grains.

Except for Ethiopia, the plateau is highest near the Equator and slopes gently southward, so that the mean annual temperature is more or less the same everywhere. North and northwest of the highlands extends the Sudan—the transition from desert to forest —stretching east and west from the Red Sea to the Atlantic. Here desert yields to grassland and grassland to savanna, which is grassland dotted with flattopped acacia trees and clumps of bush. Beyond the savannas are open forests of the kind that lose their leaves in the dry season, and beyond the open forest belt, where the savanna fails to meet the sea, is the dense jungle of tall, liana-hung trees that are watered by rainfall the year round, casting permanent shade on the ground below. These tropical rain forests are largely confined to an isolated strip of the West African coast and a belt across the Congo Basin extending as far as the western shore of Lake Victoria.

Although most of Africa consists of deserts, steppelands, and deciduous forests, there are several exceptions. Mediterranean climates comparable to those of southern Europe extend along the northern coast from Morocco to Tunisia, and are found in Cyrenaica and in the Canary Islands. On the Atlantic coast of Morocco there is a small strip of *Csb* climate, with cool dry summers, as in Portugal. Another small patch of this climate is found in the vicinity of Capetown, and there is a larger strip of the European maritime-type climate, *Cfb*, on the coast of Natal. The Ethopian highlands and the "white" highlands of East Africa have the same cool climate, with summer rain, as Yemen has. It is not surprising that these climatic strips and islands resembling the Caucasoid homelands should have been settled from time to time by Caucasoid invaders.

African Prehistory

DURING THE PLEISTOCENE, as later, Africa belonged archaeologically in the western camp. With a few omissions and local specializations, Africans made the same kinds of tools as Europeans and Western Asians, although for the most part somewhat later.

The key to African prehistory is the slow rate at which toolmaking innovations moved from north to south. This lag is becoming increasingly clear as absolute dating methods begin to supplement a time scale based on the alternation of pluvial and interpluvial periods, which more or less matched the glacial and interglacial sequence of Europe. Four pluvials are recognized: the Kageran, Kamasian, Kanjeran (in East Africa only), and the Gamblian. Using Carbon-14 dates, Desmond Clark and Van Zinderen Bakker[2] have identified the Gamblian with the Main Würm and the Kanjeran with the Early Würm. This equates the Kamasian with the Riss and the Kageran with the Mindel Glaciation. Günz—during which there was no ice cap in Europe—may have had no recognizable pluvial in Africa.

In North Africa the earliest implements are pebble tools and pecked stone balls found in the Villafranchian beds of Algeria and Morocco and believed to be over 1,500,000 years old. They are followed by Abbevillian hand axes, then by Acheulean hand axes accompanied by cleavers—which are large, side-struck flakes with a straight cutting edge instead of a point. There was no counterpart in North Africa to the Clactonian-Tayacian sequence of Europe.

After the Acheulean came a Levalloiso-Mousterian industry that evolved into the Aterian, which was the North African equivalent of the Upper Paleolithic of Europe and Western Asia. The principal Aterian implement was a point, in some cases notched and tanged at the base for hafting. It was made from a narrow flake retouched bifacially by pressure flaking, a technique also used in Europe and known widely throughout the world in the Neolithic.

Blade industries were brought into North Africa before the end of the Pleistocene. The oldest blade-tool site recorded to date is at Kom Ombo, Upper Egypt. It is dated at 12,200 B.C.,[3] even earlier than the oldest-known Mouillian date of 10,120 B.C. from Taforalt, Morocco.[4] The Capsian of Tunisia began several millennia later.

In Africa south of the Sahara the sequence also began with pebble tools and in the Villafranchian, but there these tools continued throughout the time span of the North African Abbevillian. The latter industry has not yet been found south of the desert. In the very top of Bed II at Olduvai Gorge in Tanzania—that is, the second bed from the bottom—Acheulean hand axes and cleavers

2 J. D. Clark and E. M. van Zinderen Bakker: "Prehistoric Culture and Pleistocene Vegetation at the Kalambo Falls, Northern Rhodesia," *Nature*, Vol. 201, No. 4923 (1964), pp. 971–5.

3 P. E. L. Smith: "Radiocarbon Dating of a Late Paleolithic Culture," *Science*, Vol. 145, No. 3634, p. 811 (I–1291 and I–1292).

4 Ferembach: *La Nécropole Épipaléolithique de Taforalt.*

appear among the pebble tools, and in small numbers.[5] This new industry had apparently been brought in from some other region, either North Africa or, more likely, southern Arabia, where similar tools have been found in abundance on the Rub' al-Khali. With it was found a human skullcap now known as LLK.[6]

Australopithecine skeletal remains, first discovered in the lower parts of the deposit, continue all the way up to the level of the Acheulean implements and LLK, after which they disappear. This evidence implies that the pebble tools had been made by Australopithecines and that human beings first entered this part of Africa bearing the Acheulean industry. The top of Bed II is now dated at about 500,000 years ago, and both the Acheulean industry and the accompanying human skullcap are a little older. This makes excellent sense, as we know that in Europe the Acheulean began about 600,000 years ago.

At Kalambo Falls, Rhodesia, where an almost complete Pleistocene sequence has been exposed, the Acheulean lasted until after 55,300 B.C., toward the end of the Würm Interstadial of Europe. The Sangoan, an industry consisting of picks, crude gouges, and narrow points, and derived from the Acheulean, followed it, and lasted until 38,750 B.C. It is believed to have been a forest culture designed largely for woodworking, and it occupied a wet period. After the Sangoan came the Magosian, a Levalloisian flake culture comparable to the Levalloiso-Mousterian of Europe and Western Asia. It has been dated at one site at 7550 B.C., which is postglacial. It in turn evolved into a local Mesolithic culture based on small flakes which lasted in South Africa into modern times.

This sequence more or less covers the stone industries of Africa, from Egypt to South Africa, before the advent of blades. In the rain forests of the Congo basin the Sangoan pick and gouge industry was characteristic and lasted almost until the invasion of this region by the Bantus. In West Africa, we have little evidence, as not too much work has been done. In Ghana, O. Davies found pebble tools and choppers, Sangoan picks, and flake tools that he hesitantly equates with the Magosian, and later an abundance of microliths.[7]

In postglacial times the archaeological history of food-gathering cultures in Africa consists, as we have already indicated, of a gradual drifting southward of industries originating in the north.

[5] Reported at the Wenner–Gren Conference on the Origin of Man, Chicago, April 2–5, 1965.

[6] Originally designated as Chellian-3 Man, and so-called in *The Origin of Races*.

[7] O. Davies: "The Climatic and Cultural Sequence in the late Pleistocene of the Gold Coast," PTPA, 1957, pp. 1–5.

This movement terminated in the survival, among the Bushmen, of the "Wilton" culture, a micro-blade derivative of the Capsian which had entered Africa from Western Asia some eight or nine thousand years earlier, and which had itself been derived from the Aurignacian. According to C. van Riet Lowe an even more remarkable instance of survival was that of the use of large chopping and scraping tools, made from cores, by some of the Bugisu (or Bagishu) people who lived near Mt. Elgon, in Uganda, as late as the beginning of the present century.[8]

Food-producing Cultures of the African Neolithic, Bronze, and Iron Ages

FROM ABOUT 4500 B.C. onward, Stone Age hunting cultures were gradually pushed southward and into the deep forests as cultivation and animal domestication spread. At that time food plants and domestic animals were introduced into Egypt and North Africa from Western Asia, where they had first been cultivated and tamed.[9] In Egypt the first farmers settled the high terraces flanking the Nile Valley, and the banks of the Fayum, which was then a lake. The swampy, densely wooded bottom of the valley they left to the Mesolithic natives, who lived on a lavish bounty of waterfowl, fish, hippopotamus, and other game. Later the two peoples merged as they felled the trees and began to cultivate the seasonally flooded banks.

The food plants from Western Asia, particularly wheat, barley, chickpeas, broad beans, and flax, were unsuited to the summer rains of the lands south of the Sahara, but the domestic animals had no such difficulty in the savannas and grasslands except in the tsetse-fly regions. These animals, particularly cattle, spread gradually southward from the Fezzan to the Cape of Good Hope, as shown by thousands of rock paintings all along the eastern highland route.[1]

[8] C. van Riet Lowe: *The Vaal River Chronology*, SSAB, No. 28, Vol. 7 (1952), p. 103. Cited by Sonia Cole in *The Prehistory of East Africa* (Baltimore, Md.: Penguin Books; 1954), p. 115.

[9] Surveys of this subject may be found in R. Oliver and J. D. Fage: *A Short History of Africa* (Baltimore, Md.: Penguin Books; 1962), and in G. P. Murdock: *Africa* (New York: McGraw Hill Book Co.; 1959).

[1] Coon: "The Rock Art of Africa," *Science*, Vol. 142, No. 3600 (1963), pp. 1642–5. This is a review of four extensively illustrated books: L. Frobenius: *Madsimu Dsangara, Südafrikanische Felsbilderchronik* (Graz: Akademische Druck; 1962, first published 1932); *Ekade Ektab, Die Felsbilder Fezzans* (Graz:

In the zone of Mediterranean climate in North Africa, Western Asian agriculture and animal husbandry soon reached the Atlantic Coast and was adopted by the ancestors of the Berbers along the way; eventually they reached the Canary Islands, whose Berber-speaking inhabitants, the Guanches, were still in a Neolithic stage when they were conquered by the Spaniards.

But south of the Sahara the Western Asian plants could not be grown. The situation there was much like that in China at about the same time. New plants had to be locally domesticated. This was apparently done in the bend of the Niger and in the region of Khartoum. Sudanese agriculture may have begun as early as 4500 B.C., as Murdock believes,[2] but there is no evidence of it in the Niger country before 1000 B.C., as Oliver and Fage[3] more cautiously state. They believe it began there during the third or second millennium B.C.

The plants locally domesticated in the Sudan included several varieties of millet, cow peas, okra, watermelon, and sesame. The Negroes living in the bend of the Niger also domesticated an indigenous species of rice (*Oryza glaberrina*). This assemblage of plants was suited to the narrow belt of land running east and west from Senegal to the Nile, and southeastward into Uganda and Kenya. It was not suited to the forested country to the south, which remained the domain of hunters and gatherers until after the time of Christ.

A second center of indigenous African agriculture was the Ethiopian highlands, where eleusine (*Elusine coracana*), teff (*Eragrostis abyssinica*), a banana the roots of which are eaten (*Ensete edulis*), the castor bean, safflower, and other plants were cultivated at least as early as 1500 B.C. By this time the region had already had extensive contact with Egypt. But Ethiopian agriculture was confined almost entirely to its own special environment, to which it was suited, and did not spread to other parts of Africa.

So far, we have been discussing primarily Neolithic agriculture and animal husbandry, accompanied initially by Neolithic tools, but these were eventually replaced by metal implements. Except for Egypt and a few Mediterranean coastal sites, there was no Bronze Age in Africa. Iron was introduced to Egypt from Asia Minor early in the first millennium B.C. At Meroë in Nubia a great

---

Akademische Druck und Verlagsgesellschaft; 1963, first published 1937). H-G. Bandi, ed. : *The Art of the Stone Age* (New York: Crown Publishers; 1961). R. Summers, ed. : *Prehistoric Rock Art of the Federation of Rhodesia and Nyasaland* (New York: Humanities Press; 1961).

2 Murdock: op. cit., p. 183.

3 Oliver and Fage: op. cit., p. 28.

ironworking center arose during the seventh century B.C.,[4] and owing to the abundance of ore in tropical Africa the techniques of smelting and forging spread across the cultivated belt of the Sudan, but did not reach Rhodesia until A.D. 550.[5] In North Africa, most of the Berbers used Neolithic tools into Roman times, when ironworking was introduced in the interior by Jews and later by Negroes from the south. Even today, most of the smiths in Berber lands are Negroes.

In the Sudan, iron hoes and axes replaced stone tools, facilitating the cultivation of the forested regions as soon as suitable food plants became available. The plants arrived with Indonesian navigators who reached the Indian Ocean shores of East Africa about the time of Christ. In their ships they brought taro, Asiatic yams, cocoyams, banana plants, sugar cane, Asiatic rice, and coconuts. After the discovery of America, Europeans brought maize, manioc, sweet potatoes, peanuts, pumpkins, squash, cacao, and tobacco. This type of cultivation was well adapted to most African environments, and thereafter African agriculture assumed its modern form.

The Racial Prehistory of Africa

LIKE ASIA, Africa is large enough to have given birth to more than one subspecies. But lying athwart the Equator and being less mountainous than Asia, Africa has kept her races, both native and intrusive, less effectively apart. Nor is Africa split archaeologically by any cultural divide comparable to Movius's Line. The secret of Africa's cultural and racial history is resistance in depth to penetration, or, more simply, lag. As L. Frobenius said long ago, in Africa peoples and cultures do not replace one another, they simply move aside.[6]

There seem, at the moment, to have been two local racial sequences in Africa, one north and the other south of the Sahara. The first apparently produced the Capoids, the second the Congoids. Both were discussed in *The Origin of Races*. However, a number of new discoveries have been made—some are still unpublished—which support certain conclusions tentatively offered in that book and change others.

[4] R. J. Forbes: *The History of Technology* (New York: Oxford University Press; 1954), p. 597.
[5] J. D. Clark et al.: op. cit.
[6] Frobenius: *Ekade Ektab.*

The Capoid Sequence

THE NORTHERN SEQUENCE begins with the three *Atlan-thropus* mandibles from Ternefine, Algeria; runs through the specimens from Casablanca, Temara, Rabat, and Tangier; and has now been supplemented by the discovery of two new crania, one almost complete, at Jebel Ighoud, Morocco.[7] These finds are either of Late Third Interglacial or Würm I date, older in any case than the beginning of the Aterian industry, and also older than any of the Bushman-like skulls found to date in either East or South Africa. Yet these two skulls are morphologically similar to the later ones found in geographical sequence at Singa in the Sudan, the Homa shell mounds of Kenya, the Boskop site of southwestern Transvaal, Florisbad in the Orange Free State, and Fish Hoek in Cape Province. Except for the last named, these are all full-sized skulls of unreduced ancestral Bushmen. Similar populations persisted in the northern Transvaal until after A.D. 1000, although without doubt the mysterious shrinking, fetalizing syndrome that produced the modern Bushmen had by that time begun elsewhere.

The Congoid Sequence

THE CONGOID SEQUENCE, which, such as it is, is known only south of the Sahara before postglacial time, is so far confined to only three datable specimens: the LLK skullcap of Olduvai, originally called Chellian-3 man, and yet to be studied in detail; the Saldanha Bay skullcap from Cape Province; and the nearly complete Broken Hill cranium from Northern Rhodesia. Dated respectively at about 500,000, 100,000 to 40,000 and about 25,000 years ago, the three are very similar and show little evolutionary change. The latest of them, Broken Hill, which alone has a face, has Negro features. A few later and poorly documented specimens from South Africa seem to have belonged to the same archaic line, and fill the gap between the time of Broken Hill and the arrival of the Bushmen's ancestors who presumably absorbed them.

7 E. Ennouchi: "Un Néanderthalien: l'Homme du Jebel Irhoud (Maroc)," *L'Anth*, Vol. 66, No. 3–4 (1962), pp. 279–99. Coon: "The Rock Art of Africa," pp. 1642–5.

In prime Negro country, the savannas of the western Sudan and the forests to the south as far as the Atlantic coast, one would expect to find evidence of Congoid evolution as this is its heartland. No such evidence exists; not a single Pleistocene skeleton, skull, or scrap of bone has yet been found. The origin of the living Negroes and of the Pygmies is still shrouded in a fog of mystery. So it will remain until intensive digging is done in the belt of countries from Senegal and Guinea east to Sudan and Ethiopia. But there is circumstantial evidence to suggest that East and South Africa, if not indeed all of Africa south of the Sahara, were uninhabited before the introduction of the Acheulean hand-axe and cleaver culture from southern Arabia or North Africa not long before the appearance of LLK man. That evidence is the continued presence until that time of at least two species of potentially competing bipedal primates, after which they vanish. Had man been present earlier, these species would not have been, as the prolonged coexistence of these creatures with man is unlikely.[8]

The Caucasoid Sequence

THE LAST of the three races of Africa to appear on the scene was the Caucasoid, which acted as displacing agent and catalyst to the two indigenous ones. The oldest evidence of its presence is the blade tools discovered in Upper Egypt (see page 87) dated at about 12,200 B.C., but so far we have no skeletons of the men who made them.

Postglacial Capsian skeletons found in Kenya and Tanzania are those of tall, lean people who were not as Caucasoid as it was once thought, but rather a Caucasoid-Negro mixture with long faces, flattish noses, and large teeth.[9] Late Capsians from North Africa are clearly Caucasoid and, more specifically, almost entirely Mediterranean.[1] But the earlier Mouillians, who occupied the coastal regions of Morocco and Algeria, were different. The many skeletons found in the caves of Afalou Bou Rhummel, Algeria, and Taforalt, Morocco, and individual ones from other sites, indicate the presence

[8] We refer to *Australopithecus africanus* and *A. robustus* in South Africa and *A. boisei* (formerly *Zinjanthropus boisei*) and *Homo habilis*, the "Olduvai child," in Tanzania. Leakey, P. V. Tobias, and J. R. Napier: "A new species of the genus *Homo* from Olduvai Gorge," *Nature*, Vol. 202, No. 4927 (1964), pp. 7–9.

[9] Oschinsky: "A Critique of *The Origin of Races* by C. S. Coon," *Anthropologica*, Vol. 5, No. 1 (1963), pp. 111–6.

[1] L. C. Briggs: *The Stone Age Races of Northwest Africa*, BASP, No. 18 (1955).

of a tall, heavy-boned people with massive skulls, wide faces, craggy jaws, and wide nasal openings. Although essentially Caucasoid, they clearly show the absorption of an indigenous element, which can only have come from the previous inhabitants, the Aterians. The Aterian people were derived from the local Ternefine-Tangier line and, according to our interpretation of the evidence, were unreduced ancestral Bushmen. Traces of this indigenous element may still be seen in living populations of North Africa.

Turning to Egypt, it is reasonable to suppose that the early hunters of the jungle-covered Nile Valley postulated by Oliver and Fage (see page 89) contained a strong native African genetic component, and the Neolithic farmers who settled on the open flanks of the valley to either side were Caucasoid, having come directly from Western Asia. Before the end of predynastic time, the two elements had probably fused. This hypothesis has recently been tested by J. M. Crichton, who made a comparison of a total of 296 predynastic Egyptian, dynastic Egyptian, and Negro skulls[2] by means of multiple discriminant analysis, using thirty-four measurements, seven indices and angles, and one computer. This mathematical exercise indicated that the predynastic Egyptians were more like the Negroes than the dynastic Egyptians were, and that the dynastic Egyptians were more Caucasoid than their predecessors. Differences between the two sets of Egyptian skulls were more marked in the face than in the vault. The predynastic skulls have broader, flatter nasal bones and more alveolar prognathism than the dynastic skulls. The predynastic skulls have relatively flat cranial bases, as shown by the difference between the auricular and basion-bregma heights. In this sense, the predynastic skulls were more like those of Negroes. Also the occipital bone extends higher on the back of the skulls of both predynastic Egyptians and Negroes than on dynastic Egyptians and Caucasoids in general. As Crichton did not have a large series of Bushman skulls to use for comparison, he could not determine whether or not the African element in the predynastic Egyptian population could have been Bushman, as suggested by R. Biasutti,[3] rather than Negro.

Further, and abundant, evidence of the racial sequence in the Nile Valley has recently come to light in Wadi Halfa, in Nubia, in two rich Mesolithic sites excavated by the University of Colorado and Southern Methodist University. They are dated between 13,000

2 J. M. Crichton: "A Multiple Discriminant Analysis of Egyptian and African Negro Crania," Harvard University Senior Honors Thesis for A.B. in Anthropology, 1964, Peabody Museum Library.
3 Biasutti: "Crania Aegyptica," AAE, Vol. 35 (1905), pp. 322–62.

B.C. and 8000 B.C., probably nearer the latter.[4] The collection of complete adult skulls will probably total the largest number of equal antiquity in the world and will provide clear information about the racial affinities of the inhabitants of the Upper Nile Valley at the end of the Pleistocene. The skulls are dolichocephalic with bun-shaped occiputs, massive browridges, sloping foreheads, extreme facial flattening in the orbital and nasal regions, great alveolar prognathism, large teeth, and large, deep mandibles. A general similarity to the Jebel Ighoud crania, but perhaps at a more advanced evolutionary level, is suggested. The later skeletons, which were dynastic Egyptian, seem to be Caucasoid.

All of these lines of evidence indicate the same thing, that Africa north of the Sahara was originally inhabited by non-Caucasoids, and that as Caucasoids first came in they mixed with some of the natives and drove others southward. Successive waves of Caucasoid invaders made the population of North Africa more and more Caucasoid, until much later the slave trade reversed the trend. Of particular interest is the massive penetration of Negro Africa by Caucasoid genes in the last fourteen thousand years. This may explain to some extent the similarity between Caucasoids and Negroes in many genetic traits that are not closely related to environmental adaptation such as some of the blood groups, earwax type, and fingerprints, which we will consider later on.

The last of the north-south movements was that of the Bantu tribes from their home in West Africa across to East Africa and down to South Africa. The living Bantu tribes of South Africa must contain Bushman, and possibly also Caucasoid, as well as Negro genetic elements.

The Languages of Africa

THE LINGUISTIC SITUATION in Africa, formerly confused with cultural and racial nomenclature, has recently been simplified and reclassified by J. H. Greenberg.[5] Although he lists 730 languages in his index and names 437 in his text, he reduces these to four superfamilies or stocks: Congo-Kordofanian, Nilo-Saharan,

---

[4] G. J. Armelagos, G. H. Ewing, and D. L. Greene: "Fossil Man Discoveries from Wadi Halfa," MS (1964), and photographs. Also, personal communication and photographs from F. Wendorf.

[5] J. H. Greenberg: *The Languages of Africa*, IJAL, Vol. 29, No. 1 (The Hague: Mouton & Co.; 1963).

Afro-Asiatic, and Khoisan. These combine many groups formerly separated or even isolated, and account for every known African language except the extinct Meroitic, known only from hieroglyphic inscriptions. Because Meroë was the center of ironworking brought from Asia, Meroitic need not have been African.

Afro-Asiatic

OF THE FOUR STOCKS only one is also spoken outside Africa. This is Greenberg's Afro-Asiatic, otherwise known as Hamito-Semitic.[6] The name "Afro-Asiatic" is appropriate because this family has five separate and equally valid branches; Semitic, Berber, Ancient Egyptian, Cushitic, and Chad. Four of these have not been found outside Africa, and only one of them, Semitic, is known to have been spoken first in Asia.

Over forty years ago, Nöldeke[7] proposed that the Semitic languages were of African origin. If so, then we may postulate that proto-Semitic was carried into Arabia over the Bab el Mandeb before 3000 B.C., and from there spread north; that Ancient Egyptian was genetically derived from the speech of the hunters and fowlers of the forested banks of the Nile; and that Berber was carried northward across the Sahara to the Mediterranean, as Berber tradition itself suggests. Some of the Semitic languages that had meanwhile become differentiated in Asia were reintroduced into Africa from about 1000 B.C. onward.

The Semitic Languages of Africa

THESE LANGUAGES include the extinct Phoenician, once spoken in trading posts on the North African coast and in the countryside around Carthage; the Ethiopian languages of this subfamily; and Arabic.

The Ethiopian Semitic languages are derived from two or more southern Arabian languages introduced by literate invaders from the Hadhramaut and Yemen a few centuries before the Christian

6 See M. Cohen's "Hamito-Semitic" in Meillet et Cohen: op. cit., pp. 82–181; and Greenberg: op. cit.

7 T. Nöldeke: "Semitic Languages," *Encyclopaedia Britannica*, 12th and 13th editions (1922-6), Vol. 24, pp. 617–30.

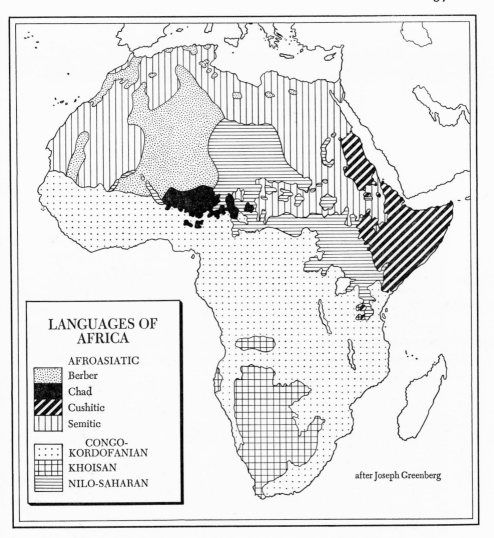

LANGUAGES OF
AFRICA

AFROASIATIC
Berber
Chad
Cushitic
Semitic
CONGO-
KORDOFANIAN
KHOISAN
NILO-SAHARAN

after Joseph Greenberg

era—no one is sure exactly when. They are spoken by over 10 million persons—or half the population of Ethiopia, which includes the former Eritrea—concentrated on one fourth of the land area. The ancient, ritual language of the local Coptic Church is Geez. The official language is Amharic, the native tongue of about 5 million people. Closer than Amharic to Geez is the Tigrinya of the Axum region, not to be confused with Tigré, which is derived from a different southern Arabian tongue and is spoken mostly in Eritrea. Other Ethiopian languages are Gafat, Argobba, Harari, and Gurage, spoken in linguistic islands cut off by the Cushitic-speaking Galla invaders of the fifteenth century.

African Arabic is divided into dialects derived mostly from the particular parts of Western Asia from which they came and to a lesser extent from local influences. The Egyptian dialect extends westward to eastern Tunisia, where it is replaced by Maghribi, which reaches the Atlantic and was once spoken in parts of Spain and Portugal. The Maghribi of herdsmen and farmers is based on a Bedawi dialect of northern Iraq brought in by the Hillali invasion of the twelfth century A.D., and is not very different from the Hassani of Mauretania and other parts of the Sahara. But the refined Maghribi of city people of North Africa, particularly of Fez, is close to the classical. In Somaliland and Ethiopia, Arab traders speak Yemeni, whereas the Arabs of Zanzibar and Indian Ocean seaports speak Omani. Swahili, a hybrid of Omani and Bantu, is spoken widely as a trade language in East Africa.

Ancient Egyptian

ANCIENT EGYPTIAN has had a long life as a written language. A form of it, written in a modified Greek alphabet, survives as a ritual language in Coptic.

Berber

IN VIEW of its supposed antiquity, Berber is astonishingly uniform over its entire area, from the Atlantic to Siwa Oasis in Egypt and from the Mediterranean to the Niger. Before the first Arab invasions twelve centuries ago, Berber speech was continuous geographically. Its present fragmentation was not completed until the time of the Bedawin invasion about 800 years ago. Although it contains many dialects, there are only two clear-cut language groups. One is Zenatia, spoken mostly in eastern Morocco and some of the Saharan oases. The other takes in all the rest, such as Rifian, Soussi, Middle Atlas, Berber, Kabyle, and Tuareg.

We have already suggested that Berber was carried north across the Sahara from a supposed Afro-Asiatic homeland. It may or may not have been spoken by the bearers of the Capsian culture; and whether or not the Mouillians spoke it is another open question. Rifian, at least, contains some "Mediterranean" suffixes (*-nth* and *-anna*) in the names of cultivated plants, and a "Mediterranean" substratum has been postulated for Guanche, the extinct Berber language of the pre-Spanish Canary Islanders, who were Neolithic in culture and anatomically Mouillian.

Cushitic

BEFORE THE ARRIVAL over two thousand years ago of the invaders of Ethiopia who spoke southern Arabian languages, Cushitic languages like Berber may have formed a solid block. Greenberg identifies fifty-four Cushitic languages divided into five regional groups. The northern is Beja, spoken also by Bisharin and Hadendoa along the Red Sea coast of the Sudan. These people are Kipling's "Fuzzy-Wuzzies," who broke the British square. Central Cushitic consists of eight isolated languages in Ethiopia. The eastern branch includes sixteen languages of several numerous peoples, mostly pastoral, including the Gallas, Somalis, and Sidamos. The western branch has thirty small units in southwest Ethiopia, and the southern consists of six languages, including Iraqu,[8] spoken in two tiny enclaves in Tanzania, each of which is located exactly east of an equally small Bushman enclave. Both enclaves have eastern Sudanic speakers to the west and Bantu speakers on the north, west, and south. This is a very curious geographical situation, suggesting the complexity of past population movements along the East African highland corridor.

Chad

THE CHAD LANGUAGES, spoken in the west-central Sudan just east of the bend of the Niger, consist of 112 languages in nine groups. Of these, by far the most widely spoken and best-known is Hausa, the language of a widespread group of Sudanese craftsmen and traders, which serves as a lingua franca over a vast region. In diversity and complexity the Chad languages stand in marked contrast to three of the other Afro-Asiatic languages, Semitic, Ancient Egyptian, and Berber. This suggests a considerable antiquity.

[8] The blood groups of these people have been intensively studied.

Congo-Kordofanian[9]

THIS STOCK, formerly called Niger-Congo, is divided into
two geographical units. One of them, by far the largest, contains
six groups and 203 languages spoken in the forests and adjacent
savannas of West Central Africa in a narrow east-west belt from
the Senegal and Liberia to the headwaters of the Uele River, at
about 30° E. longitude, and just north of the Equator.

The well-known languages of the west coast, such as Mande,
Kru, Ewe, Yoruba, and Ibo, are all members of this family. So
is Bantu, listed as only one of thirty-one "languages" of the Benue-
Congo group. Since the introduction of forest-adapted food plants
from Indonesia, Bantu has spread over most of Africa south and
east of its original home.

Fulani, one of twenty-three languages of the West Atlantic
group, is spoken by one of the most nearly Caucasoid tribes of
sub-Saharan Africa, and so is Herero, a form of Bantu spoken in
Angola. Furthermore, the famous semi-Caucasoid Tutsi (Watusi)
of Rwanda and Burundi speak Bantu. But most of the Niger-Congo
speakers are true Negroes.

The Kordofanian languages of this family are spoken by the
inhabitants of a small region of the Nuba Hills of the Eastern
Sudan who are surrounded by people who speak Nilo-Saharan
languages. Despite their small area, there are thirty-one of these
languages, divided into five groups.

Nilo-Saharan

THESE LANGUAGES, sixty-three in number, with six groups,
have a wide and discontinuous distribution. Two are spoken by
riverine peoples—Songhai along the bend of the Niger, and Nile-
Nubian or Dongola along the bend of the Nile in the Sudan above
Atbara. Meroë, the site of an extinct, unclassified language, lies
in the middle of their elongated territory. A large block of Nilo-
Saharan languages is lodged in the east-central Sahara. These are

9 In 1964 Greenberg stated, that in his 1963 classification he had changed
"Niger-Congo" to "Congo-Kordofanian" to avoid the misconception that Kordo-
fanian is excluded. He further stated that the Kordofanian languages are of the
Niger-Congo group and that their separation is merely geographical. See his reply
to H. K. Schneider: "Confusion in African Linguistic Classification," CA, Vol. 5,
No. 1 (1964), pp. 56-7.

spoken by the Teda and other partly Caucasoid peoples of the Fezzan and the Tibesti plateau country noted for a large number of rock engravings that show people of both Negro and Caucasoid appearance with cattle and wheeled vehicles. Other such languages almost surround Eastern Cushitic, which in turn completely surrounds Kordofanian, making the southwestern Sudan (in the political sense) an area of great linguistic complexity. The Chari-Nile group of languages, stretching southward to the west of Ethiopia and Somalia, and well into Tanzania, are spoken by the tall, lean Nilotic peoples, including the Dinka, Shilluk, Nuer, Bari, Turkana, Nandi, Suk, and Masai.

Khoisan

THE KHOISAN or click languages are spoken by the Bushmen, the Hottentots, and two isolated groups of primarily hunting people in Tanzania, the Sandawe and the Hatsa or Kindiga. South African Khoisan is divided into three groups—northern, central, and southern—all spoken by Bushmen. Central South African Khoisan is spoken by Hottentots as well. Sandawe and Hatsa are separate groups. Grammatically, but not genetically, Sandawe is closest to central South African Khoisan. Not very much is known about the Hatsa language. Racially the Khoisan languages are primarily identified with the Capoid subspecies, but one group of Negroes, the Bergdama in southwest Africa and Angola, also speak northern South African Khoisan. Clicks have been taken over into two South African Bantu languages, Zulu and Sotho. Attempts have been made to identify Hottentot with the Cushitic languages, as the Hottentots keep cattle. But the resemblances, largely confined to suffixes indicating gender, apply to the Khoisan languages as a whole and, if valid, suggest contact between Khoisan-speakers and Cushitic-speakers long before the introduction of cattle to South Africa. Such contact, if it existed, need not have taken place in South Africa at all.

The Living Africans

ON THE NORTH and east the living peoples of Africa, whatever languages they speak, are transitional to the Europeans and

Western Asians. Those who are the most fully African still live
in the shadowy recesses of the rain forest and on the open velds
and deserts of South Africa. The peoples of Africa as a whole
may be divided into the North African Caucasoids; the mixed
peoples of Ethiopia and the East African highlands; and the
Pygmies, the Negroes, the Bushmen, and the Hottentots.

In some parts of Africa, tribes and races have come and departed, mixing, absorbing and becoming absorbed, reemerging
and adapting to new conditions. In others, time's clock seems
to have stopped. If we hope to understand the living races of
Africa, we will do best to start with the oldest, least complicated
populations and end with the most recent and heterogeneous.
We shall start with one kind of Congoids, the Pygmies, and end
up with another, the Negroes and Negroids.

The Pygmies, or Twides: Their History, Distribution, and Numbers[1]

BECAUSE THE PYGMIES occupy a key position in the racial
history of Africa, some historical and cultural background is
necessary before they can be described. Our earliest knowledge
of these people is derived from an Egyptian document of the Old
Kingdom in which a Pharaoh instructed the leader of an expedition to the far south to bring him back a Pygmy dancer. The
mission succeeded. The next account comes from Herodotus, who
told of the Pygmies' annual battle with cranes, and gave them
their name, *Pygmaioi*, meaning people as tall as the distance
from a man's elbow to his knuckles. This name has persisted, but

1 M. Gusinde: *Die Twiden: Pygmäen und Pygmoide im tropischen Afrika*
(Vienna and Stuttgart: Wilhelm Braumüller, 1956). J. Hiernaux: "Les Carac-
tères Physiques des Populations du Ruanda et de l'Urundi," MIRSN, 2nd series,
Vol. 52 (1954); "Données Génétiques sur Six Populations de la République du
Congo," Act G, Vol. 42, No. 2 (1962), pp. 145–74. B. Adé: "Le Nanisme Raciale,"
ASAG, Vol. 19, No. 1 (1954), pp. 1–18. R. R. Gates: "The African Pygmies,"
AGMG, Vol. 7 (1958), pp. 159–218. Oschinsky: *The Racial Affinities of the
Baganda*. P. W. Morgenthaler: "Quelques remarques au sujet de l'inclinaison
et de la rétroversion du tibia," BSS, Vol. 31 (1954–5), pp. 45–59. Sauter and
A. Könz: "L'humérus des Pygmées de l'Ituri (Congo-Belge)," BSS, Vol. 31 (1954–
1955), pp. 5–6. Vallois: "New Research on the Western Negrillos," AJPA, Vol.
26, No. 4 (1940), pp. 449–71. F. Twiesselmann: "Contribution à l'Étude des
Pygmées de l'Afrique Occidentale," MMRH, Ser. 2, Fasc. 27 (1942), pp. 1–32.
D. B. Jelliffe: "The origin, fate, and significance of the umbilical hernia in
Nigerian children," TRST, Vol. 46 (1952), pp. 428–34.

Note. Extensive bibliographies on the Pygmies will be found in Gusinde: op.
cit., and Gates: op. cit.

specialists in African anthropology have created a new and more specific designation, *Twides,* from the Bantu syllable *-twa,* as in BaTwa, the Small People.

We have every reason to believe that from before the time of the pyramids the Twides were the sole inhabitants of the central African rain forest, from Liberia to Rwanda. That forest is now divided into two parts by a stretch of open country reaching the coast between Accra and Lagos. In the smaller, isolated western part, no unmixed Pygmies may be left, although small bands of them have been reported in various places until the beginning of the present century. In the much larger eastern part, three geographically distinct groups of Pygmies are recognized: the Western, the Northern, and the Southern Twides.

The Western Twides live scattered in Cameroon, Gabon, Span-ish Guinea, the Ubangi-Shari region of the Central African Re-public, and both Congos. They number about 25,000. To them may be added 80,000 to 100,000 BaTwa or Ba-Cwa living south of the Congo River, who physically resemble those living to the west. The Eastern Twides are the Pygmies of the Ituri forest, near the Uganda border and beyond it. They number about 32,000. The Southern Twides are the Pygmies of Rwanda and Burundi, numbering about 9,300. The Pygmies, then, total between 146,000 and 166,000, if these estimates are correct. If they err, it is prob-ably on the low side, because Pygmies are shy and hard to count.

Speaking primarily of the Western and Northern Twides, Gusinde[2] has convincingly shown that the Pygmies are perfectly adapted to the dark damp sour-smelling selva, where they live in small bands in an east-west belt between 5° N. latitude and 5° S. latitude from the Atlantic coast to the escarpment of the East African highlands. In their home there is no perceptible annual change in the length of the day. The temperature rises to 86° F by day and falls to 68° F at night, or a little lower if it rains, and except for a brief relatively drier season there is rain for an hour or two every day, accompanied by violent thunderstorms that send dead limbs crashing to the ground.

Whereas a European or a Negro has difficulty walking through this forest, the Pygmies glide through, jumping, grasping lianas and branches with their hands, and even running along low-lying limbs of trees. Their small size, light weight, great flexibility of joints, and sudden bursts of energy make this mode of locomotion possible for them and indeed enable them to survive as food-gatherers.

[2] Op. cit.

In the forest, fruits and seeds are scarce. So are birds and game animals. That is why Pygmies live in small bands and one band is only rarely in communication with other bands. Before the arrival of Negro pioneers who cleared small patches of forest long enough to grow a few crops in one place before the vegetation returned or elephants trampled their gardens, the Pygmies lived largely on animal products, including termites in season, and honey. Since the Negroes arrived, the Pygmies have formed symbiotic relations with them. The Pygmies give the Negroes meat and warn them of the approach of human enemies and elephants. The Negroes give the Pygmies iron objects, pottery, and bananas. The Pygmies visit the villages occasionally, speak the languages of their patrons, and send their boys to the Negroes' puberty schools, where future patron-client relationships are confirmed or created.

Despite this integrated educational system, no influx of Negro genes into the Pygmy pool takes place. To the contrary, some Pygmy women become plural wives of Negroes, remain in the relative comfort of the village, and bear half-Pygmy children who are classed as Negroes. Negro women will not go out into the forest with Pygmies, and might not survive its rigors if they did.

Because this one-way gene flow may have begun on the edges of the forest before the Negroes invaded it, the Negroes must have been partly Pygmy for a long time. When they moved into the selva they brought Pygmy genes with them and the present genetic trickle reinforces this trend, whereas the Pygmies remain unchanged.

Pygmies and Negroes both have the sickle-cell trait, one of their genetic shields against malaria. In view of the direction of gene flow, it seems more likely that the Pygmies first gave it to the ancestors of the Negroes than vice versa. But the Negroes have given the Pygmies another disease, not genetically but indirectly through bananas. That is kwashiorkor, a protein-deficiency disease that induces red hair color, bad teeth, atrophy of the pancreas, a fatty enlargement of the liver, and severe anemia. It also affects the growth of the skeleton, and body weight.

Kwashiorkor is caused by the lack of a component found in mother's milk. Since Pygmy mothers wean their babies on bananas, which are obtained from the Negroes and are easier to come by than foods suitable for weaning taken from the forest, bananas can be said to be responsible for the incidence of the disease among the Pygmies. The deficiency may even begin before weaning if the milk of a particular mother is low in this component.[3] Kwashiorkor may contribute to dwarfing, but it is not its sole cause. Many healthy Pygmies are as small as the sick ones, and at the time of the Pharaohs the Pygmies had no bananas.

The story of the Southern Twides is different. The Hutu (Bahutu) Negroes settled the highlands of Rwanda and Burundi at the time of the Bantu expansions, perhaps between A.D. 500 and 1000. Before then the whole region was forested and its only inhabitants were Pygmies. As the Hutu cleared the land to plant their crops, the edge of the forest was pushed back. Some of the Pygmies retreated behind it, and others stayed in the open country, on the bank of Lake Kivu, to serve the Hutu as potters and in other menial capacities. These stranded Pygmies became a despised caste like the Untouchables of India. While there is some disagreement on this point, sexual relations between the Hutu and the Pygmies have probably been minimal. The same is true of Pygmy-Tutsi (Watusi) relations after the arrival of the latter from the northeast at about A.D. 1450, the time of the Galla invasion of Ethiopia. The principal effect of the Tutsi on the Pygmies was to thrust the ones who were still forest hunters farther back and higher up on the slopes of the volcanoes, to make room for the Tutsi's great herds of cattle.

The Physical Attributes of the Pygmies

WITH A FEW notable exceptions, we can generalize that in every measurable or observable character known the Pygmies stand at one extreme, the African Caucasoids at another, and the Negroes in between. One exception is the Pygmies' most conspicuous feature: stature. Before more than a few groups of Pygmies had been measured, over half a century ago someone (we are not sure who, nor do we care) decreed that all groups of alleged Pygmies that had mean adult male statures of below 150 centimeters were true Pygmies, and all those with statures above that figure were Pygmoids and, by definition, had been mixed with Negroes. This obvious absurdity, which takes into account only a single character, has passed unchallenged to this day and some

---

[3] L. van den Berghe: "Le Kwashiorkor expérimental du Porc et le Facteur L," FSAC, Vol. 2, No. 1 (1956), p. 13. Detailed knowledge about the etiology of this disease was obtained through experiments with pigs.

writers still believe it. Otherwise we would not have mentioned it.[4]

The shortest Pygmies noted to date are the Northern Twides, the tribes of the Ituri forest. Their mean stature is 144.03 centimeters (4 feet, 8½ inches) for 510 men, and 137.04 (4 feet, 6 inches) for 382 women. Both the Western and the Southern Twides range from 152 centimenters (4 feet, 11½ inches) to 155 centimeters (5 feet, 1 inch) for males. The females are about 9 centimeters (3½ inches) shorter. The average weight of the Southern Twides, who are the biggest of all, is 48.7 kilos (72 pounds), and the Ituri Pygmies must be considerably lighter. In other words, they are about half the weight of most Europeans.

Except for local variations in height and weight, all are alike in body build. They have relatively short legs, particularly short in the thigh, and long arms, particularly long in the forearm. The femur head shows extreme torsion,[5] and the tibia head even more retroversion than those of the French Neanderthals.[6] These features are associated with extreme mobility and with squatting.

In conjunction with their short legs, Pygmies have relative sitting heights of 52 percent or 53 percent of stature, as do Northern and Central Europeans and the mountaineers of Western Asia. Arabs, Berbers, and Negroes have longer legs, and relative sitting heights two or three percent lower. But if the Pygmies' vertebral columns were as nearly straight as those of Europeans, their relative sitting heights might be one or two percent higher than they are. Even more than Negroes they are lordotic, that is, swaybacked. Pygmy children usually have swollen abdomens, and the combination produces umbilical hernia, which is also very frequent in Negroes.

D. B. Jelliffe found[7] that in a large sample of Negroes whom he examined 97 percent of the hernias were of the "skin" type, in which not only the intestine but the lining of the abdominal wall protrudes outward, rendering the condition harmless. This type of umbilical hernia is not found among any peoples of the world except African Pygmies and Negroes; it is not found even among Papuans, whom some anthropologists have thought to be related to Negroes. For this reason R. H. Post considers it a valid racial criterion.[8]

---

4 Someone apparently took the stature categories in Martin's *Lehrbuch* too seriously. There every series under 160 cm. is "short"; 160–170 cm. is "medium"; and over 170 cm. is "tall." Round numbers have a magic all their own.

5 Sauter and Könz: op. cit.

6 Morgenthaler: op. cit.

7 D. B. Jelliffe: op. cit.

8 Personal communication from R. H. Post.

If Negroes are loose-jointed compared to Europeans, Pygmies are even more so. Being loose-jointed not only makes them good dancers but also helps them dart through the forest. Boris Adé, who spent years as a doctor to the Pygmies in the Ituri country, attributes their flexibility to a combination of two unusual endocrine conditions, a hereditary deficiency in growth hormones in the anterior lobe of the pituitary and an excess of female sex hormone, particularly notable in the male. The former condition would explain a retarded proliferation of cartilages in the joints, affecting growth, and the latter a reduction of bony crests throughout the skeleton, a general flexibility of joints, and the frequent appearance of gynecomasty (female-like breasts) in the males.

On one occasion Adé tried in vain to save the life of a Pygmy woman who had been clawed by a leopard. Had he returned the remains to her camp, her body would have been placed in her hut and the camp abandoned. Instead he preserved the body so that he could dissect it later, planning in particular to study the endocrine glands. But the local authorities forced him to bury it, and no one has yet, to our knowledge, published a detailed autopsy of a Pygmy cadaver—or injected growth hormone into Pygmy children year after year to see what would happen.

Such an experiment, which would harm no one, could help us determine what makes the Pygmies dwarfs and whether different dwarfing mechanisms might be found to operate in different dwarf populations, not only in Africa but elsewhere. At the moment we are not in a position to state from simple observation, as some have stated, that certain Pygmies are infantile, others partly achondroplastic, and so on. We can state that the Pygmies are well adapted to their environment, where it is to their advantage to be small and lithe, that they are very fertile, and that at least as far as their genitalia are concerned they are not infantile, for their male organs are as large as those of Negroes.

The Pygmies also differ from most Negroes in skin color. The Western Twides have been described as having yellowish skin and pink lips. The Eastern Twides are said to have a clay-yellow skin color with brownish overtones, and also pink lips. Gates[9] calls the skin color of the Ituri Pygmies mahogany. He has postulated that the Pygmies possess three genes for skin color: mahogany, yellow, and brunette. The Bushmen have only the last two, and the Negroes all three and in addition a fourth, which makes them black.

[9] Gates: op. cit.

The darkest-skinned Pygmies are the potters of Lake Kivu, who, according to Hiernaux,[1] have reddish brown skins more or less matching Numbers 28 and 29 on von Luschan's widely used skin-color chart, on which Number 30 is the darkest. This makes them little if any lighter than their overlords the Hutu, but unlike the latter, many Kivu Pygmies have large, relatively unpigmented yellow patches on their bodies. The Kivu Pygmies also have deeply furrowed foreheads, wrinkles on their bodies, and their skin is characteristically coarse-grained. In these respects they differ from the Western and Eastern Twides.

Pygmies are born covered with a thick lanugo, or fetal hair, which is usually blond to reddish, and when retained in adults turns dark brown. Both sexes also have rich terminal hair, particularly on their armpits and pubis. In some males it is distributed over much of the body, and males characteristically have heavy beards. This rich body hair must be well equipped with apocrine glands, for the Pygmies exude a strong and pungent body odor that their Negro neighbors find offensive. Pungent body odor may offer protection against insects. This suggestion has been offered because Negroes are less frequently bitten than whites.

As one would expect in dwarfs, the Pygmies' heads appear large in proportion to their body size. Their heads are usually submesocephalic, with cephalic index means between 75 and 77 for both sexes. They are also relatively high-vaulted, except for the Lake Kivu potters, who are also aberrant in other respects. Pygmies' heads are usually oval to globular, like those of infants, and bulbous foreheads are common, particularly in children and women. The eyeballs usually protrude from shallow sockets, the sclera is unpigmented and the iris is brown.

Their noses are broader than they are long, with nasal indices characteristically over 100, except among the Lake Kivu potters. Among the males of this group, the mean is 90, with a range from 68 to 117. Most Pygmy noses have depressed roots and low bridges, with very broad wings. The tip is either flattened or shaped like a double funnel. The Kivu Pygmies are again exceptional in that 10 percent of them have convex nasal profiles.

Most Pygmies, the Kivu potters included, have long, convex upper lips with little eversion. Most of them have much alveolar prognathism, and retreating chins are common. To our knowledge, nothing has been published about their teeth.

[1] Hiernaux: "Les Caractères Physiques des Populations du Ruanda et de l'Urundi."

Pygmies resemble Negroes in the blood groups so far studied among Pygmies, and in that they have the sickle-cell trait. This will be discussed in more detail in Chapter 9. Here we need say only that this resemblance is not surprising. Because the genes that flow between Pygmies and Negroes characteristically follow a one-way channel, the logical deduction is that the Pygmies gave these genes to the ancestors of the Negroes, among whom further selection subsequently took place in response to local selective pressures.

According to J. P. Bouckaert,[2] the Pygmies have the highest basal metabolism rate in the world, which, through the agency of a high thyroid level, could explain their protruding eyeballs. In comparing the Rwanda-Burundi Pygmies with their neighbors the Hutu and Tutsi, Hiernaux found that the Pygmies have the lowest heart beat and the highest blood pressure of the three, but there is little difference in respiration rate. It would be interesting to know if other Pygmies, those who live in the forest, for example, are the same.

The Importance of Being a Pygmy

THE PYGMIES, as we have indicated, are a distinctive people who cannot be shown to have migrated into their rain forest from anywhere else or to have been produced by mixture. They are very much alike everywhere except in the highlands of Rwanda and Burundi, where most of them have been living for centuries in open country at a high altitude in the midst of Negroes. Hiernaux believes that these particular Pygmies are mixed. When the Pygmies which he measured are divided according to stature into the potters of Lake Kivu and the hunters of the forested mountain slopes and crests, we see that the former have a mean stature of 159 centimeters (5 feet 3 inches) and that some of the others fall as low as 149.5 centimeters (4 feet 11 inches), an ordinary figure for Pygmy height.

The Kivu Pygmies may, as Hiernaux says, be mixed, but if so, perhaps less with the Hutu or Tutsi than with earlier peoples moving down the highland corridor. This is indicated by the fact that the body proportions of the potters are still those of Pygmies

2 J. P. Bouckaert: "Étude de métabolisme de base de certains groupes d'indigènes au Congo belge," CIAN (1949), pp. 241–2. Cited in G. A. Heuse: *Biologie du Noir* (Brussels: Les Éditions Problèmes d'Afrique Centrale, 1957).

in general, that they are the hairiest of all, and that their skin is wrinkled. None of these traits occur among the Hutu or Tutsi. An alternative hypothesis is that for the thousand years or more that the potters have been living at a high altitude and in open, less humid country the selection that has kept the forest Pygmies small and button-nosed has been relaxed. Thus the Lake Kivu potters may have returned to an approximation of their ancestral body size, and acquired a less extreme nose form.

According to Gates, the Pygmies derive from a hypothetical full-sized ancestor with mahogany-colored skin, heavy body hair, a flat nose, and great prognathism. If such a race ever existed, the rule of parsimony may warrant the theory that it had evolved from an ancient African line whose last-known representative was Rhodesian Man. Such a people may have been driven into the forest by drought, in which case mutations for dwarfing, which appear everywhere, would ensure a precarious survival, impossible for simple food-gatherers on the desiccated plain. This hypothesis is a combination of Gates's reconstruction and our own study of the evidence of archaeology and human paleontology. It must remain a hypothesis until more fossils are found. Its bearing on the origin of the Negroes will be discussed later in this chapter.

The Bushmen

WE HAVE already discussed the problem of the origin of the Bushmen and have mentioned, in our survey of language, their historic geographical distribution. All that remains is a physical description of these people, with special reference to their environment and their adjustments to it.[3]

Today the 50,000 Bushmen—more or less, as their exact numbers are undetermined—live mostly on the Kalahari Desert. Four hundred and fifty years ago they hunted on well-watered grasslands and in scrub forests teeming with game. In contrast to the Pygmies, who are perfectly adapted to moving rapidly through dense vegetation in the cathedral-like shade of the tall, interlock-

[3] The bibliography on the subject is extensive. The most comprehensive single source is Tobias: "Les Bochimans Auen et Naron de Ghazni," *L'Anth*, Vol. 59, No. 3–4 (1955), pp. 235–52; No. 5–6 (1955), pp. 429–61; Vol. 60, No. 1–2 (1956), pp. 22–52; No. 3–4 (1956), pp. 268–89.

ing trees of the rain forest, the Bushmen walk and run great distances over open ground, and are exposed to the brightest sunlight of Africa except for that of the eastern Sahara. The Pygmies live in a moisture-laden atmosphere varying no more than a few degrees in temperature either daily or annually; the Bushmen are exposed to a temperature range from below freezing to 104° F in the shade and 140° F in the sun. Two entirely different sets of adaptations are indicated. Whether the ancestors of the Bushmen came from North Africa, as the present evidence indicates, or evolved locally, as most South African scholars believe, makes little difference in this respect. The Sahara and the Kalahari are climatic counterparts to each other, flanked by strips of Mediterranean climate on their poleward sides.

As before the Bushmen were forced onto the desert they had luxuriant game and ample wild vegetable foods within reach, there seems to be no reason for them to be small, but they are. The mean stature of local groups of males ranges from 149 centimeters (4 feet 11 inches) in the south to 158 centimeters (5 feet 2 inches) in the north. The women are 8 to 10 centimeters (1 inch) shorter. Their stature increases in the groups that live nearer the Equator and decreases in those nearer the South Pole. We are reminded of the situation in Europe, where the mean stature decreases with the mean winter temperature on the poleward side of the line of maximum stature, and reaches its minimum among the Lapps, who are not much taller than the Bushmen.

On the basis of a brilliant paper by Alice Brues entitled "The Spearman and the Archer,"[4] Tobias suggests that the size of Bushmen is somehow related to his use of the small weak bow and arrows tipped by poison.[5] The poison is made from either an insect or a plant, depending on which is available locally.[6] Armed with his diminutive weapons, the Bushman hunter, who need not be big and strong, creeps up, with consummate skill and sometimes in disguise, close to his prey. A rapid volley of tiny arrows pierces or scratches the animal's skin, and its fate is sealed. It runs off, eventually staggers and falls to its knees or haunches, and the Bushmen, who have been following patiently for hours or even days, move in for the kill.

This type of hunting sets a premium on litheness, endurance, economy in consumption of water, and a defiance of the elements.

[4] A. Brues: "The Spearman and the Archer," AA, Vol. 61, No. 3 (1959), pp. 457–69.
[5] Tobias: "Bushman Hunter-Gatherers: A Study in Human Ecology," in D. H. S. Davis, ed.: *Ecology in South Africa* (The Hague: W. Junk; 1965).
[6] E. M. Thomas: *The Harmless People* (New York: Alfred A. Knopf; 1959).

All these the Bushman is capable of. Although short, he is well built according to the artistic canons of the West. His legs are of medium length in proportion to his stature. In contrast to the bunchy, long-tendoned muscles of the Pygmies and the Negroes, his limb muscles are long-bellied and have short tendons, like those of Mongoloids, and his hands and feet are small. His yellowish skin, which tans to light or medium brown, reflects 43 percent of sunlight, as compared to the 23 percent reflected by the black skin of the Bantu.[7] In this the Bushman is as well adapted to life in the desert as are the Arabs and the American Indians. In contrast to the bulging eyeballs common in Pygmies, the Bushman's eyes are protected from the glare by slitted, often fat-laden lids, like those of Eskimos. His glabrous body, bare neck, and pepper-corn hair, which leaves patches of scalp exposed, facilitate heat loss at high temperatures. He protects his body against the cold with warm skins.

Certain features of the Bushman's physique which have been commonly noted have led to a theory that they are pedomorphic, or infantile, a trait more apparent in some individuals than in others. One of these features is a bulbous forehead, found among children, some women, but not many adult males. Another is a flattish face with a low nasal bridge and a flattish nasal tip. These features are racial as well as infantile, and contribute, along with their yellowish skins, to the oft-noted Mongoloid appearance of the Bushmen.

The usual pubertal form of the feminine nipple, with its swollen areola, is exaggerated among Bushman girls, to the extent that the nipples look like bright orange balls loosely attached to the breasts, a startling sexual attraction that wanes after the first baby has been suckled and weaned. Another Bushman specialty concerns the female genitalia. Owing to a deficiency of growth in the labia majora which thus fail to seal the vaginal entrance, the inner lips fall through the gap. As a Bushman woman grows older, her inner lips protrude all the more, and they may ultimately hang down three or four inches. Despite much study, no one really knows to what extent this sexual feature is a product of nature and to what extent of artifice. It is quite possible that both factors are involved.

According to early accounts, all unmixed Bushman males have penises which protrude forward as in infants even when not in erection, but this is not always true. Another oddity of Bushmen

7 J. S. Weiner, G. A. Harrison, R. Singer, R. Harris, and W. Jopp: "Skin Colour in Southern Africa," HB, Vol. 36, No. 3 (1964), pp. 294–307. The amount of light reflected was measured on the upper arm at 685 mμ (6,850 angstroms).

is monorchy, or the descent of only one testicle, but this also is not universal among Bushman males.[8]

The most famous physical attribute of the Bushman is of course steatopygia, which is most commonly found and most highly developed in the women. The gluteal fat is held out by fibrous tissue, preventing the buttocks from sagging.[9] The Bushmen are not the only steatopygous people in the world, nor is the protrusion of their buttocks wholly or even largely an artifact of lordosis, or forward-curvature of the lumbar region. The Bushman buttocks have often been compared to the hump or humps on camels and zebus and to the tail of the fat-tailed sheep. It has been proposed, without proof, that the fat on the Bushman's buttocks provides nourishment needed for survival. If so, its absence or minor development in the males seems contradictory. On the other hand, the Bushmen gorge themselves after a successful kill, as their deeply wrinkled abdominal skin indicates. One suggestion that we have not heard is that steatopygia is advantageous in the nutrition of the mother and the fetus during pregnancy and also during prolonged lactation when associated with a scarcity of food and especially of foodstuffs suitable for weaning. This suggestion is only an idea, and needs to be tested.

Several other features distinguish the Bushmen. Their skins wrinkle deeply in maturity and old age, and not just in the abdomen. They lack the body odor of Pygmies and Negroes. Their ears are small, square on top, and often lobeless, though the contour pattern of helix and antihelix is deep and complex. Their hands and feet are quite different from those of Negroes, and their nails much more curved. Despite the evidence of blood-group studies, to date incomplete, the Bushmen are a race *sui generis,* and their relationship to Negroes is probably due to the Negroes' having absorbed Bushman genes, for of the two the Bushman seems to be the older race.

The Hottentots

W H E N   T H E   D U T C H settled Capetown in order to provide a watering and ships' chandlering station for their vessels sailing

[8] Gusinde: "Monorchie der Buschmänner als ontogenetische Spezialisation," in Festschrift für Hans Plischke, *Von Fremden Völkern und Kulturen"* (Düsseldorf: Droste-Verlag; 1955), pp. 175–81.

[9] L. H. Krut and R. Singer: "Steatopygia: The Fatty Acid Composition of Subcutaneous Adipose Tissue in the Hottentot," AJPA, Vol. 21, No. 2 (1963), pp. 181–8.

to and from the rich East Indies, they saw more Hottentots than Bushmen. Once the Dutch had begun to farm and graze the rich Cape Province, they competed for pasture with the cattle-breeding Hottentots more than with the Bushmen. Today the Bushmen outnumber the Hottentots, who have been largely absorbed through mixture.

The origins of the Hottentots are obscured by legends and complicated by anthropological interpretations.[1] Because the Hottentots must have obtained cattle and the art of metallurgy from the northeast before the Bantu invasions, some anthropologists have concluded that they got these cultural advantages from "Hamites," that is, Caucasoids, whom they absorbed racially and linguistically. Their present physical appearance, however, indicates that whomever they mixed with was more Negro than Caucasoid.

The living Hottentots are larger than the Bushmen, with a mean stature of 163 centimeters (5 feet 4 inches) for males. They tend to be a little darker in skin color, and if anything even more steatopygous. In general features, particularly of the face and hair, they are partly Negroid. Their blood groups do not help clarify the question of Hottentot origins, partly because the Bushmen and the Negroes are similar in most of the blood-group factors so far studied among the Bushmen, and partly because the Hottentots show certain serological peculiarities of their own. The Hottentots are, in sum, a clinal South African population mostly but not entirely of Bushman origin.

The Sandawe and Hatsa

THE SANDAWE and Hatsa (or Kindiga) are two groups of Khoisan-speaking peoples living in Tanzania. The Sandawe have been studied anthropometrically,[2] the Hatsa have not.

According to their own tradition, the Sandawe were originally yellow-skinned hunters with peppercorn hair who came into their present country about a hundred years ago. Before that time they had met the Bantu-speaking Nyaturu and the Tatoga, who speak a dialect of Nandi (Eastern Sudanic). Both were herdsmen, and the Tatoga were also cultivators. The Sandawe traded women for

1 Tobias: "Physical Anthropology and Somatic Origins of the Hottentots," *Africa*, Vol. 14, No. 1 (1955), pp. 1–15.
2 J. C. Trevor: "The Physical Characteristics of the Sandawe," JRAI, Vol. 77, Part 1 (1946), pp. 61–78.

cattle with both these tribes, before they entered their present country, and in recent times the Sandawe themselves have absorbed some Nyaturu genes. The living Sandawe are anthropometrically closer to Hottentots than to Bushmen, but have little steatopygia. Their hair form grades from peppercorn to frizzly, their skin is mostly brown. The Nyaturu, themselves part Sandawe, are intermediate between the latter and West African Negroes in many features.

The Berbers

THE THIRD discrete racial element in Africa is the Caucasoid, which, as indicated earlier, first entered the continent in massive invasions about 15,000 years ago, certainly from Western Asia and possibly also from Europe. The descendants of those invaders who are still fully or essentially Caucasoid are the Berbers.

From the beginning the Berbers have had relationships with older African peoples. As their skeletal remains suggest, the Mouillians probably mixed with the preceding Aterian population. According to J. H. Greenberg, the Berber languages, like Ancient Egyptian, are of African origin and replaced whatever European or Western Asian languages the Caucasoid invaders may have spoken.

All the living Berbers have some form or forms of symbiotic relationship with native Africans. In every Rifian village of any size, the ironwork is done by a Negroid smith. Other Negroids serve as butchers and town criers at weekly markets, and still others are musicians who wander from tribe to tribe enlivening weddings and other festivities. Negroids, then, are the principal service personnel among agricultural Berbers, and probably have been so since the introduction of iron into North Africa early in the Christian era.

Among the part-time and full-time nomads the interracial relationship is more complicated. The Ait Atta, for example, who pasture their sheep in the Middle Atlas in summer and in the Dades Valley to the south in winter, have their castles and gardens in the Dades Valley. There they delegate the agricultural work to a caste of Negroid serfs, the Haratin. Other Haratin are found in oases all along the northern fringe of the Sahara, and indeed throughout the desert.

The camel nomads, particularly the famed Tuareg, or People of

the Veil, are divided into castes of nobles, imghad, or camel-breed-
ing dependents who also have their Haratin, and slaves. The
merchant communities of the great oases, like the Mzabites of
Ghardaïa, foster endogamy as they belong to a schismatic sect
of Islam, that of the Khawarij, or Kharijites. They too have their
gardens tilled by Haratin.

Wherever or however they live, the Berbers refuse to mate with
the Negroid lower classes, but human nature being what it is,
there evidently has been a certain amount of mixture. In Morocco,
the most Caucasoid tribes are those of the Rif and the Middle
Atlas; in Algeria they are the Kabyles and the Shawia; and in
Libya, the sedentary tribesmen of Jebel Nefusa. In certain regions
the trickle of mixture with Africans has been balanced by the
absorption of Arabs, not so much tribe by tribe but through the
establishment of saintly families derived from the earlier of
the two main Arab invasions. These Arabs came mostly from al-
Hijaz and Yemen, and were not Bedawin.

In various series of Berbers,[3] the means for body, head, and
face measurements fall somewhere between those of the Western
Asian mountain peoples, the southwestern and western Europeans,
and the Arabs. The range of stature is from about 165 centimeters
to 172 centimeters (5 feet 4 inches to 5 feet 7 inches). The range
in body build is from stocky to lean, with relative sitting heights
usually around 51, but falling to 49 in desert tribes. Most Berbers,
none of whom practice cradling, are dolichocephalic or mesocephalic. Most of them have straight or convex nasal profiles.
Their faces and jaws tend to be narrow, although some broad faces
with snub noses may be seen.

The lightest pigmentation recorded is that of the Rifians, the
most European-looking Berbers. They have a 65 percent incidence
of pinkish-white unexposed skin color (von Luschan Numbers 1–3
and 6–9). This goes as high as 86 percent in some tribes. Twenty-
three percent are freckled. Ten percent have light brown or blond
head hair; in some tribes, 25 percent do. In beard color, 45 percent
of Rifians are reddish, light brown, or blond bearded; in some tribes,
this figure rises to 57 percent, with 24 percent completely blond.
The ratio of red head hair among Rifians is 4 percent, as in Scot-

[3] Coon: *Tribes of the Rif*, HAS, Vol. 19 (1931). W. B. Cline: "Anthropometric
Notes on the Natives of Siwah Oasis," *Varia Africana V*, HAS, Vol. 10 (1932),
pp. 3–19. H. H. Kidder, Coon, and L. C. Briggs: "Contribution à l'Anthropologie
des Kabyles," *L'Anth*, Vol. 59, No. 1–2 (1955), pp. 62–79. Briggs: *The Living
Races of the Sahara*, PMP, Vol. 28, No. 2 (1958). N. Puccioni: "Berberi e Arabi
nell'Africa Mediterranea," in Biasutti: *Razze e Populi della Terra*, Vol. 3 (1959),
pp. 109–47. The bibliographies in these works cover the field.

land and Ireland. Seventeen percent have reddish beards; in some tribes 28 percent do. Light hair among Rifians is mostly golden or reddish, rarely ash blond.

In the Rif, dark eyes are found among 43 percent of the men, mixed eyes in 35 percent, and light eyes in 2 percent; and the mixed eyes have green or blue elements rather than gray. The tribe with the lightest pigmentation in general, the Beni Amart, has an incidence of 18 percent, 73 percent, and 9 percent in each of these categories. These mountain tribesmen and some of their neighbors on the coast are a little fairer than most southern European populations.

Their blondism is comparable to the blondism of Western Europe and Western Asia, not to that of Northern and Eastern Europe. They resemble the Western Europeans, however, rather than the Western Asians in development of body hair, which is light to moderate. Only 5 percent of Rifians have the bushy, concurrent eyebrows seen among Western Asian mountaineers. The hair of most Rifians is curly—that is, it forms ringlets—in over 50 percent of the men. No individuals with frizzly or woolly hair were measured or seen. This African form of hair, however, is found among 12 percent of Shluh, Berbers of the Atlas Mountains and the Sous Valley. The Shluh also have a 12 percent incidence of epicanthic fold.

African traits manifest themselves among various Berber populations in different ways and to different degrees. Among the Rifians and Kabyles it shows itself mostly in broad faces, heavy jaws, and snub noses. These features are sometimes associated with red hair, greenish eyes, and freckles. Among the Soussis the same broad-faced element is present, and some individuals actually look Mongoloid. The Soussi depicted on Plate 109c has a recombination of Bushman features: flattish face, low nasal profile, everted lips, and Bushman ears.

Legends persist along the fringes of the Sahara about the presence of an earlier, non-Caucasoid people. According to the paramount chief of the Ait Atta, when their ancestors first came down from the mountains to their present winter quarters in the Dades Valley they found that region occupied by yellow-skinned people whom they conquered and reduced to the status of agricultural serfs. Later these yellow people mixed with Negro slaves, producing the present-day serfs, who are called Haratin. Many of the Haratin resemble Hottentots.

In the Fezzan in southern Libya live a people—the so-called Duwwud or Dawwada (worm-folk)—who speak Arabic, hunt jerboas, raise a few dates, and above all harvest the salt lakes, where they live, for *Artemesia,* a brine shrimp that multiplies in prodigious numbers.[4] These shrimp are dried and compressed into cakes, which the Duwwud trade to Arab caravans. The Duwwud also look like Hottentots. Other partly Bushman and partly Negro people are also to be found in the Sahara.

The Arabs

SINCE THE RISE of Islam, or for the last twelve centuries, Arabs have been invading and infiltrating Africa by land and by sea. The first wave to reach North Africa came mostly from al-Hijaz or Yemen. Some of them passed quickly into Spain, along with many Berbers, whence both were ejected in A.D. 1492, along with the Sephardic Jews. These Arabs founded cities, converted Berbers to Islam, traded, and established centers of learning and religious foundations. Few of them settled on the land.

The second wave came in the twelfth century and consisted of entire tribes of Bedawin off the Syrian desert, with their sheep, camels, and horses. Like swarms of locusts, they crossed the lowlands of North Africa and the high plateau, and some of them moved on into the Sahara, where their descendants still live. After this second invasion, most of the Berbers of the lowlands either became Arabized or withdrew to the mountains. Finally, in A.D. 1492, many so-called Moors returned to North Africa from Spain and Portugal to settle in the cities as merchants and skilled craftsmen.

It is easier to tell a Berber from an Arab by dress and behavior than by external physical characteristics, but there are statistical differences, particularly between the tribal Arabs of Bedawin origin and the mountain Berbers. The Arabs of this second group tend to be darker-skinned, less frequently light-eyed, and rarely blond. Compared to the Berbers, fewer have broad faces and more have convex nasal profiles.

The aristocratic city Arabs who have for centuries provided leadership in North Africa are descended from the first wave of invaders, who were mostly city people and traders in Arabia. Many of these families are also descended in part from converted Jews. These city Arabs tend to lack the hawk-like features of the descen-

---

4 L. Cipriani: "Un Interesante Pueblo del Sahara: Los Dauada," RGA, Vol. 2, No. 2 (1934), pp. 141–52.

dants of the Bedawin, and many of them, whose ancestors have lived for centuries in shaded streets, are blond. The descendants of the Andalusian Moors, endogamous for almost five centuries, are anthropometrically indistinguishable from Spaniards. Most of their ancestors may have been converts to Islam.

The Egyptians[5]

WHEN THE INVADING ARABS reached the Nile Valley, some stayed in the cities, but most of them moved on, because the country was already densely populated, and with more than one kind of people. Since predynastic times, various invaders had settled in the Delta and on the banks of the Nile. And after the Arabs had come and gone, the Turks took over, bringing with them Caucasians, Albanians, and other fellow Muslims.

It is the fellahin and the Copts who most faithfully represent in a physical sense their already mixed ancestors, the Ancient Egyptians. They are people of medium stature and physique, brown-skinned, most of them with curly hair, with brown eyes except that 10 percent have mixed or light-colored eyes. They have straight nasal profiles, nasal tips of medium size, lips of medium thickness, and moderate beard development. They look like what they are—the product of an ancient blend of Caucasoid and indigenous African elements, reinforced from time to time by Caucasoid elements from Europe and Western Asia, and African elements from the Sudan.

Peoples of the Horn of Africa

AT THE OTHER END of the Red Sea from Suez, the Bab el Mandeb has also served as a major corridor between Western Asia and Africa. As its name, "The Gate of Tears," indicates, traffic flows in both directions, with Arabs moving westward and African slaves eastward. West of the Bab el Mandeb rises the steep escarpment of the Ethiopian highlands, a refuge of prime

[5] A. M. Ammar: *The People of Sharqiya*, PSRGE, 2 vols. (1944). Twiesselmann: "Expedition Anthropologique du Dr. D. J. H. Nyessen. I. L'Oasis de Kharga," BIRSB, Vol. 27, No. 14 (1950), pp. 1–36. For other references dating back to 1939, see Coon: *The Races of Europe.*

historical importance, and between the highlands and the Red Sea stretches the Dankali Desert, parts of which lie below sea level. It is one of the hottest places on earth.

The peoples of this region are all or nearly all products, in various degrees and in different forms, of mixture between Caucasoids and Negroes.[6] Except for slaves recently imported from the steamy marshes of the lower Sudan, the most Negroid people are the Wattas, hippopotamus hunters along the rivers of Somaliland and southern Ethiopia. They are an endogamous caste, feared as magicians and despised because they eat hippopotamus meat. As far as we know, they have been neither measured nor subjected to blood-group studies.

Next most Negroid are the sedentary peoples of western Ethiopia who speak Central Cushitic languages: the Kafacitos, Soddo Galla, Sidamos, Agaus, and Falasha (Black Jews). These people are curly- or frizzy-haired, have dark brown skins, and are relatively short in stature. Their mean stature is about 164 centimeters (5 feet 4½ inches). Their facial features are partly Negroid.

The least Negroid peoples of the highlands are the Ethiopians proper—who speak Amharic, Tigré, and Tigrinya—and the Gallas. The former are descended from southern Arabians who invaded Ethiopia during the first millennium B.C., and the latter from cattle people who entered the highlands from the west in the sixteenth century A.D.

Both are essentially Caucasoid in body build and facial features. Both vary in skin color from a light yellowish brown, in some cases almost yellow, to the various shades of brown that they themselves recognize and of which they are acutely conscious. None is black. The majority have frizzy hair. The next commonest is curly hair, like that of Berbers and Egyptians. Both wavy and woolly hair are rare, and no straight hair was observed. All hair is black. Eyes are either dark brown or light brown, or a mixture of the two. No black eyes were found; mixed light eyes are found in only a few individuals.

The cast of facial features known to the world because of the wide publication of Emperor Haile Selassie's picture is not uncommon, although his are somewhat extreme. Nasal profiles are more often straight than convex among both Amharas and Gallas, and

6 The most detailed study of all these peoples is Coon: "Contribution to the Study of the Physical Anthropology of the Ethiopians and Somalis" (1935)—unpublished. L. Oschinsky has published most of the means of the measurements in his *The Racial Affinities of the Baganda and Other Bantu Tribes of British East Africa*. Other pre-1939 references may be found in Coon: *The Races of Europe*. Biasutti's *Razze e Popoli della Terra* is excellent on this subject.

rarely concave. Nostrils, as seen from the side, are highly arched; nasal tips are medium to thick, and lips are medium to thick. There is no body hair or it is slight; and beards are characteristically of moderate development. In these respects the Amharas are more variable than the Gallas.

Both are fairly tall peoples, with mean statures of around 169 to 170 centimeters (5 feet 7 inches ca.) and relative sitting heights of about 51 for the Amharas and 50 for the Gallas. This puts their body build in the category of most Mediterranean whites, and of many Negroes. In other details of body build they are essentially Caucasoid, and so they consider themselves, particularly the Amharas and the upper-class Gallas, who call themselves Ormoma. The Gallas recognize two other classes, the Tumtu, some of whom are blacksmiths, and the Faki, or tanners. The two latter have not been measured. Both are descended from peoples who lived in southern Ethiopia before the Galla invasion.

The Somalis and the Dankalis are closely related and may be considered as a unit. Their stature and the proportions of their limbs are the same as those of the Amharas and the Gallas, but they have much narrower bodies and heads and faces. Most of them could be categorized as ectomorphs. Almost without exception, their skins are a rich chocolate brown. Their hair is black, and their eyes are dark brown or black. More than a third have wavy hair, and a few have straight hair. Frizzly hair, which is the most prevalent among Amharas and Gallas, has only a 6 percent incidence among Somalis. These people are strikingly homogenous, so much so that Hiernaux considers them a separate race.[7] In this context it must be remembered that the Somalis and the Dankalis live in desert country near or below sea level, where the heat is intense, the sunlight bright, and the water vapor pressure high, whereas the Amharas and the Gallas live at a high altitude in cool cloudy country. Environmental pressures cannot be discounted in a comparison of these two groups of people. Both are essentially Caucasoid, but in different ways.

Peoples of the Southern Sahara and the Sudan

NORTH of the Ethiopian highlands, the swamps of the Upper Nile, and the equatorial forest of central and western Africa, live

[7] Hiernaux: "Les Caractères Physiques des Populations du Ruanda et de l'Urundi."

a medley of clinal peoples who resemble the Gallas in some ways and the Somalis in others. Starting on the east with the Beja and the Bisharin of the Red Sea coast of Sudan and southern Egypt, one continues westward to the Ennedi and Tibesti plateaus, inhabited by the Bäle, the people called Tibbu, Tubu, or Teda, and other cattle-breeding tribes. Interspersed among them are various tribes of nomadic Arabs, and to the west live the Tuareg.

In northern Nigeria are the Hausa, a numerous and widespread people who are skilled craftsmen and clever traders. Beyond them and among them are the Fula or Peul, and the related Fulani, cattle people who have invaded the agricultural regions of the western Sudan, founded dynasties, and been overthrown from time to time. All of them are Caucasoids in a sense, and somewhat Negroid. The Fula are noted for their lean build and narrow faces, like the Somalis, but they are lighter in skin color, being usually a light reddish brown.

These various peoples are probably descended from the cattle breeders depicted on the rock surfaces of the Tibesti and of Fezzan, who dispersed at various times with the progressive desiccation of the Sahara and gave rise directly or indirectly to such distant herdsmen as the Hottentots and to the cattle peoples of East and South Africa.

Despite the differences in body build, facial features, and skin color among these people—with the Fula at one extreme and the southern Bantu at the other—it would be unwise to try to estimate to what degree the various racial elements have gone into any one group. Environmental selection can steer the course of morphological combinations in its own direction in any given area no matter how much or how little of each element was present in the beginning.

The Proper Negroes

BY "PROPER NEGROES" we mean those peoples of Africa who are neither Pygmies nor Bushmen, Berbers, Arabs, or any of the clinal populations with a readily visible Caucasoid racial element. We mean the West Africans, some of the East Africans, and most of the Bantu. It was from these populations that most of the Negroes transported to the New World and to Arabia were drawn. We have left them to the end of the chapter because although they are the most numerous race in Africa, their origins are at the moment the least known. Moreover, we can understand them best after having reviewed the racial characteristics of the other peoples of Africa.

Earlier in this chapter we stated that to date no one has found a fully identifiable Negro skull, in the modern sense, in a Pleistocene deposit. This does not mean that Negroes as we know them did not exist then or that such a skull will not eventually be unearthed. Meanwhile we may note that a detailed analysis of 571 modern Negro crania, made by advanced mathematical techniques, has shown that these crania gravitate between two poles, a Mediterranean Caucasoid and a Pygmy one. The former type is again divisible into an ordinary Mediterranean and a Western Asian type, which suggests more than a single northern point of origin for the Caucasoid element.[8] As we shall see in greater detail in Chapters 8 and 9, the Negroes resemble the Caucasoids closely in a number of genetic traits that are inherited in a simple fashion. Examples of these are fingerprints, types of earwax, and the major blood groups. The Negroes also have some of the same local, predominantly African, blood types as the Pygmies.

This evidence suggests that the Negroes are not a primary subspecies but rather a product of mixture between invading Caucasoids and Pygmies who lived on the edges of the forest, which at the end of the Pleistocene extended farther north and east than it does now. To this combination may have been added remnant Capoid genes acquired in the Sahara and East Africa. Variations among Negroids and Negroes would depend not so much on the relative proportions of the parent elements as on where a given group of people lived at a particular time and to what selective influences they had been exposed. We suggest that such a mixture has been going on for at least 15,000 years, or more than 600 generations, ample time for the present regional and local variables to have arisen. We must also remember that Negroes have been numerous only since the introduction of agriculture, which occurred in three successive stages, the last two dating only from the Christian era. In Chapter 7 we will see, with better documentation, that the Melanesians, who superficially resemble the Negroes in many ways, arose in a similar fashion.

Negro racial characteristics include tightly coiled black hair; black or dark brown skin color; black or dark brown eyes with pigmented spots in the sclera; pigmented lips and gums; a dolichocephalic or mesocephalic head, with a protruding occiput; broad

[8] A. Wanke: "Anthropological Characteristics of African Skulls," MIPA, No. 67 (1964), pp. 5–28.

noses; large, often prominent eyeballs; everted lips; highly variable nasal bridge form and prognathism; large teeth; small ears with intricate antihelical patterns; broad shoulders; narrow hips; a relatively small rib cage, and considerable lordosis, usually without steatopygia; long arms; relatively long distal portions of the limbs; limb and shoulder muscles with short, thick bellies and long tendons; an unusual mobility of the extremities; large feet with low arches, both transverse and longitudinal, and thick underlying fat pads; and when young and in good health, little subcutaneous fat.

Comparative physiological studies of Negroes and whites have shown that the Negroes surpass the whites in tolerance of damp heat but are more vulnerable both to dry heat and to cold, and excel at sports requiring short bursts of intense energy and great flexibility.

In reviewing these anatomical and physiological characters, we can find nothing except deep pigmentation that cannot also be found in Mediterranean Caucasoids, Pygmies, and Bushmen. But virtually black Caucasoids can be found in parts of India, the Somalis are deeply pigmented, and the Negroes have been subjected to intense selection for local environmental conditions, some of which undoubtedly favor deep pigmentation, although exactly how we are not sure. At any rate the hypothesis that all Negroes are partly Caucasoid eliminates the need for creating an artificial taxonomic barrier between Negroes and Negroids, which makes our work much easier.

In the predominantly Negro populations of Africa regional variations are evident, as would be expected, because they mirror environmental differences.[9]

In the damp regions of the West Coast and the Congo, where the temperature is seldom extreme, Negroes tend to be short,

9 The most complete regional anthropometric survey is Oschinsky: *The Racial Affinities of the Buganda and Other Bantu Tribes of British East Africa.* Means of series measured before 1929 are also covered in M. J. Herskovits: *The Anthropometry of the American Negro,* CUCA, Vol. 9 (1930). See also Hiernaux: "Les Caractères Physiques des Populations du Ruanda et de l'Urundi"; "Les Caractères physiques des Bashi," IRCB, Vol. 23, No. 5 (1953), pp. 5–50. Herskovits: "Physical Types of West African Negroes," HB, Vol. 9, No. 4 (1937), pp. 483–97. Vallois: "Les Badjoué du Sud Cameroun." BMSA, Vol. 1, No. 1–3 (1950), pp. 18–59. G. I. Jones and H. Mulhall: "An Examination of the Physical Types of Certain Peoples of S. E. Nigeria," JRAI, Vol. 79, Parts 1–2 (1949), pp. 11–19. M. E. de Castro e Almeida: "Contribução para o estudo dos caracteres descritivos dos nativos 'Tongas' e 'Tonghuinas' da Ilha de São Tome," CIAO, Vol. 5, Sess. 6 (1958), pp. 41–54. P. A. Talbot and H. Mulhall: *The Physical Anthropology of Southern Nigeria* (Cambridge: Cambridge University Press, 1962). D. F. Roberts and D. R. Bainbridge: "Nilotic Physique," AJPA, Vol. 21, No. 3 (1963), pp. 341–66.

stocky and mesocephalic, and some are even obese. On the West Coast the mean stature runs around 165 centimeters (5 feet 5 inches) and one tribe in the eastern Congo, bordering Rwanda and Urundi, has a mean as low as 160 centimeters (5 feet 3 inches). The Warega and their neighbors the Bashi both have a visible Pygmy component and resemble the potters of Lake Kivu. At the other extreme are the Dinka, Shilluk, Nuer, Suk, and other Nilotic tribes dwelling in the hot steamy swamps of the lower Sudan. They reach an extreme of tall stature, 183 centimeters (6 feet), combined with extremely slender bodies and long thin limbs. Some individuals even exceed the limits of ectomorphy specified by the somatotypists.

Ectomorphs are also common among some of the tribes of the East African highlands, but except for some individuals among the much-photographed Tutsi (Watusi), their linear body build is not as extreme as that of the Nilotes. What is more characteristic of the highlanders is an accent on long, high-bridged, narrow noses, probably in response to cool dry air, as we shall see in Chapter 8. The South African Bantu, who have lived for almost five centuries in a climate which is cool during part of the year and who have mixed with their Capoid predecessors, are relatively large, heavily muscled, and in some cases fat.

Conclusion

THIS is a long chapter. It had to be, because Africa is a large continent. Its prehistory goes back to the beginning of the Pleistocene. It contains three of the world's five subspecies, spatially distributed in a complex pattern. It belongs with Europe and Western Asia racially as well as archaeologically, and forms an integral part of that half of the world which lies west of Movius's Line. We shall presently cross that line and find on the other side a much simpler racial situation.

5

East Asia and the Americas

The Mongoloid Realm

THIS CHAPTER deals with the homeland of the Mongoloids and the previously uninhabited regions in northeastern Asia and the New World where Mongoloids were the first settlers. It is a vast realm covering nearly half of the land area of the inhabited world. Its heartland is China, where the Mongoloids probably evolved. Crude quartzite implements have been found in southern Shansi in deposits attributed to the Villafranchian, dating back over one and a half million years, but both their age and their status as man-made artifacts need confirmation.[1] The Sinanthropus finds at Choukoutien are now dated at about 1,100,000 years ago. The Mongoloids evolved in China from at least that time onward, and later spread as far afield as the banks of the Volga, Madagascar, and Tierra del Fuego.[2]

---

[1] Chia Lan-po, in WW, No. 4–5 (Peiping, 1964), pp. 25–6, after Kwang-chih Chang: *The Archaeology of Ancient China* (New Haven: Yale University Press; 1963), p. 28.

[2] In various sections of this chapter we shall make use of Chang's book and of the three published volumes of Cheng Te-K'un's *Archaeology in China* (Cambridge: W. Heffer & Sons): Vol I. *Prehistoric China*, 1959; Vol II. *Shang China*, 1960; and Vol. III. *Chou China*, 1963.

The Geography of the Mongoloid Realm

A S I A resembles, on a grand scale, some of the high islands of the Pacific that have a central cone ribbed with ridges sweeping to the sea and enclosing compartmented valleys, each occupied by its private avian fauna. Instead of a cone, Asia has the Tibetan Plateau and the Himalayas, and instead of ridges it has a spider-web of mountains dividing it into subcontinents, the largest of which is China. Almost equal in size to all of Europe, China occupies a natural geographic area shut off by mountains to the southwest, west, and northeast, and by deserts to the north. Like the eastern half of North America, China is situated on the wrong side of its continent to be tempered by the cooling effect of the westerly winds off the oceans. Its climate is continental, with mostly summer rainfall.

Because most of the rivers of China flow from west to east, the land divides itself into discrete geographical zones following a combination of latitude and altitude. Northern China consists of the Yellow River valley, with loess to the west and alluvial soils to the east, and the Shantung Peninsula. Southern China is to a large extent mountainous or hilly. It has several river systems, the principal ones being the Yangtze, the Hwai, and the Pearl.

Chang contrasts the two as follows.[3] The north has limited, uncertain rainfall with from 16 to 32 inches annually. It has cold winters, hot summers, and little snow; a semiarid climate; unleached, calcareous soils; mixed deciduous forests and grass-lands; and is brown and dust-blown during the winter. The south (or more accurately the southeast) has abundant rainfall with from 32 to 63 inches; cold winters; hot moist summers; infrequent snow or ice; a subtropical climate; summer monsoon rains and typhoons; leached, noncalcareous soils; subtropical and tropical forests; and a green landscape at all seasons.

Stating it in more conventional geographical terms, the whole bulge of China east and south of a diagonal line running from eastern Kwangsi to a point north of Shanghai has a climate like that of the most populous part of the United States from Connecticut westward to Nebraska and then south to the mouth of the Rio Grande. This is Köppen's *Cfa* climate, with hot summers, mild winters, some rain the year round, and only moderate cloud cover—quite different from that in which Western Europeans

[3] This is a close paraphrase from Chang: op. cit., p. 24.

evolved. Inland from this *Cfa* zone is a belt running northeast to southwest which has completely dry winters. East of central China rises the plateau of Tibet, a vast region of thin air, much of it over 13,000 feet high, with a circumpolar-like climate in which the average temperature in the warmest month is below 50° F (10° C), except in deep valleys, where it may rise to 68° F (20° C). North of this forbidding barrier-refuge lies a huge region of steppes and deserts in which what little rain there is falls in summer, unlike the northern Sahara and the Arabian desert.

Southern Korea and most of Honshu are climatically similar to eastern China. Manchuria, northern Korea, and Hokkaido are colder, with climates more or less similar to those of New York State and northern New England, except that in some places more rain falls in summer and less in winter.

Siberia consists of two unequal parts: a wide, swampy eastern lowland from the Urals to the Lena, and a series of mountains and river valleys from the Lena to the Pacific.[4] This last is the coldest region in the inhabited world. The world's lowest temperature, −90° F., has been recorded there—at Verkhoyansk. Although it was largely unglaciated during the Pleistocene, it was probably too cold to be inhabited at that time, and there is no evidence of habitation. Yet at least some of the ancestors of the American Indians must have walked along its coast during the latter part of the Würm-Wisconsian Glaciation, because at that time some had already arrived in America. Then the world's principal centers of glaciation flanked the shores of the North Atlantic, but the North American ice also reached the Pacific in an irregular jumble of expanded river glaciers. The Yukon Valley was unglaciated, however.

Bering Strait was then an expanse of dry land 1,300 miles wide from north to south; even at present it is only 180 feet, at the maximum, below sea level. Because the seas fell 460 feet during the Würm-Wisconsian, the Strait must have been closed for some time after the ice caps had begun to melt and the seas to rise. It must also have been warm enough and ice-free enough to permit the passage from Asia to North America of such animals as the bison, sheep, goat, wapiti, camel, and horse, as well as the more cold-adapted mammoth, musk-ox, and reindeer.[5]

As the oceans were lower at that time, the shallow Yellow Sea

4 L. S. Berg: *Natural Regions of the U.S.S.R.* (New York: The Macmillan Company; 1950).

5 Charlesworth: op. cit., p. 1237. W. G. Haag: "The Bering Strait Land Bridge," SA, Vol. 206, No. 1 (1962), pp. 112–23.

area was probably out of water, along with parts of the Sea of Okhotsk, and the shores of the Maritime Province north of Vladivostok and of the Kamchatka Peninsula must have extended farther out than they do today. With the exclusion of Arctic water from the Pacific by the Bering land bridge, the temperatures of these shorelines may have been warmer than they are at present. The remains of the ancestors of the American Indians who gradually hunted their way along these shores may now be underwater.

Once these migrants were in Alaska, we have no certain indication of the route or routes they took to move southward. We only know they must have done so.[6] Today a wet foggy climate like that of northwestern Europe (*Cfb*) extends along the Pacific islands and parts of the coastal fringe from Vancouver to Juneau. Some of the local glaciers calve into the sea, but it is not certain that they did so then, as the sea level was lower and the Japanese current may have been warmer. There may have been room between the glaciers and the sea for people comparable to the Alakalufs to have made their way to California. It has also been proposed that during interstadials a corridor existed between the Keewatin ice sheet to the east and the Cordilleran glaciers to the west, connecting the Yukon Valley with the plains east of the Rockies. Both these explanations are speculative.

North and South America differ profoundly from either Eurasia or Africa in having a backbone of mountains on their western, windward sides, and older, lower mountains on the east, with, most notably in North America, a central lowland trough running north and south. This orientation gives most of the United States and Canada an exaggeratedly continental climate, with colder winters and hotter summers than in any region of equal area in the Old World. It also provides an elevated, mostly cool highway from the southwestern United States into Mexico, and all the way to the tip of South America, except for a short corridor of warm climate in Panama. But even there the range of temperature between the coldest and the warmest months is less than 9° F (5° C).[7] The highland corridor of the New World may be compared to that of East Africa, where it served a similar purpose.

The types of climate in which Caucasoid man evolved are poorly represented in the New World. The maritime climate of Western Europe (*Cfb*) is limited to the northwest coast islands and adjacent pinpoints of mainland, a few spots in the Appalach-

[6] H. M. Wormington: *Ancient Man in North America* (Denver: Denver Museum of Natural History; 1957), Popular Series No. 4, 4th ed., pp. 249–60.

[7] James: *An Outline of Geography* (Boston: Ginn & Co.; 1935), p. 378.

ians and coastal Massachusetts, the southern coasts of Brazil and Argentina, and a larger area in Chile from about 37° S. latitude to the Strait of Magellan. Mediterranean climates of both kinds (with hot or cool summers, *Csa* and *Csb*) are limited to the Pacific coast of the United States, to the Columbia River valley of the United States and Canada, and to certain parts of Chile.

On the whole the ancestors of the American Indians found in North America climates like those they had left behind. They could even hunt some of the same animals. In South America east of the Andes, as in the lowlands of Yucatán, Guatemala, and British Honduras, they encountered something new—tropical forests and savannas. In South America these take up most of Brazil, Venezuela, and the Guianas, from about 10° N. latitude to the tropic of Capricorn, mirroring those of Africa west of the highlands in the same latitudes. For Mongoloids whose ancestors had survived Kamchatka, the Bering land bridge, and the fringes of the Wisconsian ice sheet, the fetid, seasonally flooded jungles and scrub-covered, eroded hills offered a new physiological challenge for which they had brought with them no genetic defenses.

The Paleolithic of China

I T   I S   G E N E R A L L Y believed that throughout the Pleistocene China was shut off from the West and had an open cultural frontier only with Southeast Asia. It is also believed that in China a single stone-tool industry, related to those of Southeast Asia and Java, evolved largely on its own from coarser to finer tool types, without much outside influence. An industry based on choppers, chopping tools, and simple flakes began with the earliest occupation of the Sinanthropus site at Choukoutien, during the Mindel glacial period. As time passed, the tools in this site became more refined. After a gap of over a half a million years, the same tradition may be seen in the industry found in the Upper Cave of the same site, dated at about the end of the Pleistocene.

Geologically there were no marked changes in China during the Pleistocene. During this epoch the land table rose steadily and the temperature decreased constantly. It is hard to tell when the Pleistocene began and when it ended, particularly in the absence of Argon-40 and Carbon-14 dates. In any case, there were apparently no dramatic events, as in Europe, to foster extensive movements of populations.

Our knowledge of the outside influences at work during the Pleistocene in China is still meager, but implements have been found at Ting-tsun in Shansi, along the banks of the Fen River, which seem to resemble some of the Mousterian artifacts of Uzbekistan and northern Afghanistan. Of these implements Bushnell and McBurney have said: "This industry, in which only the eye of faith can distinguish the slightest traces of Chopper–Chopping-Tool influence, is undeniably of general Middle Paleolithic character in the Western sense."[8] If these two scholarly gentlemen are correct, the presence of this industry in northern China could have far-reaching implications. It might even be cited as evidence that Neanderthals penetrated deep into China before the departure of the ancestors of the American Indians. Such an invasion might be construed to explain the beaky faces and other Neanderthaloid features seen on some of the living Indians and also on other peripheral Mongoloids such as the Nagas of Assam.

The trouble with this theory is that we do not know the exact age of this site. The discoverers call it Late Middle Pleistocene;[9] Movius places it in the Third Interglacial;[1] and Bushnell and McBurney say it is only a little earlier than two sites in the Ordos that contain small blades and burins.[2] Of the three, Movius's dating is the best suited to the Neanderthal–American Indian hypothesis. This theory cannot be either proved or disproved with the Pleistocene skeletal material at our disposal at the present time—which we discussed in Chapter 10 of *The Origin of Races*. There is, however, the fact that the Upper Cave male from Choukoutien, dubiously dated at the end of the Pleistocene, would be indistinguishable in a grouping of American Indian skulls.

The two blade and burin sites referred to above are in the Ordos loess country of the Upper Yellow River valley, only 1,000 miles from the shores of Lake Baikal, on which a similar industry, of uncertain date, has been found. According to G. F. Debetz, a single frontal bone found in one such site, that of Afontova Gora, has nasal bones attached to it, and the form of these bones suggests a depressed bridge. Debetz interprets this fragmentary information as evidence of Mongoloid penetration of Siberia at that time.[3] Whether or not he is right, the archaeological contin-

---

[8] Bushnell and McBurney: "New World Origins Seen from the Old World." The quotation is on page 100.

[9] Cheng: Vol. I, pp. 24–6.

[1] Movius: "New Paleolithic Sites near Ting Ts'un on the Fen River, Shansi Province, North China," *Quaternaria*, Vol. 3 (1956), pp. 13–26.

[2] Bushnell and McBurney: op. cit.

[3] G. F. Debetz: *Palaeontropologiia SSSR*, TIE, n.s., Vol. 4 (1948).

uity between these two regions lying athwart Movius's Line offers
another possibility of genetic exchange between Caucasoids and
Mongoloids which has been going on ever since.

Postglacial China

ALTHOUGH China is far from the edge of any ice sheet, its
climate changed at the end of the Pleistocene. What is now a
treeless, overtilled plain in northern China was then heavily forested, and the river bottoms to the east were swampy. Two
Mesolithic cultures arose in the north: that of the Gobi dune and
oasis dwellers, and the forest culture which extended from the
Upper Yellow River valley to Manchuria. Both were of western
inspiration.

South of the Tsinling Mountains the rest of China may be
divided into two archaeological provinces, subdivided according
to the modern zones of high and low rainfall in that region. One
of the provinces extended along the western mountains, crossed
southern China to the sea, and reached out to Formosa. This
culture had cord-marked pottery and chipped or flaked axes with
ground cutting edges, of a style known as Hoabinhian, after a
site in Vietnam. Eventually it was carried into Southeast Asia
and Indonesia. Chinese anthropologists have expressed the opinion
that the Corded-ware People were "Negroid" (in our terms, Australoid) as far north as the Tsinling Mountains, but this is far
from demonstrated. Their evidence consists of one skull fragment
of dubious date, from Kwangsi, said to have non-Mongoloid features in its nasal aperture and zygomatic bone.[4]

Whoever these Corded-ware People were, and we think they
were essentially if not wholly Mongoloid, they and their culture
were pushed southward as the northern Chinese acquired agriculture and expanded in a southern direction, particularly along the
eastern plain. There they introduced rice cultivation before 1500
B.C., and thence carried it into Southeast Asia.

So far we have no Neolithic skeletons to represent these movements.[5] But we do have a detailed report on 84 Copper and Bronze
Age skeletons from Kansu and Honan, which compares them with

[4] Chia Lan-po and Woo Ju-Kang: "Fossil Human Skull Base of Late Paleolithic
Stage from Chilinshan, Leipin District, Kwangsi, China," VP, Vol. 3, No. 1 (1959),
pp. 37–9.
[5] Some have been excavated, but no measurements have yet been published.
See Hsai Nai: "Our Neolithic Ancestors," in CR, Vol. 5, No. 5 (1956), pp. 24–8.

a collection of modern skulls from northern China.[6] The early skulls are essentially those of mesocephalic Mongoloids no different in general from the living population of northern China. Of them, three skulls from Kansu, which have less facial flatness than the others, deviate in a Caucasoid direction, but remain within the modern range.

Another early Chinese skull collection consists of specimens from the sacrificial grave pits of the Shang Period at Anyang. At least two of the female skulls of this collection have Caucasoid traits in the eyesockets and nasal skeleton. A few others are brachycephalic and exaggeratedly Mongoloid, like the skulls of modern Buriats. The rest are of the usual northern Chinese type, with a mesocephalic braincase and moderately long, flattish face.[7] No comparable material is available from southern China.

Japanese Prehistory

J A P A N E S E archaeological research, late in starting, is now being feverishly pursued. Any summary is therefore liable to need revision with little notice.[8] In general, Honshu and the southern islands constitute one province and Hokkaido another, although there is some cultural overlap. There is a possibility that the three southern islands were once connected to the mainland by way of Korea—which would in part account for the difference—whereas Hokkaido's connection was by way of Sakhalin. Hokkaido, too, is climatically distinct from the rest of the islands.

On Honshu the oldest recognized industry is the so-called Gongenyama, an assemblage of choppers and chopping tools with coarse, unfaceted flakes. Because some of the chopping tools are

[6] D. Black: *A Study of Kansu and Honan Aeneolithic Skulls and Specimens from Later Kansu Prehistoric Sites in Comparison with North China and Other Recent Crania,* PS-D, Vol. 6, Fasc. 1 (1928). Part 1. *On Measurement and Identification.*

[7] Coon: "An Anthropogeographic Excursion around the World," HB, Vol. 30, No. 1 (1958), pp. 29–42.

[8] The following sources are recommended. J. Maringer: "Einige faustkeilartige Geräte von Gongenyama (Japan) und die Frage des japanischen Paläolithikums," *Anthropos,* Vol. 51 (1956), pp. 175–93; "Some Stone Tools of Early Hoabinhian Type from Central Japan," *Man,* Vol. 57, No. 1 (1956), pp. 1–4; "Die Industrie von Iwajuku I (Japan), und ihre kulturelle Einordnung," *Anthropos,* Vol. 52 (1957), pp. 721–31. J. E. Kidder, Jr.: "Japan," AP, Vol. 1, No. 1–2 (1957), pp. 28–30. C. Serizawa and F. Ikawa: "The Oldest Archaeological Materials from Japan," AP, Vol. 2, No. 2 (1958), pp. 1–39.

pointed or rounded, Maringer sees in them a hand-axe tradition derived indirectly from Java and ultimately from India, as will be explained in the next two chapters. These were followed by other chopping tools ground at the cutting edge in Hoabinhian style, and two successive Mesolithic industries called Iwajuku I and II. After this comes cord-marked pottery of the same general type found in southwest China, southern China, and Formosa, but showing distinctive features. It is called Jomon and is divided into Earliest, Early, Middle, and Late. With it are found finely pressure-flaked blades, thumbnail scrapers, and winged arrowheads, a sophisticated tool kit. After Jomon appears Yayoi, a type of pottery accompanied by both bronze and iron objects, from Korea.

The northern sequence, centered on Hokkaido, begins with an assemblage of large obsidian tools, including blades and steep scrapers, then continues with blades and burins, then bifacial projectile points, and then Jomon pottery with its accompanying industry. These industries resemble the Upper Paleolithic of Afghanistan on the one hand and the American paleo-Indian and Woodland assemblages on the other.

But these resemblances cannot be shown to prove that contacts existed with either Central Asia or America. Intermediate sites are lacking, and the Japanese industries are either undated or their dating is incongruous. Only the Jomon cultures have Carbon-14 dates. In Honshu, two Carbon-14 dates put the Earliest Jomon back to 7500 B.C. and 6450 B.C., the oldest dates for pottery anywhere in the world.[9] In Hokkaido the same pottery is dated, in two samples, at about 5700 B.C.,[1] still earlier than pottery anywhere else. In Honshu, Middle Jomon is 2560 B.C., and "Latest" Jomon is 1220 B.C.[2] Yayoi is dated by analogy with Korea and China at shortly before the time of Christ.

How these sequences and dates will eventually be sorted out and related to those of other regions remains to be seen. At any rate, archaeologists have begun to show that, far from being a cul-de-sac, Japan was an archaeologically variable and busy region in late Pleistocene and early post-Pleistocene times. There is even the suggestion of racial and cultural ties with the Australoid and Caucasoid as well as with the Mongoloid regions.

[9] Kidder: "Japan," AP, Vol. 4 (1960), pp. 21–34.
[1] Ibid.
[2] T. Oba and C. S. Chard: "New Dates for Early Pottery in Japan," AP, Vol. 6 (1962), pp. 75–6.

Japanese Cranial History

THE EARLIEST Japanese skeletal materials are a very small humerus[3] and a skull[4] found in two different Pleistocene sites. We know little of racially diagnostic value about either. At least one Early Jomon skull has been found,[5] and a detailed study of thirty-four Late Jomon skulls has been published.[6] There is nothing from the critical Yayoi period, but five later series carry the record of Japanese cranial changes from the fourth to the nineteenth centuries A.D.,[7] and three more or less recent series represent the Ainu.[8] Speaking of the Jomon specimens, H. Suzuki has said: "The skeletons of the Neolithic ages are so different from those of the protohistoric period that there is some dispute as to whether or not they are directly related."[9]

The Jomon skulls represent the pre-Yayoi population and the "protohistoric" skulls the post-Yayoi Japanese. The Yayoi epoch, then, began with a true population movement and not mere cultural diffusion. The Jomon skulls have larger bases, lower vaults, greater cranial circumferences, larger faces, and wider interorbital distances than any of the skulls from the fourth to the nineteenth centuries, and in these respects they resemble the Ainu crania, all of which are of more or less recent date. This does not simply mean that the Jomon people were the only ancestors of the living Ainus, but it implies some degree of genetic relationship. Because early Jomon pottery has been found in Hokkaido as well as farther south, we may suppose that Japan as a whole was more of a unit racially as well as culturally before the Yayoi invasion than after it.

After the Yayoi invasion, Japanese faces tended to become

[3] H. Suzuki and F. Takai: "Entdeckung eines Pleistozänen Hominiden Humerus in Zentral-Japan," *AAnz*, Vol. 23, No. 2–3 (1959), pp. 224–35.

[4] Suzuki, in 1960 press release.

[5] Coon: "An Anthropogeographic Excursion Around the World."

[6] T. Sakakibara: *Kraniologie der Otoshibe-Aino*, Sonderabdruck von *Crania Ainoica*, Sapporo, 1940.

[7] Suzuki: "Changes in the Skull Features of the Japanese People from Ancient to Modern Times," FICA (1956), pp. 717–24; "Changes in the bodily features of the Japanese people from the protohistoric to the present time" (in Japanese), in "Papers in Memory of the Hundredth Anniversary of the Publication of Darwin's *Origin of Species*" (Tokyo, 1960), pp. 140–6. Suzuki, H. Sakura, T. Hayashi, G. Tanabe, and Y. Imai: "Craniometry of the Japanese Skulls of the Final Edo Era," ZZ, Vol. 70, No. 733 (1962), pp. 47–120.

[8] Sakakibara: op. cit.

[9] Suzuki: "Changes in the Skull Features of the Japanese People from Ancient to Modern Times," p. 717.

progressively narrower, with narrower noses, eye sockets closer together, and skull vaults shorter and higher. In effect, a racial element resembling the Turko-Korean was introduced, along with horses and iron, and it expressed itself increasingly, particularly in the cities and in the Samurai class.

Although the three series of Ainu crania studied vary regionally, they are all closer to the Jomon model than to the Japanese skulls of the Christian era. A series from Otoshibe, a small fishing village on the southern peninsula of Hokkaido, is the most like the Jomon. A general Hokkaido series shows two different concentrations in head height, suggesting that some are pure Ainu and the others a product of Japanese or other admixture. The Sakhalin Ainu skulls have the largest faces of all, as might be expected in view of the geographical position of their island.

The Archaeological Evidence for Racial Origins in the New World

THE DETAILS of the early peopling of the New World are still a mystery. All we know is that human beings entered Alaska from Asia well before the end of the Würm-Wisconsin glaciation, as early as 30,000 or 40,000 years ago, or as late as 15,000 years ago, according to various estimates based on the interpretation of sites farther south, on linguistics, and on other types of evidence.[1] Somehow or other some of these people worked their way southward into the American Southwest and to California, reached Venezuela probably by 13,000 years ago, and came to the Strait of Magellan—we are more certain here—by 8,000 years ago.

In Alaska the oldest dated material is a sophisticated blade and burin culture which began between 4000 B.C. and 2200 B.C., as determined by a battery of Carbon-14 tests.[2] This industry resembles the comparable blade and burin culture of Hokkaido, to which it may or may not be related, and was too late to be involved in the initial peopling of America. However, it may have had something to do with the origin of the Eskimo.

Elsewhere in the New World, three main archaeological complexes dating before the time of agriculture are generally recog-

[1] J. D. Jennings and E. Norbeck, eds.: *Prehistoric Man in the New World* (Chicago: University of Chicago Press; 1964).

[2] J. L. Giddings: *The Archaeology of Cape Denbigh* (Providence, R.I.: Brown University Press; 1964). Dates are on p. 248. I am also quoting unpublished dates.

nized. The first is a culture of crude choppers, chopping tools, and flakes resembling that of China. It is limited largely to the intermontane Great Basin and Plateau areas which extend from Oregon southward to Mexico. Its earliest date so far is about 9000 B.C., from material found in Danger Cave, Utah. It persisted until modern times among tribes like the Northern Paiute, and spread down the Pacific coast of South America as far as the Strait of Magellan. Elements of it lasted until recently among Chonos and Alakalufs.

The second is a culture founded on big-game hunting and located generally in butchering stations just east of the Rockies, from Wyoming to Mexico. It is characterized by large, finely pressure-flaked bifacial projectile points of several types, and initially dated at the period just after the Valders or Manketo advance of the Wisconsin ice, with an average Carbon-14 age of 9300 ± 360 B.C., for six sites.[3] These points have been found as far east as Ipswich, Massachusetts, where hunters followed mammoths as the ice sheet shrank. Either this technologically sophisticated industry was introduced from Siberia from an ultimately Solutrean source, as Bushnell and McBurney[4] have postulated, or it arose through independent invention in the New World, as Chard[5] has suggested. We do not pretend to know.

The third is the Woodland culture, with pottery resembling northern Asiatic pottery, and with ground stone axes and bifacially chipped knives and projectile points. This culture filled the great void of northern and northeastern North America after the ice retreated and the huge Pleistocene mammals became extinct. That it came into the region relatively recently is indicated by its cultural homogeneity and also by the fact that except for the historically intrusive Iroquoian, and possibly the extinct and almost unknown Beothukan of Newfoundland, only two families of languages, Algonkian and Athabascan (Na-Dené) are spoken there by the living Indians.

To this threefold sequence may be added the Eskimo cultures of the polar fringes from Siberia to Greenland and the related Aleut culture, all of which seem to have evolved from a Neolithic economy on the Pacific coast based on fishing and the hunting of sea mammals.[6] Again we are reminded of some of the cultural aspects of the Hokkaido material.

[3] C. V. Haynes, Jr.: "Fluted Projectile Points: Their Age and Dispersion," *Science*, Vol. 145, No. 3639 (1964), pp. 1408–13.
[4] Bushnell and McBurney: op. cit.
[5] Chard: op. cit.
[6] Levin: *Ethnic Origins of the Peoples of Northeastern Asia*, AITR, No. 3 (1963), Chapter 4, pp. 192–233.

The object of this review, which may seem complicated, is not to teach archaeology, but to help elucidate the troublesome problem of the origins of the American Indians and the Eskimo. The evidence suggests that although the obvious source of genetic material in both cases was Mongoloid, Northeast Asia may have been a point of convergence of Australoid elements creeping up the island chain and of Caucasoid elements breaching Movius's Line, particularly through the Amur River valley. We do not suggest a succession of racially distinct invaders taking turns entering America and preserving their racial identities after they arrived there. That widely publicized idea was a product of the misinterpretation of a typological analysis of a cranial series of Southwestern Indians[7] which its author never intended. We do suggest the possibility that certain non-Mongoloid elements contributed to the formation of the gene pool or pools that entered America in pre-Columbian times. As for later contacts by sea, that is another matter. The best evidence that America was reached by seafarers across the Pacific is the discovery, along the coast of Ecuador, of pottery closely resembling that of Middle Jomon at the date when the move would have taken place, 2500 B.C.[8]

Concerning the skeletal evidence for early man in America, little need be said here. There are few early skulls and fewer skeletons, and none of them fall outside the range of living American Indians or Eskimo. Some authorities have claimed that the Lagoa Santa skulls of Brazil, the Pericu crania of Lower California, and some early Ecuadorean skulls show Melanesian or Australoid affinities, but Oschinsky finds them all typically Mongoloid in the morphology of the cheekbones, and completely different from the Melanesian and Australoid crania in this respect.[9] Six newly excavated skeletons from the Tehuacán Valley, Mexico, dated by Carbon-14 from 6800 B.C. to 5000 B.C. are also fully Mongoloid.[1] The numerous and well-documented skeletons from later pre-Columbian times from all the Americas, studies of which have been assiduously published, show evidence of local population movements, but hold few if any surprises. Where these skeletons need to be mentioned, it will be done in the context of the living.

7 E. A. Hooton: *Indians of Pecos* (New Haven: Yale University Press; 1930).

8 E. Estrada, B. J. Meggers, and C. Evans: "Possible Transpacific Contact on the Coast of Ecuador," *Science*, Vol. 135, No. 3501 (1962), pp. 371–2. The date is (W-631) 4450 ± 200 B.P.

9 Oschinsky: "The Supposed 'Melanesian Affinities' of Ancient New World Mongoloids," paper read at 33rd AAPA Conference, Mexico, D.F., June 21–5, 1964.

1 J. E. Anderson: "The Skeletons from Tehuacán, Mexico: A Preliminary Report," paper read at 33rd AAPA Conference, Mexico, D.F., June 21–5, 1964.

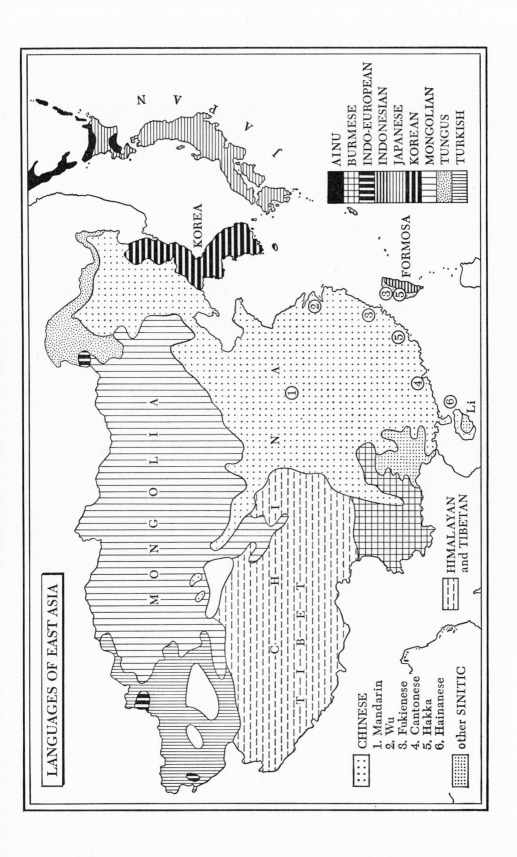

LANGUAGES OF EAST ASIA

CHINESE
1. Mandarin
2. Wu
3. Fukienese
4. Cantonese
5. Hakka
6. Hainanese

other SINITIC

HIMALAYAN
and TIBETAN

AINU
BURMESE
INDO-EUROPEAN
INDONESIAN
JAPANESE
KOREAN
MONGOLIAN
TUNGUS
TURKISH

Languages of East Asia[2]

EXCEPT for the Altaic languages, which are spoken from the Mediterranean to the Pacific, the languages of East Asia have no demonstrable relationship to the languages of the Caucasoid homelands or of Africa. They may be divided roughly by latitude into four bands, reading from north to south.

In the far north are the Ugrian languages, mentioned in Chapter 3, the Samoyed languages, the Tungus-Manchu group, and the Paleo-Asiatic languages. All but the latter are Ural-Altaic. The Paleo-Asiatic languages, which have not been shown to constitute a phylum, include two families and one isolated language group. The families are Yukaghir or Odul, and Chukchian. Yukaghir is a single language. Chukchian includes Chukchi, Koryak, and Kamchadal, and possibly also Gilyak (Nivkh) and Ainu. The language group is Yeniseian, or Ket, and its affiliation is unknown. For the benefit of readers who are accustomed to seeing these languages and the peoples who speak them referred to by their Russian names, Table 5 gives a correlation of terms. Most of these languages are spoken today by very few people, and two of them, Yeniseian and Kamchadal, have been replaced wholly or largely by Russian.

The next tier of languages consists of Turkish, Mongolian, Tungusic, Korean, and Japanese. The first three are Altaic. Korean and Japanese, both of which have borrowed heavily from Chinese, may be ultimately of Tungusic origin, like Manchu.

South of this zone are spoken the Sinitic languages, a phylum which Seboek has divided into nine co-equal families: (1) Han Chinese, (2) Miao-Yao, (3) Kam-Thai, (4) Burmese, (5) Karen, (6) Bodo-Naga 1–Kachin, (7) Naga 2–Chin, (8) Gyarung-Misir, and (9) Tibetan. Chinese and Tibetan have by far the most speakers in the area with which we are now concerned. Chinese itself is divided into the official Mandarin of the North, Wu of the lower Yangtze Valley, Cantonese, Hainanese, Fukienese, and Hakka. The last two are also widely spoken on Formosa.

The Miao-Yao and Kam-Thai language families both originated north of their present ranges in central or northern China and have been progressively pushed southward by the expansion of

2 The principal sources used in this section are Trager's "Languages of the World," in *Collier's Encyclopedia*. T. Sebeok: "Languages of the World: Sino-Tibetan Fascicle One," AL, Vol. 6, No. 3 (1964), pp. 1–13. Meillet and Cohen: *Les Langues du monde. Atlas Narodov Miri* (Moscow, 1964).

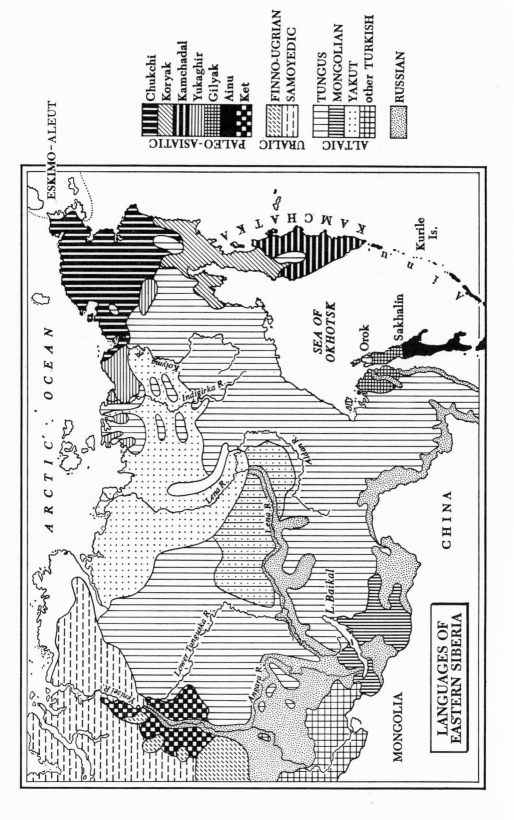

LANGUAGES OF
EASTERN SIBERIA

TABLE 5

SOME NAMES OF SIBERIAN PEOPLES IN RUSSIAN AND ENGLISH

Russian	English	Russian	English
I SAMOYED GROUP		III PALEO-ASIATIC GROUP	
Nentsi	Samoyeds of area from Kanin Peninsula to Yenisei	Chukchi	Chukchis
		Koriaki	Koryaks
Entsi	Samoyeds of Lower Yenisei	Itelmeni	Kamchadals
Ngansani	Samoyeds of Taimyr Peninsula	Iokagiri	Yukaghirs
		Nivkhi	Gilyaks
Selkupi	Ostyak-Samoyeds of Upper Ob–Yenisei		
		Ket Group	
		Keti*	Yeniseians
II TUNGUS-MANCHU GROUP			
Evenki	Tungus Proper		
Eveni	Lamuts		
Nanaitsi	Golds		
Ulchi	Ulchs (Olchs, Ulchans, Mungans)		
Oroki	Oroks		
Orochi	Orochs		
Udegaitsi	Udeghe		
Manchjuri	Manchus		
Sibo	Sibo		

* The affiliation of the Ket language is not certain.

the Chinese empire. Today they are spoken mostly in Southeast Asia. In southern and southwestern China they are spoken by many isolated tribes and villages of aborigines living on the slopes and ridges above the river valleys, which are occupied by Chinese-speakers. Languages (4) and (8) on Sebeok's list are spoken in Burma and India.

American Indian Languages[3]

WHEN Columbus reached America, about 20 million people in the New World were speaking about 900 languages, with an

[3] Trager: op. cit. J. W. Powell: "Indian Linguistic Families North of Mexico," BAE, 7th Annual Report for 1891 (1892), pp. 1–142. E. Sapir: "Central and

average of 11,000 persons per language. In a linguistic sense, America was thus the most diversified part of the world, in great contrast to East Asia. Its linguistic complexity was known long before other facts were determined which made it seem all the more curious. We now know that the ancestors of the American Indians could only have entered the New World over the Bering Strait, not necessarily earlier than 15,000 years ago and almost certainly not earlier than 30,000 years ago. We know that these people, like the living Indians, were essentially Mongoloid. And archaeological research indicates that the advanced cultures of the New World grew up locally out of a basic cultural substratum of hunting and gathering which was all these people had brought with them from the Old World.

Before any of this was known, a number of imaginative writers versed in Old World lore—discounting the facts of independent invention—sought to derive the Indians, in part or as a whole, from the lost tribes of Israel, from ancient Egypt, the west coast of Africa, Atlantis, or the equally imaginary lost continent of Mu. Meanwhile professional linguists have shown that most of the North American Indian languages can be grouped into a few phyla, and that their extraordinary diversity was probably a product of mutual isolation. Powerful states, such as those of the Aztecs and the Incas, arose too late before the Conquest to spread single languages far afield.

The effort to reduce the number of languages into families and larger categories resulted in 1892 in a classification by J. W. Powell that set the number of families north of the Mexican border at fifty-eight. His work has been the basis for subsequent reductions, particularly that of E. Sapir in 1929 which involved languages spoken on both sides of the Mexican border. Sapir established six phyla: (1) Eskimo-Aleut, (2) Na-Dené, (3) Algonkian-Wakashan, (4) Uto-Aztecan, (5) Penutian, and (6) Hokan-Siouan. Thirty-five years later Trager used the same general classification, with a few changes. The third phylum has become Algonkian-Mosan; the fourth, Azteco-Tanoan; and the fifth, Marco-Penutian.

Except for Eskimo and Aleut, which were probably the last to arrive from Asia, each of the others shows a diversified geographical range and is spoken by Indians of quite different cul-

North American Indian Languages," Encyclopaedia Britannica, 14th ed. (1929), Vol. 5, pp. 138–41. S. Tax: "Aboriginal Languages of Latin America," CA, Vol. 1, No. 5–6 (1960), pp. 430–6. M. Swadesh, in *Discussion and Criticism:* "On Aboriginal Languages of Latin America," CA, Vol. 4, No. 3 (1963), pp. 317–8.

LANGUAGES OF
NORTH AMERICA

ESKIMO—ALEUT
NA—DENÉ
ALGONKIAN—MOSAN
AZTECO—TANOAN
PENUTIAN
HOKAN—SIOUAN
MACRO—OTOMANGUEAN

MAYAN
TARASCAN
ARAWAKAN
CHIBCHAN

tures. Sapir once suggested that Na-Dené was related to Sinitic, but his documentation has been lost. These languages are spoken by many hunters and trappers in Alaska and western Canada, by a number of tribes along the Pacific coast from Alaska to northern California, including the highly artistic Tlingit and Haida, and by the Navajo and Apache.

Languages now labeled Algonkian-Mosan are spoken from the Pacific to the Atlantic, and if Mary Haas is right to include the Gulf languages among them, from the Gulf of Mexico to Hudson's Bay.[4] Trager lists these languages under Hokan-Siouan.

Uto-Aztecan has likewise been expanded into Azteco-Tanoan. This phylum is notable in that its speakers cover the whole gamut of cultural complexity among the Indians of the New World, from the simple food-collecting economy of the Utes and Paiutes to the sophisticated civilization of the Aztecs. All of the Pueblo languages except Keresan have now been incorporated into this phylum, as have Kiowa and Comanche.

The Penutian phylum was originally created to encompass many local languages of California, particularly those of the Sacramento Valley: Miwok, Maidu, Yokuts, Wintun, and Patwin; but it has been expanded to include northwestern languages such as Nez Percé, Yakima, Klamath, and Modoc, and possibly Maya and related languages in Yucatán and Central America.

Hoakan-Siouan has been the most contested of Sapir's six phyla. It encompasses all the Sioux languages, including those spoken on the east coast of the southern United States and inland; Caddo and Arikara; the Keresan Pueblo language; certain languages of the southern Colorado basin such as Yuma, Walapai, and Havasupai; and those of the Lower California coast, as well as Serian on the opposite coast. The Iroquoian languages, those of the Seven Nations of the eastern Great Lakes and the St. Lawrence Valley, and the southern tribes, Cherokee, Tuscarora, Nottaway, and Meherrin, were originally included in Sapir's Hokan-Siouan and then rejected, but have recently been proposed for inclusion again.[5] In northeastern Mexico, Hokan-Siouan languages are widely spoken, such as Coahuiltec, Tamaulipec, and others. Small enclaves of this phylum are also found on or near the Pacific coast as far south as Nicaragua.

The United States–Mexican border, then is non-existent insofar

[4] M. R. Haas: "A new linguistic relationship in North America, Algonkian and the Gulf Languages," SWJA, Vol. 14, No. 3 (1958), pp. 231–64.

[5] W. L. Chafe: "Another Look at Siouan and Iriquoian," AA, Vol. 66, No. 4, Part 1 (1964), pp. 852–62.

as language is concerned. All six northerly languages, except Eskimo-Aleut, extend south of the border, where only two localized phyla have resisted amalgamation: Macro-Otomanguean and Tarascan. Both of these are spoken in central Mexico and were isolated by the spread of the Aztec state. The principal languages under each phylum are Otomi, in the first, and Tarascan, a single language usually designated as an independent isolate. If the New World contains a linguistic frontier, other than that separating Eskimo-Aleut from the rest, it is not along the Rio Grande but in Honduras and Nicaragua and in the Straits of Florida, where North American and South American languages meet. In both Central America and the West Indies, South American languages encroached on the territory of the northern languages. In post-Columbian times one of them even penetrated southern Florida.

The South American languages are difficult to classify. To the obscurity of extinction, one may add the fact that some South American Indians are still unconquered and their tongues unrecorded. Of the known languages, 108 families were postulated before 1924. Then the number was reduced to seventy-five, the largest of which are Carib, Arawak, Tupi-Guarani, Gê, Chibchan, Aymara, Quechua, Araucanian, Puelche, and Tehuelche. Since then several attempts have been made to reduce them still further. In 1960 Sol Tax, for example, proposed three phyla; twenty superfamilies, which he calls stocks; and fifty-nine families.[6] The three phyla are Macro-Chibchan, Gê-Pano-Carib, and Andean-Equatorial. The first has eight stocks and twenty-five families, extending from Honduras and El Savador to Ecuador and Brazil. The second, with seven stocks and eleven families, extends from the Caribbean, where it is spoken by the Black Caribs among others, to the highlands of Brazil, and Argentina. The Andean-Equatorial phylum, with five stocks and twenty-three phyla, includes Arawakan, the family that penetrated Florida, and covers the West Indies and South America to Cape Horn. Among its languages are Tupi; Guarani, which is an official language of Paraguay; Quechua and Aymara, which the highland Indians of Peru and Bolivia speak; all the languages of Southern Argentina; and the Fuegian languages.

Trager, who is more conservative, has not wholly accepted this scheme, and it will probably be a long time before linguists agree on any overall classification of the languages of South America. However, the fact that contemporary linguists have been able to bring together hundreds of American Indian languages

[6] Tax: op. cit.

CHIBCHA

C A R I B

ARAWAK

JIVARO

C A R I B

ARAWAK

TUPI

TUPI

←QUECHUA

GÊ

AYMARA

GUARANI

ARAUCANIAN

PUELCHE

TEHUELCHE

ALAKALUF

ONA

YAHGAN

INDIAN LANGUAGES
OF
SOUTH AMERICA

into a relatively small number of linguistic networks is something of a success and may help dispel some doubts about the origins of the American Indians. Both J. H. Greenberg and M. Swadesh, who are "lumpers" rather than "splitters" in linguistic taxonomy, agree that all American languages are essentially related.[7] To physical anthropologists unversed in linguistic intricacies, this concept suggests only one thing—that the American Indians came from northeast Asia in a single migration or in a series of migrations and all from an essentially Mongoloid line. The multiplicity of American Indian languages does not substantiate theories of multiple origins for the American Indians—genetically, geographically, or culturally—or necessarily place them in a more remote time than the archaeological evidence warrants. In other words, all pertinent disciplines are beginning to lead to the same general conclusion.

The Racial Characteristics of the Mongoloids of East Asia

THE CONCLUSION is that the ancestors of the American Indians were Mongoloids from Eastern Asia. Let us now review the racial characteristics of the Mongoloids. These peoples include the northern Chinese, the southern Chinese, the Tibetans, the tribal peoples of southern China, the Mongols, some of the Turks, and the Tungus, Koreans, Japanese, and Paleo-Asiatic peoples. From the standpoint of physical anthropology, all these peoples, taken together, are less variable than are the Caucasoids or the Africans. There is no wide variability among them in pigmentation or hair form, and none are dwarfs. Although they vary less among themselves than members of other subspecies, they differ more from the rest of mankind than any others.

The Mongoloid morphological characteristics are well known and require little review.[8] The peoples of East Asia vary in stature

[7] Greenberg: "The General Classification of Central and South American Indian Languages," in A. F. C. Wallace, ed.: *Selected Papers of the Fifth International Congress of Anthropological and Ethnographical Sciences* (Philadelphia: University of Pennsylvania Press; 1960). Swadesh: op. cit.

[8] The literature is extensive. Reviews and bibliographies may be found in G. W. Lasker: "Migration and Physical Differentiation," AJPA, Vol. 4, No. 3 (1946), pp. 273–300.

Levin: *Ethnic Origins of the Peoples of Northeastern Asia.*

Hulse: "Physical Types among the Japanese," PMP, Vol. 20 (1943), pp. 122–33. See also S. M. Shirakogarov: *Anthropometry of Northern China*, RAS-NCB, extra vol., No. 2 (1923); *Anthropometry of Eastern China and Kwangtung Province*, RAS-NCB, extra vol., No. 4 (1925).

from a mean of 158 centimeters (5 feet 2 inches) among some Japanese groups to a mean of 168 centimeters (5 feet 6 inches) among northern Chinese. They have relatively long trunks and short extremities, with relatively short forearms and lower legs. Their hands and feet are small; their nails, like those of Bushmen, are curved. Their backs are relatively straight, with little lumbar curvature; their chests are large and their hips narrow. Their skin, which regionally varies little in color, is mostly glabrous; they have little pubic and axillary hair, but abundant hair on the head and usually sparse beards. Their hair is coarse, tubular in section, and grows very long on their heads. Balding is rare and men do not usually gray until they are very old.

Head form is variable. The northern Chinese are mostly meso-cephalic; the southern Chinese are brachycephalic. The Koreans and the Japanese are mostly brachycephalic, with steep occiputs and high vaults. The Mongols and the Kirghiz, whose ancestors came from the Yenisei,[9] have very large heads, both long and broad, but low-vaulted. Their cranial capacities, because of a deep curvature of the occipital portion of the cranial base, are greater than would be expected on the basis of the low vaults.

Most Asiatic Mongoloids have small browridges if any at all. Their eyeballs, which are smaller than those of other races, are set wide apart and are placed forward in the orbits. As with the Bush-men, eyefolds narrow the opening, and a Mongolian or epicanthic fold may cover the inner edge of the lid. Two forms of nasal bridge are found among nearly all Mongoloid populations: a very low, flattish bridge, sometimes so low that the surfaces of the eyeballs protrude in front of it; and an aquiline one. Intermediate, straight forms are uncommon.

The lower margin of the Mongoloid orbit lies farther forward than in other races, and the malars (zygomatic bones) tend to protrude both forward and laterally, giving the so-called "high-cheekboned" appearance. As Oschinsky has pointed out, an ex-treme form of zygomatic development is found among Siberian peoples and Eskimo; in it the zygomaxillary tuberosity extends forward, and both the anterior malar surface and the lower border of the malar are concave.[1] To match this extreme development of the zygomatic region, the mandibles of Siberians and Eskimo have pronounced gonial eversion, along with mandibular tori. These

[9] A. Bernshtam: "On the Origin of the Kirghiz Peoples," in H. N. Michael, ed.: *Studies in Siberian Ethnogenesis*, AINA, No. 2 (1962), pp. 119–28. Debetz: "The Origin of the Kirghiz in the Light of Physical Anthropological Findings."

[1] Oschinsky: "Facial Flatness and Cheekbone Morphology in Arctic Mongoloids," *Anthropologica*, n.s., Vol. 4, No. 2 (1962), pp. 349–77.

adaptations can be readily seen in the peoples of the Arctic, who also have overdeveloped masseter muscles. Other Mongoloids, living below the Arctic. also have prominent malars and broad mandibles, but without the extreme development seen in their northern brethren.

Most Mongoloids, whether they live in the Arctic or elsewhere, have shovel-shaped incisors—principally the upper centrals—and their incisors and canines are relatively large in proportion to the size of their molars. When Mongoloids live on soft foods and do little or no heavy chewing, they tend to have a so-called psaliodont occlusion of the front teeth. That is, instead of the pronounced overbite of most modern Caucasoids, among the Mongoloids both upper and lower incisors project forward, giving a bucktoothed appearance, particularly common among Japanese.

Facial flatness, as measured by a series of chords and subtenses invented by T. L. Woo,[2] is a well-known Mongoloid characteristic. It involves the skeleton and soft parts of the forehead, eyes, nose, cheeks, and jaws. As one would expect, it reaches a peak in Siberia, particularly among the Tungus and some of the Paleo-Asiatic-speaking peoples who live in the coldest inhabited regions of Asia. As one moves into warmer regions, the selection that governs this condition is relaxed. The Mongoloid facial features are still present, but in a less extreme form.

The Ainus and Gilyaks[3]

NO SINGLE PEOPLE in the world has had more written about its origins, which are unknown, and its racial classification, which is undetermined, than the Ainu. These familiar-looking solidly built, bearded, hairy people living in the dim light of Hokkaido, Sakhalin Island, and formerly in the Kuriles, have been called outliers of an ancient migration from Europe; bleached Austra-loids whose ancestors moved up the island chain in remote an-tiquity; and Mongoloid variants. Without doubt they have been mixed with Mongoloids, both with the Japanese who drove them north out of Honshu, and with Siberian peoples whom they met in Hokkaido and elsewhere. But they have retained their distinctive

2 T. L. Woo and G. M. Morant: "A Biometric Study of the 'Flatness' of the Facial Skeletal in Man," *Biometrika*, Vol. 26 (1934), pp. 196–250.

3 Levin's *Ethnic Origins of the Peoples of Northeastern Asia* contains a bibliog-raphy of the extensive literature on this subject, much of which is in Japanese. See also Coon: "An Anthropogeographic Excursion Around the World," pp. 31–42.

features: a Caucasoid type of skin, brunette, white, hairy, and well provided with sweat glands; and a Caucasoid type of hair that varies from straight to curly, as among the Ainu who formerly inhabited the Kurile Islands.[4] Typical of the Ainu are a broad forehead, moderately heavy browridges, a moderately low nasal bridge, snubbed tip, eyes far apart but usually without folds, and a light brown eye color, with a mixed greenish and grayish iris patterns in a few cases.

Today the indications are that they were originally Caucasoid, for the following reasons. The Ainu fingerprints show more loops than whorls. This is a Caucasoid characteristic. Both among Mongoloids and among Australoids whorls exceed loops. The Ainu have an incidence of 63 percent of sticky earwax.[5] Sticky earwax is characteristic of Caucasoids; crumbly earwax of Mongoloids. The upper incisor teeth of the Ainu, although they are shoveled in one third of the individuals studied, do not show the extreme forms of shoveling seen among most Mongoloids, but are rather like the moderately shoveled teeth found occasionally in Northern Europe.[6] Among the Ainu, upper molar teeth have pearl-like excrescences of enamel along the outer gingival border in 30 percent of the individuals studied. Three percent of Japanese skulls also show this. Enamel pearls are also found among the Eskimo and among Northern Europeans, particularly the medieval Icelanders.[7]

The Icelanders were in no sense Mongoloid. They had some of the arctic adaptations of the Siberians and the Eskimo, notably the mandibular torus and the thickened tympanic bone under the earhole, but these adaptations were probably convergent. The Moriori of the Chatham Islands off New Zealand had them too. The dental pearls of the Ainu, however, cannot be so easily accounted for, and imply a genetic continuity. It would seem as if after the Pleistocene had ended this genetic trait was carried eastward along the edge of the Siberian forest from the Urals to the Amur River, rather than having moved in the opposite direction. In this trait as in others, it would appear that the Eskimo may have started out Caucasoid and ended up Mongoloid, the opposite of the Ottoman Turks.

Whatever one may say of the Eskimo, it now seems most likely that the Ainu are of Caucasoid origin. The same must be true in

[4] R. Torii: "Les Ainou des Iles Kouriles," JCS, Vol. 42, Art. 1 (1911), pp. 1–337.
[5] E. Matsunaga: "Polymorphism in ear-wax types and its anthropological significance," ZZ, Vol. 67, No. 722 (1959), pp. 171–84.
[6] M. Suzuki and T. Sakai: "Shovel-Shaped Incisors in Polynesians," AJPA, Vol. 22, No. 1 (1964), pp. 65–76.
[7] Coon: "An Anthropogeographic Excursion Around the World."

part of the Gilyaks, another heavily bearded people of Sakhalin and the Lower Amur River valley. Old photographs of other Paleo-Asiatic-speaking tribesmen, like the Yukaghirs, also show European-like features, including beards. But these people are now so decimated and mixed that it is difficult to draw any conclusions about their racial composition before the Russians reached the Pacific.

The Racial Characteristics of the American Indians[8]

THE ESKIMO and the Aleuts belong racially with the Siberian Mongoloids and represent a later migration to the New World than that of the Indians. This is easily shown by blood-group studies and also on the basis of morphological features. These people may not be much more than 5,000 years old in the New World, but that figure is only a guess based on archaeological finds made to date.

The American Indians are more uniform racially than any other group of people occupying an equally vast area. In fact, they are more uniform than many peoples who occupy an area a tenth as large. All of this indicates that a relatively small number of people crossed the Bering Strait during the last part of the Wisconsin glaciation, and that their descendants gradually filled the uninhabited regions of the New World. They are Mongoloid in general and despite some of their peculiarities in blood groups do not necessarily merit classification as a subspecies of their own. This will be explained in Chapter 9. But they are Mongoloids of a particular kind, just as they would be Caucasoids of a particular kind had the New World been peopled by a small band of Upper Paleolithic Europeans—as W. C. Osman Hill has proposed.[9] One objection to his hypothesis is that the American Indians have a much greater incidence of shoveled incisors than any Asiatic peoples, and in more extreme forms.[1]

The differences between the American Indians and the Asiatic Mongoloids are found principally in their facial features. Most of

8 For a bibliography on the North American Indians see G. K. Neumann: "Archaeology and Race in the American Indian," YPA, Vol. 8 (1952), pp. 213–55. For the South American Indians, see J. H. Steward, ed.: *Handbook of the South American Indians*, SIBAE, Bull. 143 (1950).

9 W. C. Osman Hill: "The Soft Anatomy of a North American Indian," AJPA, Vol. 21, No. 3 (1963), pp. 245–70. Hill based this theory on his dissection of the cadaver of a sixty-seven-year-old male Cherokee of blood group B.

1 Suzuki and Sakai: op. cit.

the Indians show less facial flatness than Asiatic Mongoloids and have more prominent noses, many of them with convex profiles. Noses like those of American Indians may be seen in Asia, particularly among Tibetans, and among the Nagas of Assam, but they are less common among the Chinese and the Siberians. If the prevalence of beaked noses among American Indians is due to Caucasoid mixture, there is an additional problem, as the mixture cannot have resulted from a Caucasoid movement along the Siberian forest lands (a movement such as that which may explain the Ainu). At the time the Indians entered the New World, such a movement was impossible. Moreover, the Ainu do not have aquiline noses. It could only have been a movement of central Asiatic Neanderthals through the Zungarian Gate into northern China at the time that Levalloisio-Mousterian-like flake implements appeared. Such a relationship is possible, but cannot be proved. American Indian skulls with heavy browridges and receding foreheads have been found in archaeological sites, and also among the recent Ona Indians of Tierra del Fuego, but none of the oldest fossil remains are of this type. If genes for this primitive condition were brought from the Old World, they were brought as infrequent alleles, and were not characteristic of any population yet known.

American Indians also differ from Asiatic Mongoloids in pigmentation, for some of the Indians are darker-skinned. The Seminoles of Florida are almost mahogany-colored, and the Papago and other Indians who live in the part of the New World that has the brightest sunlight are dark brown—and these colors are not entirely due to tanning. Ninety percent of Alaskan Indians have brunette untanned skin color.[2] Alakaluf Indians are all of brunette skin color except for blue spots of deep-lying pigment in various places, and blue genitalia. Many of the Indians who live in the Amazonian forest are light-skinned, and among them beaked noses are rare. Some of these Indians resemble the forest-dwellers of Borneo—probably a case of simple parallel selection from the same original source.

From time to time aberrant or atypical Indians have been studied or reported upon. For example, some of the villages around the shore of Lake Atitlán in Guatemala are occupied by Indians who are small enough to be called Pygmies, whereas the inhabitants of neighboring villages are of normal stature. Stunted Indian populations have also been found in the mountains of Colombia.[3]

[2] R. A. McKennan: "The Physical Anthropology of Two Alaskan Athapaskan Groups," AJPA, Vol. 22, No. 1 (1964), pp. 43–52.

[3] Gusinde: "The Yupa Indians in Western Venezuela," PAPS, Vol. 100, No. 3 (1956), pp. 197–220.

These instances of stunting can probably be explained by local inbreeding and by dietary deficiencies, which are indicated by goiter. Equally small people were found in isolated Alpine valleys a century ago.

Although the mean stature of American Indians follows regular climatic lines, with the tallest tribes situated in the North American Plains and in Patagonia, and the shortest in the warmer, wetter regions between, exceptions have been noted. Mayas of high rank exhumed from the elaborate tombs in Tikal, Palenque, and other romantic ruins were bigger men than most Mayas of today, but they were not necessarily invaders and conquerors of an alien race. Any tourist who visits the market at Sololá, Guatemala, will see that the dozen and more Indian mayors who convene there are a good five inches taller than their fellow villagers, and just as Indian. The royal family of Saudi Arabia is also tall, as is the nobility of the Tutsi (Watusi).

The conquistadors commented on Montezuma's light skin, but did not remark that this ruler rarely exposed himself to the bright sun. George Catlin, in his portraits of the Mandan Indians, depicted some of them as blond. M. T. Newman, however, has suggested that what Catlin took for blondism was a hereditary tendency to early graying of the hair.[4] This question cannot now be answered because there seem to be no full-blooded Mandans left. Another case of allegedly aberrant Indians is that of the Pomo, Hupa, and neighboring tribes in north-central California whose beard growth seems to have been Caucasoid when they were first seen, but this is *sub judice*.

Conclusion

THE MONGOLOIDS of East Asia and the Americas are a basic, ancient human subspecies, quite homogeneous in general, but showing regional variations that mirror differences in climatic stress. The Ainu and Gilyaks probably owe their Caucasoid appearance to an ancient migration from eastern Siberia. The American Indians differ from the Asiatic Mongoloids mainly in that they have less facial flatness, particularly in the nasal skeleton, and a more variable skin color. There is no valid evidence that the Indians were derived from more than one source or that they came into the New World by a route other than the Bering Strait.

[4] M. T. Newman: "The Blond Mandan: A Critical Review of an Old Problem," SWJA, Vol. 6, No. 3 (1950), pp. 255–72.

6

Southeast Asia, Australia, The Pacific Islands, and Madagascar

❈❈❈

The Australoid and the Southern Mongoloid World

THIS CHAPTER covers a wide and watery territory. It stretches from the Tropic of Cancer to 50° S. latitude, and from Easter Island to Madagascar, more than halfway around the world. It includes about 770,000 square miles, or 4½ percent, of Asia; the Australian continent; the four largest islands of the world entirely below the Arctic Circle—New Guinea, Borneo, Madagascar, and Sumatra; about fifty middle-sized islands; and a majority of the small islands and atolls of the world which were inhabited at the time of European discovery.

The reason why these far-flung land masses, ranging in size from about 3 million square miles (Australia) to less than three square miles (Bikini), are grouped together is simple. All of them have or have had something to do with the Australoid subspecies. Southeast Asia and Indonesia (speaking in the geographical, not the narrower political sense) were the Pleistocene homelands in which the Australoids evolved. New Guinea and Australia were uninhabited until Australoids migrated to them before the end of the Pleistocene, the very time that Mongoloids invaded Southeast Asia out of China. These invasions resulted in the isolation of dwarf Australoids, or Negritos, in these regions, and also in an absorption of Australoid genes by the invaders, particularly the Indonesians. The admixture is shown quite clearly in blood-group studies though it may not be as evident from details of external anatomy. Seafarers of mixed Mongoloid-Australoid origin then settled the previously uninhabited islands of Madagascar, Micronesia, and Polynesia. From New Guinea to New Caledonia some of them mixed with indigenous Australoids all over again, thus creating the Melanesians.

Geography and Climate

NEXT TO WATER, the outstanding feature of this vast region is its mountainous character. In Upper Burma peaks rise to over 19,000 feet; in Laos and both Vietnams, to between 8,000 and 10,000 feet; and even the Malay Peninsula has a mountain 7,350 feet high. In all of the region under consideration there is hardly an island big enough to hold a peak or ridge of over 9,000 feet that does not have one. New Guinea rises to 16,500 feet, Hawaii to 13,796, Borneo to 13,763, Formosa to 13,414, Sumatra to 12,753, New Zealand to 12, 349, and Java to 11,504.

In Southeast Asia three principal ridges provide relatively cool highways from the jumble of mountains to the north down to the river valleys and the sea. On the west the Arakan Range separates the mouths of the Ganges from the Irrawaddy. Next, to the east, the Dawna Range fences Burma off from Thailand, and its extensions sweep almost to Singapore, knotting up in the Malayan highlands. Farther east the mountains of Laos and both Vietnams divide the lowlands of North Vietnam from those of South Vietnam and Cambodia. The Thai lowlands are split by a low range that turns east just north of Bangkok to separate eastern Thailand from Cambodia. Along these ridges Mongoloid peoples, mostly non-Chinese tribesmen from southern China and eastern Tibet, have been filtering down to the steamy jungles and swamps of the lowlands while gradually becoming acclimated on the way.

Southeast Asia has a variety of tropical climates with summer rainfall of varying amounts, producing types of vegetation ranging from true rain forest in Malaya to a semi-deciduous, dry tropical forest in South Vietnam, and savannas in eastern Cambodia and southern Laos.

Sumatra, Java, and the Sundas are extensions of the Southeast

Asia mountain system rising from the sea; Formosa, the Philippines, Borneo, and the Celebes belong with the Japanese chain. All the Indonesian islands that are large enough to be climatically variable have tropical climates in the lowlands, with the usual summer rain. The larger islands have cool refuges in the highlands. In the highlands of New Guinea the temperature falls to 40° F. at night at an elevation of 5,000 feet, and most settlements are higher up. The parts of this highland country that are south of the mountain ridge are dry enough for grasslands.

Even islands as small as Viti Levu in the Fijis and New Caledonia have tropical forests on their windward sides and grasslands to leeward. The lowlands of Indonesia are as hot as those of Southeast Asia, and so are the coasts of New Guinea and much of Melanesia, but New Caledonia is cooler. During most of the year the windward side of Fiji, where most Fijians live, is cooler also. Samoa, Yap, and Palau can be hot and muggy for a few weeks each year between winds, but most of the time the trade winds keep the tropical islands of Polynesia and Micronesia comfortable, and Polynesians and Micronesians cool their bodies by swimming and bathing.

Tasmania is far enough south so that large parts of it were glaciated during the late Pleistocene, and it is possible that some of the ice was still there when the first human beings arrived. New Zealand, which was settled much later, was also partly glaciated. Both have maritime climates comparable to that of the British Isles.

Australia, being a continent, has a variety of climates, with deserts in the center and the west, monsoon forests subject to seasonal flooding in the north, some rain forest on the northeast coast, and a strip of maritime and mediterranean climates from Sydney around the coast to Adelaide, and in the southwestern corner. These meteorological data are pertinent here because the ancestors of the Australians, the Tasmanians, and the Maoris all came from the damp tropics and had to make fairly rapid adjustments, both physiological and cultural, in their new homes.

Madagascar has rain forest on the eastern slope of the island and savannas skimpily watered by summer rain on the western plain. In between is a strip of cool grassland variegated with patches of mountain vegetation. The division of the island into these three zones has had an effect on the racial distribution of its inhabitants, as we shall see shortly.

The Prehistory of Southeast Asia and Indonesia: the Paleolithic

IN 1944 H. L. Movius, Jr., delivered an opinion that has been accepted as dogma by many specialists and has been challenged by others—that in all Southeast Asia, Indonesia, and China the Pleistocene industries consisted entirely of local variants of a single complex.[1] This was a combination of choppers (unifacial core tools), chopping tools (bifacial ones), and coarse flakes, which persisted until postglacial times. When he wrote, before World War II, only Burma,[2] Java,[3] and the Philippines,[4] among the regions covered in this chapter, had been explored in this sense. Since then discoveries of Paleolithic tools have been made in Thailand,[5] North Vietnam,[6] Sumatra,[7] Malaya,[8] Bali,[9] Borneo,[1] the Celebes,[2] and again in Java.[3] On the whole, these later finds have shown that essentially he was right.

The oldest site is that of Kota Tampang, four miles east of Lenggong on the Perak River in Malaya. There implements of the usual kinds, made mostly from quartzite pebbles, were excavated from a thin gravel bed 236 feet above the river. It is dated

1 Movius: *Early Man and Pleistocene Stratigraphy in Southern and Eastern Asia.*

2 Movius: "The Stone Age of Burma," TAPS, n.s., Vol. 32, Part 3 (1943).

3 Summarized in H. R. Van Heekeren: *The Stone Age of Indonesia* (The Hague: Martinus Nijhoff; 1957).

4 Although this material is largely unpublished, it has long been available to qualified visitors in H. Otley Beyer's collection in Manila. C.S.C. was shown it on December 4 and 5, 1956.

5 K. G. Heider: "A Pebble Tool Complex in Thailand," AP, Vol. 2, No. 2 (1958), pp. 63–6. Chin You-Di: "Thailand," AP, Vol. 5, No. 1 (1962), pp. 54–7. Chin's report refers to the collection of over a million tools from a stratified site at Kanchanaburi, 60 miles northwest of Bangkok, excavated by a Danish expedition in 1961 and 1962. C.S.C. was shown some of these implements, which are in the Danish National Museum in Copenhagen, on December 4, 1962.

6 W. G. Solheim II: "Vietnam," AP, Vol. 6, No. 1–2 (1963), pp. 23–31. Solheim combines in translation and paraphrase two articles by P. I. Borisovsky: "Exploration of Ancient Sites of the Stone Age in the Democratic Republic of Vietnam," SoA, Vol. 2 (1962), pp. 17–25; and "Archaeological Discoveries in Vietnam," HASR, Vol. 4 (1962), pp. 98–101.

7 Van Heekeren: op. cit., p. 35. Also R. P. Soejono: "Preliminary Notes on New Finds of Lower Paleolithic Implements from Indonesia," AP, Vol. 5, No. 2 (1961), pp. 217–32.

8 A. Sieveking: "The Paleolithic Industry of Kota Tampan, Perak, Northwestern Malaya," AP, Vol. 2, No. 2 (1958), pp. 91–102.

9 Soejono: op. cit.

1 Van Heekeren: op. cit. T. Harrisson: "New Archaeological and Ethnological Results from the Niah Caves Sarawak," *Man*, Vol. 58, No. 1 (1959), pp. 1–8.

2 Van Heekeren: op. cit., p. 50.

3 Soejono: op. cit.

at a time of high sea level near the end of the First Interglacial or at the very beginning of the Mindel glaciation. These implements may thus be as old as the oldest human remains in this part of the world, Pithecanthropus 4, the Modjokerto child, and the "Meganthropus" mandibles.[4] Because these implements were older than the earliest hand axes found in India, they could not be expected to include that kind of tool.

Both the Irrawaddy Valley sites and the site near Kanchanaburi in Thailand go back only to the Early Middle Pleistocene, or the Second Interglacial. The oldest Javanese sites that contain implements are no earlier than the Upper Middle or Late Pleistocene, later than the Trinil Pithecanthropus specimens. The others mentioned are either late or undated.

On the whole, in all dated, stratified sites, the original types of tools carry on through the Pleistocene with only local evolutionary changes and without the evidence of diffusion from outside the original Australoid region. We have no reason to doubt the continuity of Australoid peoples throughout this epoch. But there is some evidence of a possible penetration from India of the technique of making Acheulean hand axes. This comes from the Pajitanian culture of Java, dated at Late Middle or Early Upper Pleistocene time—that is, at the time of the Riss Glacial or the Riss-Würm Interglacial. In the Pajitanian tool assemblages found before World War II, Movius noted that some 6.3 percent of the tools partly or fully resembled Acheulean hand axes, and since the war Van Heekeren has found some excellent specimens. On this basis Van Heekeren favors the interpretation that such tools were indeed introduced from India at the time indicated. In his favor it may be said that we have no tools at all from the west coasts of Burma and Malaya, only from inland valleys. But if he is right, the contact did not necessarily continue, as there are no hand axes in the later chopper, chopping tool, and flake industries of Java or elsewhere in Indonesia.

His interpretation could help explain some of the puzzling resemblances between the aquiline facial features of some of the Papuans and those of Caucasoids. But on the whole, and with this possible exception, Southeast Asia and Indonesia were cultural backwaters suitable for the slow evolution of Australoid peoples from the end of the First Interglacial until well into postglacial time.

---

[4] See *The Origin of Races,* pp. 375–84.

The Postglacial Archaeology of Southeast Asia and Indonesia

DURING the postglacial Mesolithic two trends may be noted. In the Irrawaddy Valley sites of Burma and at Katchanaburi in Thailand, the old cultures continued with little change for a long time. But in Vietnam cultural influences were soon felt from the north. Polished stone axes and adzes of several kinds were introduced from China. First came celts with only the cutting edge polished, in some cases consisting of pebbles only. These were called Hoabinhian I, after a site in Vietnam. This technique was carried down the Malay Peninsula to Sumatra. We do not know whether the industry preceded or was accompanied by the earliest slash-and-burn agriculture, which is still practiced in the highlands to the present day.

Meanwhile a fine flake and microlithic industry moved southward from the Philippines along the island chain to the Celebes, Java, and the Sundas. In some of the latter islands it lasted so long that some of the implements were made by chipping glass. In the Celebes it lasted almost to the present day. After this microlithic industry, polished stone axes and adzes with rounded sections and pointed butts followed the same route and were taken out to the Pacific and moved by other routes to India.

The full Neolithic came from China with the Hoabinhian II or Bacsonian adzes and axes, which were rectangular and flat-surfaced and had parallel ground sides. Later on they had notched shoulders to facilitate hafting and, as some say, in imitation of metal prototypes. These also reached India. No firm dates for these movements have been recorded, but judging by dates elsewhere, the Hoabinhian II could not have begun in parts of Southeast Asia much before 1750 B.C. After that the special agricultural complex of Southeast Asia arose, with a combination of dry rice and millet in the uplands and wet rice in the lowlands, with taro, yams, and many tropical fruits that were later carried to East Africa, Madagascar, and the Pacific Islands.

Racial Continuity and Changes in Southeast Asia and Indonesia

MEAGER FINDS of Pleistocene date from Java and Borneo indicate that the Australoid subspecies evolved from the first small-brained Pithecanthropi into people resembling the living Australian aborigines.[5] More abundant remains have been found to document the later racial history of this region. They come from Vietnam, Thailand, Malaya, and various islands of Indonesia. Many skulls and bones, being unfossilized, are in too poor a condition for accurate racial diagnosis, and of those that are sufficiently whole, few have reached the hands of physical anthropologists. All that we know about many of them is the racial labels given them by archaeologists.[6]

Most specialists agree that four racial types are represented in the Mesolithic and Neolithic populations of Southeast Asia and Indonesia. In Vietnam, where careful work has been done, these are called "Australoid," "Melanesian," "Negrito," and "Mongoloid." The "Melanesian" crania, which are in the majority, are apparently the product of mixture between Australoids, Negritos, or both, and Mongoloids who had come down from the north in small numbers compared to their more massive invasions of modern times. The populations of Vietnam and Laos during Mesolithic and early Neolithic times, if not also later, probably resembled the Munda-speaking peoples now living in east-central India, who will be described in the next chapter.

Remains of full-sized Australoids have been found in eastern Java in association with a Mesolithic bone-tool industry, the Sampung. Elsewhere most of the remains seem to be those of Negritos. One skeleton was found in the Mesolithic level at Kanchanaburi in Thailand, and others have been found in Sumatra, Java, Borneo, Palawan, and Luzon. Some of the skeletons taken from shell heaps in Wellesley Province, Malaya, which Thomas Huxley examined in 1860, were probably Negrito also. During the Late Neolithic, Mongoloids had moved out the Sunda Island chain as far as Sumba, where one skull, found buried in a jar, was of mixed Australoid-Mongoloid type, like some of the people in the Lesser Sundas today.

In sum, the Neolithic inhabitants of Southeast Asia were mainly a mixed group of Australoid and Mongoloid origin, with pockets of Negritos much more widespread than they are today. Some of

[5] For details, see *The Origin of Races*, Chapter 9. In this context we are not concerned with the problem of peripheral gene flow.

[6] J. Fromaget and E. Saurin: "Note Préliminaire sur les Formations Cénozoiques et plus Récentes de la Chaîne Annamite Septentrionale et du Haut Laos (Stratigraphie, Préhistoire, Anthropologie)," BSGI, Vol. 22, No. 3 (1936), pp. 1–48. H. Mansuy: "Contribution a l'Étude de la Préhistoire de l'Indochine," Parts 5, 6, 7, BSGI, Vol. 12, No. 1, 2, 3 (1925). Van Heekeren: op. cit. And also numerous regional reports in *Asian Perspectives*, Vol. 1–6 (1957–62).

these Neolithic peoples moved west into India and became the ancestors of the Munda-speaking aborigines and of the Khasis of Assam. Others went out to Micronesia, Melanesia, and Polynesia. The predominantly Mongoloid phenotype of the modern Southeast Asians and many of the Indonesians is a more recent acquisition, dating from historic times. It arose from population pressure from China, which pushed the Burmese, Thais, Miaos, Yaos, Laos, and other tribal people southward. The movement is still going on today.

Historic Genetic Contacts in Southeast Asia and Indonesia[7]

WHOLLY ASIDE from these continuing tribal incursions of undiluted Mongoloids from the north, since the beginning, Southeast Asia and Indonesia have had contacts with and experienced invasions from four quarters: imperial China, India, southern Arabia, and Europe. The Chinese came mainly from southern China; the Hindus from the southeastern tip of the peninsula; the Arabs from Hadhramaut; and the Europeans from Portugal, Spain, the Netherlands, and Britain. Java probably absorbed the greatest amount of Indian genes, particularly in the upper classes. The Malay Peninsula may have received the greatest Arab influence, and the Philippines the greatest amount of European genes. Probably Indochina, being nearest to China, felt the greatest impact of Chinese genes. The official or prevailing religions of these countries reflect these influences. They are Islam in Malaya and in Java, which had previously been Hindu, then Buddhist; Hinduism in Bali; Catholicism in the Philippines; and Buddhism in Burma, Thailand, Laos, Cambodia, and Vietnam.

Languages of Southeast Asia[8]

MOST of the languages spoken in Southeast Asia today belong to the same families of the Sinitic phylum also found in southern China and cited in Chapter 5, and are relative newcomers. Not one

7 For Indonesia, see B. H. M. Vlekke: *Nusantara* (Cambridge, Mass.: Harvard University Press; 1943).
8Trager: op. cit. Sebeok: op. cit. Meillet and Cohen: op. cit. Murdock: "Genetic Classification of the Austronesian Languages: A Key to Oceanic Culture History,"

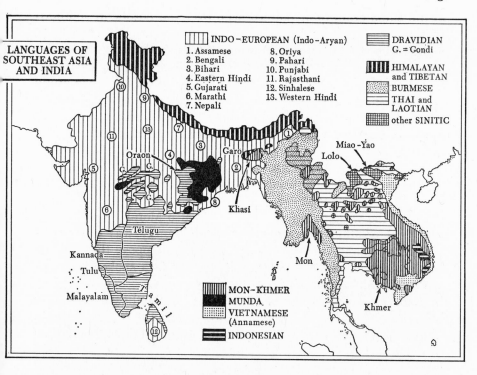

LANGUAGES OF SOUTHEAST ASIA AND INDIA

INDO – EUROPEAN (Indo–Aryan)
1. Assamese
2. Bengali
3. Bihari
4. Eastern Hindi
5. Gujarati
6. Marathi
7. Nepali
8. Oriya
9. Pahari
10. Punjabi
11. Rajasthani
12. Sinhalese
13. Western Hindi

DRAVIDIAN
G. = Gondi

HIMALAYAN and TIBETAN

BURMESE

THAI and LAOTIAN

other SINITIC

MON–KHMER
MUNDA
VIETNAMESE (Annamese)
INDONESIAN

of them has genetic ties with languages spoken farther west on the mainland except for languages also introduced into India and Pakistan from the east and the north.

Several Sinitic languages are spoken in Burma, particularly Burmese itself, Chin, and Karen. There are three principal Kam-Thai languages: Shan, Laotian, and Siamese. Shan is the chief language of Upper Burma, and Laotian of northern and eastern Thailand and adjacent parts of Laos. Siamese, the official language of Thailand, is spoken in the Menam River valley north of Bangkok and along the entire coast of the Gulf of Siam from the Cambodian border almost to Malaya. Vietnamese, or Annamese, may also be a Thai language much altered by contact with the older Mon-Khmer languages of Vietnam, although this is not certain. It is spoken in the Red and Mekong river deltas, and along the coast in between. Languages of the Miao-Yao family are scattered throughout the mountains of northern Laos and northern Vietnam,

Ethnology, Vol. 2, No. 2 (1964), pp. 117–26. (This article is "an expository review" of I. Dyen's *The Lexicostatistical Classification of the Austronesian Languages* [New Haven, 1963].) A. Capell: "Oceanic Linguistics Today," and comments by 20 other scholars, CA, Vol. 3., No. 6 (1962), pp. 371–428. G. G. Grace: "The Linguistic Evidence," CA, Vol. 5, No. 5 (1964), pp. 361–8.

in the same crazy-quilt pattern seen over the border in southern China.

Mon-Khmer is a subfamily of the Austro-Asiatic family, which seems to be older in Southeast Asia than the Sinitic languages that have largely replaced it. Mon is the principal language group of the Burmese coast near and about the mouth of the Salween River, with a linguistic island in Thailand just east of Bangkok. Related languages, such as Palaung, are spoken in other linguistic islands in northern Burma and northern Laos. Khmer is the chief and official language of Cambodia. More than a dozen Mon-Khmer languages are spoken in the middle of southern Vietnam and southern Laos. Nicobarese, the language of the Nicobar Islands lying off the western tip of Sumatra, is also Mon-Khmer. Its geographical position suggests that this subfamily was once widespread in Indonesia. It seems reasonable to suppose that at least some of the Neolithic peoples of Southeast Asia spoke languages of the Austro-Asiatic family.

Whereas Sinitic languages have invaded Southeast Asia from the north, Indonesian[9] languages have entered it from the south. Cham, Chru, Jarai, and Rade are Indonesian languages spoken in south-central Vietnam. Cham at least is believed to have been introduced there from the Atjeh region of Sumatra by the founders of the historic Cham kingdom, liquidated in the fifteenth century A.D.

Malay, spoken in the Malay Peninsula and on the Mergui Archipelago off the coast of Burma, is also Indonesian. Modern Malay is a lingua franca that has borrowed heavily from Arabic. Archaic, pre-Arabic Malay languages are still spoken by the aborigines of the central mountains of the peninsula, including the Semang Negritos, and by the Selungs of the Mergui Islands.

The Settling of Australia and New Guinea

AUSTRALIA and New Guinea were first settled during the latter part of the Würm glacial period, when the sea level was lower than it is today. The Sunda and Sahul shelves were then exposed, and the stretches of sea to be crossed by raft or canoe were shorter than they are now. At such a time Timor and the Australian coast were no more than 100 miles apart.

9 The word "Indonesian" is used here in the conventional sense. Dyen's new classification of these languages will be discussed later in this chapter.

The earliest isolated Carbon-14 date so far recorded in Australia is 16,850 ± 800 B.C. (GaK 335), and the earliest of a series in a stratified site is 14,180 ± 140 B.C. (NPL 68).[1] In the latter site, Kenniff Cave in southern Queensland, the choppers, chopping tools, and coarse flakes of the usual Southeast Asian industry were deposited from the initial occupation until after 3,070 ± 90 B.C. (NPL 66). These are the same kinds of tools used by the natives of Tasmania at the time the island was discovered. It is, however, unlikely that Tasmania was settled before the end of the Pleistocene, as parts of that island were glaciated.

During the second millennium B.C. a more advanced industry appears in several Australian sites, including Kenniff Cave. It consists principally of flakes in the form of points, made from prepared cores, and microliths. Because this second industry resembles certain Indonesian ones, particularly the Mesolithic industry of the Celebes, it is more likely to have been introduced into Australia than to have been invented there. During the second millennium B.C. the sea was as high as it is today, but even so, no stretch of water more than 60 miles wide had to be crossed. Newcomers using bark canoes or rafts like those made by Australian aborigines at the time of discovery could have done it. And they need not have been numerous to have introduced new toolmaking techniques.

At the time of European settlement the Australian aborigines were making a variety of stone tools, from the most ancient types of choppers and chopping tools (still used along the northern coast) to flakes struck from prepared cores (in central Australia) to microblades (in Victoria)—in other words, all the types found in Kenniff Cave. Many were also using stone axes with ground cutting edges, of Hoabinhian tradition. These axes have been found at archaeological sites, but have not been dated. Some of them, picked up on the beach at Snake Bay, Melville Island, had been used, then discarded and finally reworked by crude flaking into old-fashioned chopping tools.

In New Guinea archaeological work has scarcely begun, but two sites recently excavated in the central highlands, and so far undated, show a simple and interesting succession of tool types. From the bottom to the top are found the usual choppers, chopping tools, and coarse flakes, but in the uppermost layers they are accompanied by pottery and by a sequence of polished stone axes and adzes. The earliest polished stone tools are celts notched on the

[1] D. J. Mulvaney: "The Pleistocene Colonization of Australia," *Antiquity*, Vol. 38, No. 152 (1964), pp. 263–7.

sides for hafting—a familiar Southeast Asian technique. They are followed by the round-polled and rectangular types still made in this century. In the pre-pottery and pre-axe levels are found many bones of birds and marsupials which, because of clearing and planting, are not seen near the sites today.[2] At least in the highlands, the people of New Guinea passed directly from the stage of chopper, chopping tools to the Neolithic, just as their descendants are passing from the Neolithic to the mid-twentieth century.

Languages of Australia, Tasmania, and New Guinea[3]

AUSTRALIA, as might be expected, contained many languages at the time of colonial settlement. There were probably at least five hundred, or roughly one to a tribe or breeding isolate. Many individuals could speak more than one language, and a sign language was commonly employed, as among the Plains Indians of North America. On the basis of their structure, Capell has divided these languages into five geographical groups: Southeastern, Central, New South Wales, Queensland, and Kimberley, the latter including most of Arnhem Land. All that have been well recorded and carefully studied seem, despite their grammatical differences, to be genetically related and thus to form a single superfamily.

The Tasmanians, it is believed, spoke five languages, which have been divided in two groups, three in the east and two in the west. Because the last Tasmanian died in 1877, the data concerning these languages are inadequate. W. Schmidt considers them to form a single genetic unit, but not necessarily part of the Australian language family.

Two kinds of languages are spoken in New Guinea: Melanesian and "non-Austronesian," or "Papuan." Melanesian, which is limited to certain coastal regions, belongs to the Austronesian family, which we shall discuss next. "Non-Austronesian" is actually a grab bag of languages that have not yet been fully classified. In fact, some of them have not even been recorded. Over 650 languages had been listed by 1952; the number may well run into more than 1,000. Outside of New Guinea, "Non-Austronesian" languages are spoken in the following islands of Melanesia: the Admiralties, New Ireland, New Britain, and the Solomons. In Indonesia several of the latter are spoken on Halmahera, and in

2 S. and R. Bulmer: "The Prehistory of the Australian New Guinea Highlands," AA, Vol. 66, No. 4, Part 2 (1964), pp. 39–76.

3 Trager: op. cit. Meillet and Cohen: op. cit. Capell: op. cit. S. A. Wurm: "Australian New Guinea Highland Languages and the Distribution of their Typological Features," AA, Vol. 66, No. 4, Part 2 (1964), pp. 77–97.

Portuguese Timor. There may also be some on Alor. This distribution indicates that languages of this kind or kinds were widely spoken in Indonesia and parts of Melanesia before the introduction of Indonesian and Melanesian.

Recent work in the highlands of Australian New Guinea has begun to untangle the linguistic web of this region, where, because of the cool climate, white Australians are now settling. S. A. Wurm[4] has found that fifty-two of sixty languages spoken in that area belong to a single phylum, and are also related to three other families of languages spoken in other parts of New Guinea. On lexico-statistical grounds Wurm believes that this highland phylum must go back 5,000 years, a date which the archaeological evidence so far unearthed would support.

Austronesian Languages[5]

THE LANGUAGES of the Austronesian phylum are conventionally divided into four groups: Indonesian, Polynesian, Melanesian, and Micronesian. Between them Indonesian and Polynesian together are spoken over a wide area from Madagascar to Easter Island and from Formosa to New Zealand. Micronesian and Melanesian are spoken in the islands so named, which lie between Indonesian and Polynesian waters.

The relationships of these four groups to one another are obscure, and have been the source of much study, speculation, and controversy. If we follow the writings of Capell and the commentaries on them, however, a tentative theory emerges. At some time in the past there lived a group of people in southern China or northern Vietnam, or both, who spoke a non-Chinese language and were pressed from the north and west by the rising might of the Chinese Empire. Some of them put to sea in ships, probably at various times, setting off on lengthy odysseys from which none returned to their counterpart of Ithaca. First their route took them to Formosa and the Philippines. From the Philippines some went east across the Micronesian atolls. Others went southwest into Borneo and continued eventually as far as Madagascar. Still others sailed southeastward to the northern coast of New Guinea, along the shores of New Britain, New Ireland, and the northern Solomons, and out to Fiji and thence to the islands now known as Polynesia.

[4] Wurm: op. cit.

[5] Trager: op. cit Capell: op. cit. Murdock, op. cit. Grace: op. cit. Meillet and Cohen: op. cit.

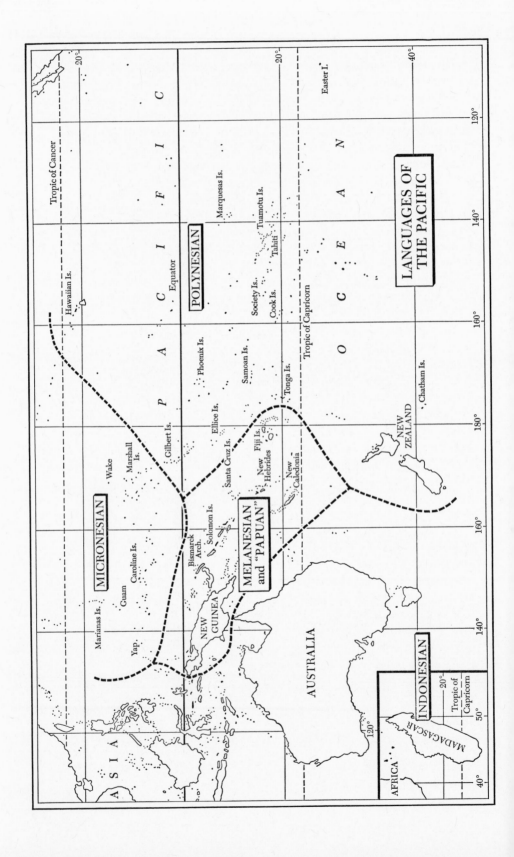

LANGUAGES OF
THE PACIFIC

POLYNESIAN

MICRONESIAN

MELANESIAN
and "PAPUAN"

INDONESIAN

PACIFIC OCEAN

ASIA

AUSTRALIA

NEW GUINEA

NEW ZEALAND

Tropic of Cancer

Equator

Tropic of Capricorn

Hawaiian Is.

Marquesas Is.

Tuamotu Is.
Tahiti
Society Is.
Cook Is.

Phoenix Is.

Samoan Is.

Tonga Is.

Ellice Is.
Gilbert Is.
Fiji Is.
Santa Cruz Is.
New Hebrides
New Caledonia

Marshall Is.
Wake

Caroline Is.
Guam
Marianas Is.
Yap.

Solomon Is.
Bismarck Arch.

Chatham Is.

Easter I.

AFRICA
MADAGASCAR
Tropic of Capricorn

20°
20°
40°
120°
140°
160°
180°
160°
140°
20°
50°
120°
40°

The parent group of languages has been given a theoretical name, "Original Austronesian." The people who took the western route spoke what is now Indonesian. Those who went eastward encountered people speaking "non-Austronesian," or "Papuan," languages in New Guinea and its offshore islands. The languages that this contact produced retained varying amounts of the basic vocabulary of Original Austronesian, but adopted the syntax of non-Autronesian in considerable measure. The result was Melanesian.

The language or languages of the navigators who continued on past New Britain and the northern Solomons experienced further change, particularly in the reduction of consonants, and became Polynesian. As for Micronesian, it is so close to Melanesian that some linguists refuse to separate the two. It has been studied less than the other three branches, and how it got to Micronesia is not clear.

In general, Capell's reconstruction of the history of Austronesian languages agrees with that of Grace. Both men bring the languages out of Asia by way of the Philippines. Whether or not this theory is right, certainly some people followed this route, whatever they spoke—as Chang's archaeological reconstructions and Solheim's comparison of Asiatic and Oceanic pottery indicate.[6] These seafarers, who were at least partly Mongoloid, brought into the Pacific and elsewhere a southern Chinese Neolithic culture with pigs, chickens, and food plants of Southeast Asian origin. Of these generalizations there can be little question. What can be and has been questioned is whether they brought along Austronesian languages too.

I. Dyen, vigorously abetted by G. P. Murdock, believes that they did not. Dyen compared lists of 196 words each from 245 of the estimated 500 Austronesian languages—not including dialects—by means of a computer, making over seven million comparisons. He then calculated the percentages of similarities in each pair of languages, and from the results reclassified the Austronesian phylum. He divides this phylum into two main parts. Part I consists of ten divergent isolated languages or groups of languages, each of which is potentially an independent family. Seven of them have been previously called Melanesian: three from New Guinea, and one each from the Bismarck Archipelago, the Solomon Islands, the New Hebrides, and New Caledonia. A separate language group

[6] Kwang-chih Chang: "Prehistoric and Early Historic Culture Horizons and Traditions in South China," CA, Vol. 5, No. 5 (1964), pp. 359, 368–75. Solheim: "Pottery and the Malayo-Polynesians," CA, Vol. 5, No. 5 (1964), pp. 360, 376–84.

consists of Nauruan and Yapese, which are spoken in Micronesia. Two isolated languages, Atayal in northern Formosa and the language of Enggano, a small island off the southern coast of Sumatra, had previously been listed with Indonesian. (See Map 16, p. 178.)

Part II is the Malayo-Polynesian family, which is split into six subfamilies: (1) *Heonesian,* (2) Chamorro of the Marianas, (3) Palauan, (4) *Hesperonesian,* (5) Formosan, and (6) Moluccan.

Heonesian has seven branches, of which Polynesian is only one. The other six are four language groups of Melanesia and two of Micronesia which have not been given separate listing elsewhere in Dyen's scheme. Hesperonesian consists of seven language groups whittled out of what used to be called Indonesian, including Malay, Malagasy of Madagascar, and Chru of Vietnam.

Dyen's massive feat of linguistic taxonomy, made possible by the miracle of electronics, has greatly complicated the once orderly picture of Mongoloid Vikings from China setting out to sea and colonizing island after island in several directions. By following the well-known linguistic hypothesis that the origin of a group of languages is to be sought in the region of its greatest genetic diversity, Dyen has concluded that the Malayo-Polynesian languages originated somewhere in Melanesia. Murdock has tentatively narrowed their birthplace down to the vicinity of the New Hebrides and the Banks Islands. Grace agrees that this region was a center of linguistic differentiation, but not for the entire phylum. He postulates two such centers, an earlier one in the Philippines and a later one where Dyen and Murdock have placed it.

According to Murdock's reconstruction of Oceanic history, the original speakers of Malayo-Polynesian languages were preagricultural people who lived off the bounty of the sea and certain wild vegetable foods such as sago pith, coconuts, and pandanus fruit. They were skilled navigators and traded widely. During the course of their expansions they picked up agriculture from others, and brought it back. This hypothesis separates race and language as sharply as the Supreme Court divides church and state. It is as ingenious as it is bold, and we will be interested to see how it fares in the future.

Archaeology and the Settlement of the Pacific

SINCE World War II a number of archaeologists working in Melanesia, Micronesia, and Polynesia have turned up useful information derived from the careful excavation of stratified sites, and some interesting Carbon-14 dates, all of which may be of help both to linguists and to physical anthropologists. Other Carbon-14 dates from southern China and the Philippines broaden the picture.[7]

They show that the peoples living on the coast of southern China before and at the time the ancestors of the present Austronesian speakers are supposed to have left there had seagoing vessels by 2000 B.C., and were manufacturing rectangular Neolithic stone axes as late as 994 B.C. The date for a similar Late Neolithic site on the island of Masbate in the Philippines is 754 B.C.

A date of 1527 B.C. obtained from uncalcified oyster shell in Saipan has been questioned because shell may contain inorganic calcium, which makes the date too old. But it is said to be supported by geological evidence. The oldest date for Tinian is A.D. 176, but this was obtained from charcoal taken from four discrete samples belonging to a single cultural level and may or may not have been contaminated. In any case, we cannot be absolutely sure that Micronesia was occupied before the time of Christ.

The oldest date so far recorded from Melanesia is 847 B.C. at a site in New Caledonia representing the oldest occupation of that island. One sample, or reading, from Viti Levu in Fiji gives 46 B.C. as the time the island was first settled. In Samoa, dates of A.D. 9, A.D. 79, and A.D. 109, all taken at sites containing pottery, indicate the first settlement of that region. Dates from the Marquesas, Hawaii, and Easter Island are, respectively, 122 B.C., A.D. 124, and A.D. 400. Many determinations set the arrival of the Maori in New Zealand at about A.D. 1000. On the basis of archaeological evidence alone, Shapiro and Suggs set the initial settlement of the Marquesas, with implications for the islands farther east, at before 100 B.C., a date yet to be confirmed by Carbon-14 study.

Whatever the true dates of the first Polynesian movements into the open Pacific may turn out to be, Shulter's work supports the postulation, on archaeological and technological grounds, of a route via Melanesia. Pottery was made in central Polynesia at the time of the first settlement and then abandoned, and the pottery found in excavations is of Melanesian type. Art motifs, types of fishhooks, and other ethnographic details link the two cultures.

---

[7] R. Shulter Jr.: "Peopling of the Pacific in the Light of Radiocarbon Dating," AP, Vol. 5, No. 2 (1961), pp. 207–12. Shapiro and R. C. Suggs: "New Dates for Polynesian Prehistory," *Man*, Vol. 59, No. 1 (1959), pp. 12–13.

Evidence for the Date of the Initial Peopling of Madagascar

DARTING RAPIDLY from Polynesia to the other periphery of Austronesian languages, we may examine the evidence for the initial peopling of Madagascar by Indonesians. First of all, the Malagasy language contains loan words from both Sanskrit and Bantu, suggesting that Hindu influences had already begun to reach Indonesia before the settlers left their original home in the Philippines, Borneo, or wherever, and that they had visited the East African shore of the Indian Ocean after the Bantu expansion had reached Tanzania. These chronological landmarks do not take us back much before the time of Christ.[8]

Archaeological evidence suggests that the Indonesians may well have arrived later. In a site at Talakay in the southern part of the island, excavators found at the bottom of their trench the egg-shells of a giant bird. This was none other than the extinct flight-less aepyornis, known only from its eggs and skeletons, and from the tales of far-voyaging Arab seamen who described what may have been the same bird. They called it the roc. The Carbon-14 date of this site is 840 ± 80 years ago, or about A.D. 1140.[9] In other island refuges comparable birds have become extinct shortly after the arrival of the first human inhabitants. This discovery seems to support the linguistic evidence cited above. At present there is no reason to believe that Indonesians had colonized Madagascar from one end of the island to the other much before the arrival of Arab and Persian traders, who needed people to trade with. They came after the official beginning of Islam, or A.D. 622.

The Racial Characteristics of the Southern Mongoloids and Australoids

IN THE LAST CHAPTER we had a simple problem: to describe the northern Mongoloids and the American Indians. The only serious complication was posed by the Ainu, who turned out to be basically Caucasoid, as many observers had said nearly a century ago. Our present problem is more complex, as we are now dealing

8 P. Vérin: "Rétrospective et Problèmes de l'Archéologie à Madagascar," AP, Vol. 6, No. 1–2 (1962), pp. 198–218.
9 Vérin: op. cit.

with the interrelationship of the Mongoloids and the Australoids in Southeast Asia, on the islands from Easter Island to Madagascar, and on the Australian continent itself.

Our experience with Africa should have furnished us with some principles for guidance. Like Africa, Southeast Asia and the neighboring islands constitute one of the world's great foci of tropical diseases, and disease is a prime agent of natural selection. Also, Southeast Asia and the islands harbor dwarf populations. But in this region we have something that Africa lacks—an isolated, full-sized, evolutionarily archaic people, the Australian aborigines.

The Australians and the Tasmanians

A B O U T 74,000 Australian aborigines survive today, and they seem to be increasing in numbers after a decline that began with the first European contact. The Tasmanians are extinct in unmixed form. As in the case of the Americas, very few individuals need have been involved in the settling of Australia and Tasmania. The archaeological evidence neither requires nor excludes the theory of a series of invasions to explain its diversity, and the only evidence to support a hypothesis of multiple entries is the geographical distribution of certain racial characteristics.[1]

The Aborigines are people of variable stature, the tallest being those in the far north around Darwin, which is the warmest and dampest region. There the Tiwi reach a mean of 171 centimeters (5 feet 7 inches). They are long-limbed, but not as much so as the Africans who live in a comparable climate. They have neither the lumbar curvature of the Negro nor the straight back of the Mongoloids. In general body build they resemble slender Europeans and the Caucasoids of India. As one moves southward in Australia, this ectomorphic body build gradually changes: legs grow shorter, trunks longer and thicker, and necks shorter. Also, the smooth skins of the northern Aborigines give way to an abundance of body hair which has reminded more than one observer of the Ainu.

The Tasmanians, who lived almost naked in a climate like

[1] A. A. Abbie: "Metrical Characters of a Central Australian Tribe," *Oceania*, Vol. 27, No. 3 (1957), pp. 220-43. W. W. Howells: "Anthropometry of the Natives of Arnhem Land and the Australian Race Problem," PMP, Vol. 16, No. 1 (1937), pp. 1-97. J. B. Birdsell: "The Racial Origins of the Extinct Tasmanians," RQVM, Vol. 2, No. 3 (1949); also YPS (1950), pp. 143-60. N. B. Tindale and Birdsell: "Tasmanoid Tribes in North Queensland," RSAM, Vol. 7, No. 1 (1941), pp. 1-9.

that of England, were short and stocky; but with a mean stature of at least 162 centimeters (5 feet 4 inches). They were far from being dwarfs. One individual measured by a French navigator was 179 centimeters tall (5 feet 10½ inches). Among the Aborigines the men were notably larger and heavier than the women. For example, among the Melville Islanders, the men had a mean weight of 126 pounds; the women of only 96 pounds.

Except for the Tasmanians, who were very dark brown, skin color varies among the Australians from nearly black in the north to a light or medium brown in the south and particularly in the desert. The newborn are quite light and darken after only a few days. Gates believed that one less gene is involved in their skin color than in that of Negroes.[2] Eyes are brown almost without exception, and the hair is black except among some of the desert tribes. There many women and children are blond, whereas the hair on the heads of adult males usually darkens with maturity. This light hair color is not due to mixture, and may have some selective advantage because it reflects sunlight.

Most variable is the form of their hair. The Tasmanians had spiral, Negroid hair, which is found in Australia only among a few coastal tribes, and even there in just a few individuals. Among the Tiwi of Melville Island the few persons with frizzly hair had straight-haired brothers and sisters.

The cranial and facial features of the Aborigines are archaic as well as racial. Their heads are very dolichocephalic, with mean cephalic indices as low as 70. Although the vaults are not low, the skulls are to a certain extent peaked and ridged, rather than rounded. The browridges are the heaviest of any living peoples. The jaws are large, and usually prognathous, and the teeth are large. The eyes are deep-set; the noses wide and most often straight in profile. Although convex noses are common in some of the desert tribes, the nasal tips are very large and often protrude beyond the plane of the nasal skeleton and cartilage. Lips are not usually everted, and the upper lip is often convex.

Various attempts have been made to divide the Australians and Tasmanians into different types that would have come in at different times, but most of the local differences can be explained on the basis of adaptation to the regional variations in climate within a continent. In the rain forest of northeast Queensland on the Atherton Plateau near Cairns live, or formerly lived, some tribes with curly hair and short stature, with a mean of 155 centimeters

2 R. R. Gates: "The Genetics of the Australian Aborigines," AGMG, Vol. 9 (1960), pp. 1–50.

(5 feet 1 inch), like that of the Lake Kivu Pygmies in Africa. Some individuals of this population studied by Gates were actually dwarfs.

It is possible that the earliest invaders of Australia were curly-haired and that some were dwarfs, but otherwise there is no substantial evidence of a series of invasions. A likelier explanation of the marginal distribution of Negroid hair on the peripheries of Australia, including Tasmania, has to do with the ancient relationship between the Australoids and the Mongoloids in Southeast Asia and even in southern China, which must go far back in the Pleistocene to a time earlier than the first peopling of Australia. If we postulate that the Australoids as a subspecies were originally curly-haired, contact with Mongoloids may have introduced the genes for straight hair. According to this theory, peripheral Australoids remained curly-haired, and those who had received the genes for straight hair brought it to Australia later. Although this explanation does not necessarily require multiple invasions, it suggests that gene-flow from Indonesia took place over a considerable period. It may be no coincidence, also, that the curly hair is concentrated in cool damp regions, because matted, curly hair has a function as insulation, as we shall see in Chapter 8.

A lesson learned from our comparison in the last chapter of the American Indians and Mongoloids of Eastern Asia may also be applicable here—that a peripheral people who moved into an uninhabited continent may not be representative of the ancestral race as a whole.

The Papuans and the Melanesians[3]

COMPARED to Australia, New Guinea is a poor place for hunters. The terrain is rugged, the vegetation dense, game is scarce, and the whole central highland region is cool or even chilly. Before the introduction of agriculture, the population away from the coast must have been relatively thin. Not only is the supply of animal food scanty, but mobility is also restricted. We

[3] Howells: "The Racial Elements of Melanesia," PMP, Vol. 20 (1943), pp. 38–49. D. L. Oliver and Howells: "Micro-Evolution: Cultural Elements in Physical Variation," AA, Vol. 59, No. 6 (1957), pp. 965–78. D. R. Swindler: *A Racial Study of the West Nakanai*, MMUM (1962). O. Schlaginhaufen: "Zur Anthropologie der Admiralty-Inseln in Melanesien," BSGA, Vol. 26 (1950), pp. 12–23; "Die Variabilität, geographische Verteilung, und Stellung der Körpergrösse der Eingeborenen Neuirlands," GH, Vol. 1 (1953), pp. 18–28. Gates: "The Melanesian Dwarf Tribe of Aiome, New Guinea," AGMG, Vol. 10, No. 3 (1961), pp. 277–311.

must therefore look upon the interior of New Guinea as a more marginal region than Australia itself.

The non-Melanesian-speaking Papuans are Australoids whose ancestors must have come from the same place and during the same period as the ancestors of the Australian aborigines. Like the Tasmanians and the tribes of the Atherton Plateau, the Papuans have tightly curled hair that can be combed out into an impressive mop. They also differ from the aborigines of Australia in having a high frequency of high-bridged, convex noses. Such noses are not unknown in Australia, but they are mostly limited to the desert tribes. We have seen high-bridged noses, associated with a long upper facial height before, among desert people and mountain people in Western Asia and Arabia, and among American Indians, all of whom are exposed to moderate cold dry air, thin air, or some combination of these. We need not postulate an undemonstrable invasion in order to explain the Papuan nose.

In New Guinea stature goes down with altitude, and more importantly, with temperature. Some of the highland tribesmen are small enough to be called Pygmies, and perhaps they are indeed Pygmies. But if so they are living in the midst of unreduced kinsmen, as is evident by the fact that they look no different from the full-sized Papuans near them. It would be interesting to see how tall the children of these so-called Pygmies would grow to be if they were brought up in the lowlands.

Some of the highland Papuans are also pink-skinned and have light reddish hair. They are not albinos. Among the Gimi tribe and its neighbors in the Fore area, where much medical work has been done on a local nervous ailment, these pink-skinned people constitute about 1 percent of the population.[4] R. R. Gates found an Englishman in the highlands who had blond children by three brown-skinned Papuan wives, but they may have carried the gene for blondism as a recessive.[5] Both in Australia and in New Guinea, then, genes for blondism are present.

The Melanesians of New Guinea differ from the Papuans mainly in that their skin is blacker, they have less rugged or Australian-like facial features, and fewer prominent convex noses. But on other islands the Melanesians themselves vary. The Solomon Islanders are the blackest.

The New Caledonians are thickset and heavy-boned, with heavy browridges and jaws, and some of them also have the Papuan nose. At the same time they are light to medium brown in skin

4 Personal communication from Dr. Jared Diamond.
5 Gates: "Studies in Race Crossing," AGMG,, Vol. 9 (1960), pp. 165–84.

color, quite hairy, and some have blond hair. How much of their blondism is genetic and how much is due to bleaching in salt water is hard to determine.

Pink-skinned individuals with reddish or blond hair are found on Fergusson Island of the D'Entrecasteaux group off the eastern tip of New Guinea. The Fijians, who are the easternmost Melanesians, are well known for their tall stature, powerful build, and frizzly hair, and many of them also have the Papuan nose.

The Southeast Asians and the Indonesians

LET US RETURN to the Southeast Asian mainland, whence the ancestors of some of the people we have been describing must have come. We must also include the principal islands of Indonesia, particularly those west of Wallace's Line, because they were part of Asia during much of the Pleistocene.

The critical geographical division in this area is not between mainland and islands, but between the mountain ridges which extend like fingers southward from Tibet and China on the one hand, and the lowlands and the offshore islands on the other. On the mountain ridges live tribesmen related to those in eastern Tibet and southern China, and physically similar to their kinsmen to the north. These are the Burmese, Miao, Yao, and some of the Laotians and include the "Montagnards" of Vietnam. They have not been in Southeast Asia very long, and are still pushing slowly southward.

Then we come to the Thais and the lowland Laotians, who have been living in Thailand and Laos somewhat longer. A still older ethnic stratum is that of the Vietnamese, the Khmers of Cambodia, and the Mons of Lower Burma; to this category may be added the Indonesians and the Malays. Oldest of all are the food-gathering peoples of two races, Mongoloid and Australoid. The Mongoloid ones are the Yumbri, or People of the Yellow Leaves, in northeastern Siam and Laos; the Sakai of the Malay Peninsula; the Punans of Borneo; the Kubu and Lubu of Sumatra; and probably the Shom Pen of the Nicobar Islands. The Australoid ones are the Negritos of the Philippine Islands, the Semang of the Malay Peninsula; possibly some relict groups in Cambodia; and the Andamanese.

In describing the physical characteristics of these people, let us work backward from the oldest to the most recent, starting

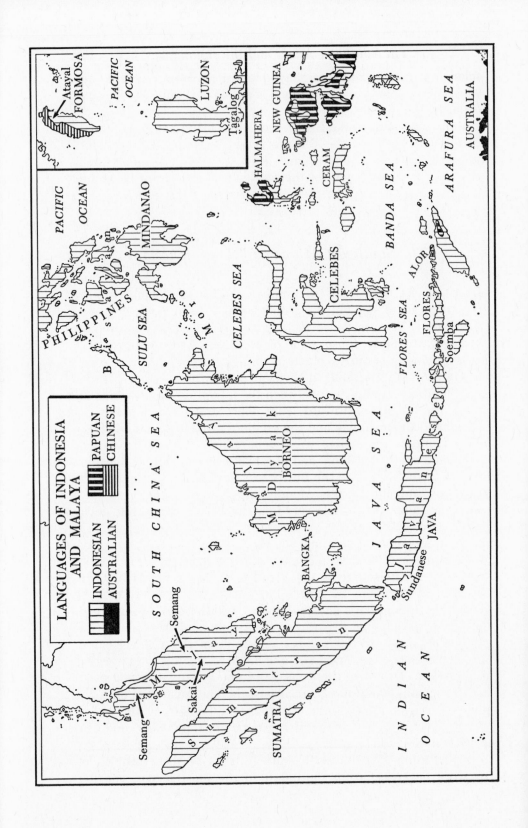

LANGUAGES OF INDONESIA
AND MALAYA

INDONESIAN   PAPUAN

AUSTRALIAN   CHINESE

with the Negritos.[6] Five separate groups of Negritos live on Luzon, and one each on Mindanao and Palawan. All of them live in forested, hilly or mountainous, country. All are agile and quick, like the African Pygmies, and they are expert in tapping water from lianas and collecting vegetable foods from their environment, as well as in hunting small game.

The males have a mean stature of about 147 centimeters (4 feet 10½ inches); their skin color ranges fom yellowish brown to almost black; their hair is tightly curled; and their facial features resemble those of Australian aborigines, without the latter's excessive browridges. Some individual Negritos could be matched on the basis of facial features with individual Australian aborigines.

The Semang of the Malay Peninsula are a little taller than the Negritos, with a mean stature for males of 152 centimeters (5 feet). Their skins are nearly black, and their hair is like that of the Philippine Negritos. Some of them, particularly the women, have an infantile appearance, but others have facial features like those of Australian aborigines.

The Andamanese form three distinct groups: the inhabitants of most of Great Andaman, the Önge of Little Andaman, and the Jarawa of North Sentinel Island and the southern part of Great Andaman. The Great Andamanese are nearly extinct; the Önges are protected from visitors by the Indian government; and most of the Jarawa are still wild and hostile.

All are of about the same size, as far as we know, with mean male statures of about 149 centimeters (4 feet 10½ inches), and all have nearly black skins and the usual tightly curled hair. All are more or less infantile in appearance. The Önges, who spend much time in the water, are fat, particularly the Önge women, who are noted for a combination of lordosis and a development of steatopygia rivaling that of the Hottentots.[7]

All of these Negrito peoples are remnants of the pre-Mongoloid population of Southeast Asia and parts of Indonesia. Some of them, particularly the Great Andamanese, show signs of having mixed, before they became dwarfed, with an early wave of Mongoloids. The next racial tier is that of the food-gathering

---

6 A. L. Kroeber: *Peoples of the Philippines*, (New York: AMNH Handbook No. 8; 1919). E. Genet-Varcin: *Les Negritos de Luçon, L'Anth*, Vol. 8 (1949). J. Wastl: "Beitrag zur Anthropologie der Negrito von Ost-Luzon," *Anthropos*, Vol. 52 (1957), pp. 768–812.

7 E. H. Man: "On the Aboriginal Inhabitants of the Andaman Islands," JRAI, Vol. 12 (1883), Appendix C. Man's measurements were taken on the Great Andamanese. Most of the information on the Önges and Jarawa is derived from photographs.

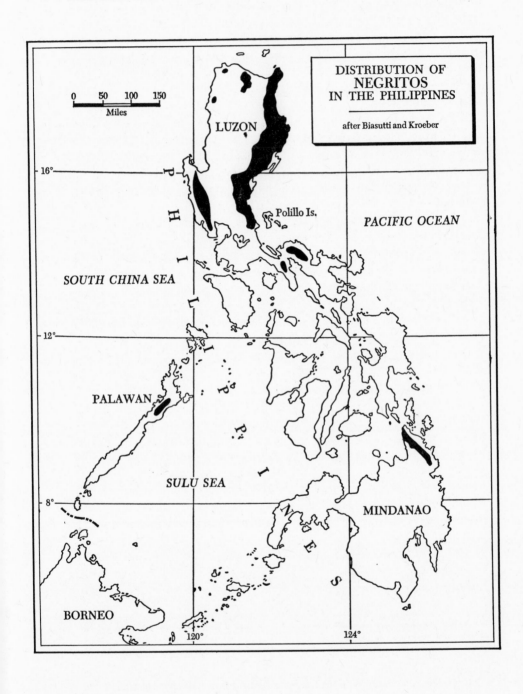

DISTRIBUTION OF
NEGRITOS
IN THE PHILIPPINES

after Biasutti and Kroeber

0   50   100 150
Miles

LUZON

16°

PHILIPPINES

Polillo Is.

PACIFIC OCEAN

SOUTH CHINA SEA

12°

PALAWAN

SULU SEA

8°

MINDANAO

BORNEO

120°   124°

Mongoloids, who are very rare, although, according to local tradition, they were once much more widely spread.

The Yumbri,[8] who hunt tapirs with wooden spears in the forests of northeastern Thailand and Laos, are nearly extinct, and those that have been seen are badly diseased. Photographs of them show a Mongoloid racial type and some of the men have moderately heavy browridges.

The Punans of Borneo are more numerous and in better health and circumstances than the Yumbri because the Punans have established a symbiotic relationship with the agricultural Dyaks comparable to that between Pygmies and Negroes in Africa. They too are fully Mongoloid, and some have convex nasal profiles.[9]

The Sakai or Senoi, as they are sometimes called, are part hunters, part shifting-cultivators. They live in the mountains just south of the Semang in the Malay Peninsula. They are not a homogeneous people. Some are mostly Mongoloid; others show Australoid or Negrito features, particularly wavy or loosely coiled hair.[1]

The Kubu and Lubu are forest-dwellers of north-central Sumatra who exchange their wild forest products, such as fibers and beeswax, for cloth, knives, and the like, by silent trade with cultivators —that is, by leaving offerings at a designated spot, where the cultivators in turn leave their offerings.[2]

The Shom Pen are a "wild" aboriginal people who live in the interior of Great Nicobar. Their racial affinities are still to be established. With the possible exception of these people, as far as we know all the food-gathering and semi-food-gathering peoples we have just named are essentially Mongoloid, and some of them are completely so. The commonly accepted idea that they are all Caucasoids related to the Veddas of Ceylon is a mistake originated by two energetic Swiss cousins, R. and F. Sarasin, over seventy year ago.[3]

The next racial tier consists of the lowland Vietnamese, the Cambodians, the Thais, the Mons of Burma, the Malays, and the Indonesians.[4] These peoples are mostly short, with a mean stature

[8] H. A. Bernatzik: *Die Geister der gelben Blätter*, (Munich: Bruckmann; 1938).

[9] Again we are largely dependent on photographs for our knowledge of the physical appearance of these people.

[1] R. Martin: *Die Inlandstämme der Malayischen Halbinsel* (Jena: Gustav Fischer; 1905). P. Schebesta and V. Lebzelter: "Anthropological Measurements on Semangs and Sakais in Malaya," *Anthropologie*, Vol. 6 (1928).

[2] B. Hagen: *Die Orang Kubu auf Sumatra* (Frankfort: Joseph Baer; 1908).

[3] R. and F. Sarasin: *Die Weddas von Ceylon* (Wiesbaden: C. W. Kreidel's Verlag; 1893).

[4] For a bibliography of Southeast Asia see A. Ducros: "Contribution à l'Anthro-

for males between 157 centimeters and 160 centimeters (5 feet 2 inches to 3 inches); of medium build; yellowish- or brown-skinned; mostly straight-haired; and with features of a general Mongoloid cast, but without excessive facial flatness. Among most of them the Mongolian eye fold is rare. Like the Australoids, many of them have large teeth. In fact, the teeth of the Javanese are among the largest in the world.

Most Australoid in appearance are the Cambodians, who are dark-brown-skinned, broad-nosed, and for the most part have wavy or curly hair. In 2 percent the hair is frizzly. Among them live a small tribe, the Saoch, who might be considered Negritos, as the mean stature of the men is only 153 centimeters and all have chocolate-brown skins and frizzly hair.[5]

At the opposite extreme are the Burmese,[6] who are the most Mongoloid, and the Miaos, who are Mongoloids containing a Caucasoid element. Some of the Miaos have Caucasoid facial features. Their tradition is that they came through northwestern China from a land of snow, where their ancestors wore furs.[7]

The Indonesians who live west of Wallace's Line, the Filipinos, and most of the Formosan aborigines are similar to the less Mongoloid of the Southeast Asians, and less Australoid than the Cambodians. They represent a more or less stable mixture between Mongoloid and Australoid elements, with local variations. The Atayal tribe of northeastern Formosa, however, are morphologically different from the others, in an Ainu-like direction.

In eastern Indonesia, east of Wallace's Line, from Lombok to the islands off the western end of New Guinea, the racial situation is different.[8] Some of the inhabitants are Negritos; others resemble Papuans. The Mongoloid element is minor. Racially these islands belong more with Melanesia than with Indonesia. This fact may help to explain the frizzly hair found among a few aborigines on

---

pologie des Miaos (d'après les Documents du Dr. Olivier)," BSAP, Vol. 6, No. 3 (1964), pp. 461–76. R. M. White: *Anthropometric Survey of the Armed Forces of the Republic of Vietnam* (Natick, Mass.: U.S. Army; 1964); *Anthropometric Survey of the Royal Thai Armed Forces* (Natick, Mass.: U.S. Army; 1964). G. Olivier: *Les Populations du Cambodge* (Paris: Masson et Cie; 1956). J. M. Andrews IV: "Evolutionary Trends in Body Build (Thailand)," PMP, Vol. 20 (1943), pp. 102–21. L. Oschinsky: "Races of Burma," AJPA, Vol. 15, No. 3 (1957), pp. 440–1.

5 Olivier: op. cit.
6 Oschinsky: "Races of Burma."
7 Ducros: op. cit.
8 A. A. Mendes Corrêa: *Timor Português*, MSAE, Vol. 1 (1944). W. Keers: "An Anthropological Survey of the Eastern Little Sundra Island"; "The Negritos of the Eastern Little Sunda Islands"; "The Proto-Malay of the Netherland East Indies," KVII, No. 26 (1948).

the northern coast of Australia. The trepang fishermen who visit them from time to time and seek the company of their women are mostly from Halmahera, and many Halmaherans have frizzly hair.

Madagascar

THE PEOPLES of Madagascar are divided into tribes and clans which speak related languages and are more or less culturally uniform, except for their means of livelihood. In the drier coastal plain of the west and southwest they raise cattle, and in the hilly country they practice terraced agriculture like that of Southeast Asia. As we have stated previously, their ancestors came from Indonesia over a millennium and a half ago and picked up African passengers on the way. At the time of their first arrival, probably there was still a considerable Capoid element in East Africa. Also, numerous Arab and Persian traders have been in Madagascar at least since the rise of Islam, over twelve centuries ago. As none of these peoples were noted for celibacy, one would expect the living inhabitants of the island to be descended from all five subspecies of man.

Although a recent estimate makes the peoples of Madagascar about two thirds African,[9] they have sorted themselves out racially to a certain extent. The Hovas, who are a ruling class, live in the highlands and are the most nearly Mongoloid, although many have frizzly hair. The coastal people are mostly Negro. These distributions parallel those seen in other parts of the world where Negroes and Mongoloids coexist in varied terrain. This is due to the Negro's superior tolerance of damp heat and malaria, and to the Mongoloid's predilection for mountains and thin air.

Polynesians and Micronesians

WE HAVE REVIEWED the attempts of several linguists and linguistically oriented ethnographers to explain the distribution of languages in the Pacific and, by so doing, to trace the movements

[9] R. Singer, O. E. Budtz-Olsen, P. Brain, and J. Saugrain: "Physical Features, Sickling, and Serology of the Malagasy of Madagascar," AJPA, Vol. 15, No. 1 (1957), pp. 91–124.

of the first settlers. At this point our only task is to describe the living Polynesians and Micronesians, in that order.[1]

Much fantasy has been shown in attempts to explain the racial origins of the Polynesians. Such handsome and generous people surely must have had European ancestors, reasoned nineteenth-century navigators and twentieth-century refugees from the clang of streetcars and the dunning of tax collectors. However, this ethnocentric rationalization is supported neither by local archaeology, which we have reviewed, nor by a study of what is left of the Polynesians themselves. The Polynesians are just as clearly a part of the Mongoloid-Australoid clinal world as are the Formosans, the Filipinos, or the Balinese, with more of the Australoid element in evidence than among some of the latter. As one would expect of island people scattered over a vast ocean, the Polynesians differ physically from island to island, particularly in such features as stature, skin color, the cephalic index, hair form, and the frequency of Mongolian eye folds, but on the whole they are a single people. Most of them are of medium stature, with means of about 170 centimeters (5 feet 7 inches), although some members of royal families are very tall. They are heavy people, and run to fat. Their trunks are long, their limbs heavily muscled, and their ankles rarely slender. Their skins are of various shades of brown, depending to a certain extent on exposure to the sun. Their facial features are variable but reach no extremes, which may be one reason why they appear so pleasing. Their hair ranges from loosely curled to straight. The men have beards but little body hair, and the women's head hair grows to considerable length.

The Micronesians are more variable than the Polynesians and are usually smaller. They are not only shorter, with mean statures ranging from 161 to 164 centimeters (5 feet 3 inches to 5 feet 5

[1] L. R. Sullivan: "A Contribution to Samoan Somatology," MBM, Vol. 8, No. 2 (1921), pp. 79–98; "A Contribution to Tongan Somatology," MBM, Vol. 8, No. 4 (1922), pp. 233–60; "Marquesan somatology, with Comparative notes on Samoa and Tonga," MBM, Vol. 9, No. 2 (1923), pp. 141–249. P. H. Buck: "Maori Somatology," PSJ, Vol. 31, No. 121 (1922), pp. 37–44; No. 123 (1922), pp. 145–53; No. 124 (1922), pp. 159–70; No. 128 (1923), pp. 189–99. C. Wissler: "Observations on Hawaiian Somatology," MBM, Vol. 9, No. 4 (1927), pp. 263–342. L. C. Dunn: *An Anthropometrical Study of Hawaiians of Pure and Mixed Blood*, PMP, Vol. 11, No. 3 (1928). H. L. Shapiro: "The Physical Characters of the Society Islanders," MBM, Vol. 9, No. 4 (1930), pp. 275–311; "The Physical Relationships of the Easter Islanders," BPMB, Vol. 160 (1940), pp. 24–30; "Physical Differentiation in Polynesia," PMP, Vol. 20 (1943), pp. 3–8. Shapiro and Buck: "The Physical Characters of the Cook Islanders," MBM, Vol. 12, No. 1 (1936), pp. 1–35. E. E. Hunt, Jr.: "A View of Somatology and Serology in Micronesia," AJPA, Vol. 8, No. 2 (1950), pp. 157–83. K. Hasebe: *The Natives of the South Sea Archipelago* (in Japanese), JSK, Vol. 1 (1938), pp. 1–35. H. Utinomi: *Bibliography of Micronesia*, edited and revised by O. A. Bushnell (Honolulu: University of Hawaii Press; 1952).

inches), but are less inclined to fat. A few have frizzly hair, and others have more Mongoloid facial features than the Polynesians do. These differences may be explained in two ways. They may reflect more recent ties with both Melanesia and the Philippines than the Polynesians had. And second, most of the Micronesian islands are so small that rapid selective adaptation and genetic drift may have accentuated local differences. In some of the larger islands, physical differences between social classes may be seen. In Yap, where there are nine classes, the people of the two lowest, consisting of landless tenant farmers, are shorter and more muscular than the others, and have straighter hair, broader jaws, and broader noses. What these differences mean is not clear.

Conclusion

SOUTHERN CHINA, Southeast Asia, and those Indonesian islands which were joined to the continent during the glacial periods of low sea level, constitute the homeland of the Australoid subspecies. Australoids were in contact from remote antiquity with Mongoloids living to the north of them and there has always been the possibility of gene flow between the two races.

At the end of the Pleistocene, Mongoloids pushed southward, creating clinal populations and crowding peripheral Australoids out to sea. Before or during this period of close contact, some of the Australoids became dwarfs. In fact, some may have become dwarfed after genetic contact with Mongoloids. Mixture between Mongoloids and Australoids, both dwarfed and full-sized, produced a new racial element that was more resistant to tropical diseases than were the Mongoloids alone. The end product was the Melanesians and comparable people in India whom we have yet to study. The parallelism with Africa, both in history and in the physical results, is evident.

Polynesians, Micronesians, and Indonesians, as well as Melanesians, are all of mixed Mongoloid-Australoid origin. Some show one set of features to a greater degree than the other, depending on where they have gone and what conditions they have met. The peoples of Madagascar, although Indonesian in speech and culture, have absorbed both African and Western Asian elements and are thus descended from all five subspecies.

7

Greater India

O F ALL THE PENINSULAS and subcontinents of Asia, that of India is the most complicated geographically, racially, and culturally. Once the most precious and glittering jewel in the British crown, it includes the present political units of India, Pakistan, Nepal, Bhutan, Sikkim, and Ceylon.

Three fourths the size of China, its area is almost 1,700,000 square miles, with a distance of over 2,000 miles from the northern border of Kashmir to Cape Comorin, in the south, and a spread from east to west of 2,300 miles. On its landward side it is surrounded by mountains, including the world's highest, and there are few passes. On the western frontier, desert sweeps from mountains to sea. On the east the Arakan Mountains of Burma are fronted by an intricate network of shifting channels and swampy ground. Except for Bombay, the seacoast is almost without harbors, and a long sea voyage lies between India and any other major center of population and civilization. Isolation has not prevented India from being invaded, but it has screened the invaders and limited their numbers. Once inside the barriers of mountains and sea, they have found a wide variety of terrain and climates, broad plains for some groups to expand on, and inaccessible refuges for others to hide in. India's variety caters to nearly all racial adaptations, cultures, and tastes. No invader has ever been able to homogenize India, and it is unlikely that any ever will.

Geography and Climate

THE MOST POPULOUS PART of India and the most accessible is the great Indo-Gangetic plain, formed by sediments washed down from both the Himalayas and the southern plateau. The Himalayas are new, sharply ridged mountains, and the southern "hills," which rise to 5,000 feet, are old, eroded mountains like the Appalachians. Each furnishes its own variety of refuges for Caucasoid, Australoid, and Mongoloid peoples. The open plain, however, is almost exclusively Caucasoid country.

Like Southeast Asia, India is a part of the Oriental faunal region, but the two do not have exactly the same animals. For example, only India has lions, and only Southeast Asia has orangs and gibbons. The faunal difference is to a certain extent a function of rainfall. Although India contains the wettest weather station on earth, Cherrapunji in the Khasi Hills, it is much drier than Southeast Asia. Rain forests are found only along the southwesterly coast, particularly in the Cardamon Hills, and in southern Ceylon. Monsoon forests, characterized by heavy summer rain, cover the Malabar Coast on the east side of the peninsula; northern Ceylon; the lowlands of the lower Ganges; and a strip of land known as the Terai which extends just south of the Himalayan foothills, and lies mostly in Nepal. The rest of the subcontinent is for the most part drier, with summer rain of varying quantity and reliability, and desert. These variations, along with differences in altitude, provide a cover of many different kinds of vegetation. Nearly everywhere, what rain there is falls mostly or wholly in summer, as in China and Southeast Asia, but west of the Indus and in Kashmir are semiarid regions with the winter rainfall characteristic of the Caucasoid lands to the west.

During the Pleistocene the Himalayas, like the Alps, were glaciated four times, with three interglacial periods in between. In southern India these glaciations were matched by pluvials, which were wetter than the present climates. The interpluvials, however, were more like those of today. At the end of the Pleistocene the climate dried, the landscape eroded, and present conditions arose.[1] At that time a number of Indian mammals, comprising the so-called Indo-Malayan fauna, moved into Southeast Asia, down the Malay Peninsula, and into Java and its neighboring

[1] V. D. Krishnaswamy: "Stone Age India," BASI, No. 3 (1947), pp. 11–58.

islands. At the same time, or even earlier, this eastward movement was paralleled by the penetration of certain Palearctic and Ethiopian species from the west and north. Among them were the cheetah, the wild ass, the wild sheep, the wild goat, and the wolf. Whether these faunal movements in and out of India, both in an eastward direction, included *Homo sapiens* is an open question.

The Prehistory of India[2]

THIS QUESTION cannot be answered, nor can the greater question of whether during the Pleistocene India was Caucasoid or Australoid territory, or a combination of both, be answered, until someone discovers the remains of fossil man in India. Up to the present the subcontinent represents the widest and most vital gap in our geographical coverage of this subject. At the moment we can only draw inferences from the archaeological record.

This record goes back at least to the second interglacial period, in sites both north and south of the Indo-Gangetic plain, which has been silted in since. In these sites two cultural sequences have been found. One is a chopper–chopping-tool sequence called Sohan, after a site in the Punjab. It began with pebble and core tools and large coarse unretouched flakes. As time passed, the pebble and core tools diminished in numbers and the flake tools improved. During the third interglacial these became Levallois flakes, some with faceted striking platforms. During the fourth and last Himalayan glaciation they became further refined into long, parallel-sided or pointed flakes.

The second sequence is that of hand axes, comparable to those made in Europe, Western Asia, and Africa. In one site in the Narmanda Valley, in Madhya Pradesh, Central India—which has been studied by A. P. Khatri—Sohan pebble tools lay under hand axes that either evolved out of them or were produced by cultural diffusion from the west. These hand axes then evolved in the same sequence and forms as in the other regions, and were gradually discontinued during the third interglacial, when the archaeological dichotomy of India disappeared. The situation was the same as in

2 Krishnaswamy: op. cit. A. P. Khatri: "A Century of Prehistoric Research in India," AP, Vol. 6 (1962) pp. 169–85; "Mahadevian: An Oldowan Pebble Culture of India," AP, Vol. 6 (1962), pp. 186–96. H. D. Sankalia: "Middle Stone Age Culture in India and Pakistan," *Science*, Vol. 146, No. 3642 (1964), pp. 365–75. A. H. Dani: "Sanghao Cave Excavation, the first Season: 1963," APak, Vol. 1, No. 1 (1964), pp. 1–50.

Western Europe, where the Clactonian-Tayacian-Levalloisian sequence coexisted with the hand-axe tradition, and where the two eventually merged. The Sohan, hand-axe, and Levalloisian industries could only have come from the west, in that order, and only the first effectively crossed Movius' Line into Southeast Asia, where it evolved in its own way, as stated earlier.

Later on, at some unknown period, a blade and burin culture was introduced to the neighborhood of Bombay. This resembled the "Aurignacian" of Western Asia but was probably later, as it was in Africa. Mesolithic industries of a generally Capsian or Wilton-like type began all over India in postglacial times and lasted in some out-of-the-way areas until at least 500 B.C.

Skeletons of India

WITH THIS Mesolithic industry were found, at long last, the oldest skeletons India has yielded: a series of seven from Gujarat, descriptions of four of which have been published.[3] Although the Mesolithic culture lasted a long time in some places, these skeletons are probably of quite early date, as they were buried without pottery. One male was 5 feet 7 inches (170 centimeters) tall; one female was 5 feet 4 inches (162 centimeters). The bones of their limbs were slender; their lower arms and shins moderately elongated; their skulls long and narrow, with a combination of Caucasoid and Australoid features.

The Bronze Age civilization of the Indus Valley and neighboring regions is racially documented by fifteen skulls from Mohenjo-Daro, eighty-six from Harappa, and seven from Lotha in Gujarat.[4] They show a population divided into several distinct types. In both Mohenjo-Daro and Harappa, two kinds of dolichocephals were found, both essentially Caucasoid. One is a craggy, often aquiline variety resembling somewhat the Sumerian skulls from Eridu and the "Nordics" from Tepe Hissar in Iran. The other kind is a Gracile Mediterranean, more like the Natufians of Palestine and the North

[3] I. Karvé and G. M. Kurulkar: "Human Bones Discovered So Far," *Preliminary Report on the Third Gujarat Prehistoric Expedition* (Bombay: Times of India Press; 1945).

[4] Guha and P. C. Basu: "Report on the Human Remains Excavated at Mohenjo-Daro in 1928–29," in *Further Excavations at Mohenjo-Daro. P. Gupta*, P. C. Basu, and A Datta: *Human Skeletal Remains from Harappa*, Memoir No. 9 (Calcutta: Anthropological Survey of India; 1962). B. K. Chatterjee and G. D. Kumar: *Comparative Study and Racial Analysis of the Human Remains of Indus Valley Civilization with Particular Reference to Harappa* (Calcutta: B. K. Chatterjee; 1963).

African Capsians. These two Caucasoid types occur in both sexes, and at all periods.

Large, massive brachycephals, variously Mongoloid- and Armenoid-looking, are rare, but occur both early and late. In the later levels at Harappa, large-brained brachycephals of both sexes, with narrow faces and noses, were found, along with a group of smaller-brained, dolichocephalic, narrow-faced women. Both were buried in jars. Most of these people were fairly tall, with statures ranging from 5 foot 6 inches to 5 foot 9 inches in the males, and the females considerably shorter. The molar teeth of all of them had European, not Australoid, dimensions. On the whole the Australoid element was little in evidence, although it was not entirely absent.

The seven skulls from Gujarat are sub-brachycephalic, as are the modern Gujaratis, and show no resemblance to the earlier Mesolithic skulls of the same region.

This material may be interpreted in two different ways. The first is that northwest India was invaded several times from the west and northwest. The second is that Harappa, being a huge city, was inhabited by people of different morphological types drawn from local enclaves in the surrounding countryside, just as in any large city of India today. In any event, when the Aryan invaders arrived a few centuries later, they found the country already racially complex and the northwest, at least, essentially Caucasoid.

But this generalization need not apply to eastern and southern India. The Neolithic cultures of those regions, probably not much older than the beginning of the Bronze Age of the Indus Valley seems to have been introduced from Southeast Asia, judging from the distribution of stone axes and from a comparison of their types.[5] These are believed to have come in two waves, one before and the other after 1500 B.C. Although we have no skeletons to prove or disprove it, it seems likely that the spread of these axes marked the arrival of Australoid-Mongoloid mixed peoples in eastern and southern India, and particularly of the Munda-speaking tribes of Chota Nagpur, whose languages are related to others in Burma and Cambodia.

A further complication is the recent discovery in southern India of a number of Neolithic sites of cattle herders, dated by Carbon-14 at between about 2000 B.C. and 750 B.C.[6] There are still Dravidian-speaking cattle herders of fairly low caste in the same region with a

5 E. C. Worman, Jr.: *"The 'Neolithic' Problem in the Prehistory of India,"* JWAC, Vol. 39, No. 6 (1949), pp. 181–201.

6 F. R. Allchin: *Neolithic Cattle Keepers of Southern India* (Cambridge: Cambridge University Press; 1963).

tradition that their ancestors were warriors. The Todas, a much-studied tribe of dairymen living at Ootacamund in the Nilgiri Hills, may be a culturally specialized branch of this group. The reports on the skeletal material found in these cattle-herding sites have not yet been published.

The Languages of Greater India[7]

ENVIRONMENTALLY, racially, and culturally Greater India, as defined in the beginning of this chapter, is the most complex segment of the earth's surface of equal size. Yet linguistically it is relatively simple, even when compared to such smaller areas as California, the Caucasus, and southern China. The reasons for this seeming paradox are not far to seek. Much of India is covered by flat plains on which no geographical barriers to linguistic spread exist, particularly among people who have been using wheeled vehicles for several millennia. Moreover, during these same millennia the plains have been the seats of high civilizations, and the languages of high civilizations have a way of being taken over by tribes and bands of simple hunters and gatherers who have found refuge in the forests and hills. In this area are spoken languages belonging to six mutually unrelated linguistic entities ranging in taxonomic magnitude from families to isolated languages. They are Indo-Iranian; Dravidian; Munda, Khasi, and Nicobarese; the Sinitic languages of the Himalayan borderlands and Assam; Burushaski; and Andamanese. (See Map 13, p. 163.)

The Indo-Iranian Languages

THE INDIGENOUS Indo-Iranian languages of Greater India are spoken by nearly two thirds of its five and a half million people. They are divided into two main subfamilies, Iranian and Indic. Iranian languages are spoken in West Pakistan by Pathans (Pushtu) and Baluchis. Indic languages are spoken throughout most of the northern and central portions of the subcontinent south of the Himalayas, as well as in Ceylon. Indic is split into Dardic and Sanskritic, the difference between them being that

[7] Trager: op. cit. Meillet and Cohen: op. cit. Sebeok: op. cit.

only the latter is derived from Sanskrit, as the Romance languages are derived from Latin.

The Dardic languages include Kafiri, spoken in northwest West Pakistan as well as in neighboring portions of Afghanistan, and Kashmiri. The Sanskritic languages are divided in three groups: western, central and eastern. The principal western Sanskritic languages are Sindhi, Rajasthani, Gujarati, and Marathi. The languages of the gypsies of Europe and Western Asia are also derived from this group. The central group consists of Punjabi, spoken not only in the Punjab itself but also elsewhere by the ubiquitous Sikhs; Hindi, including its Muslim branch, Urdu; and Pahari, a group of mountain languages of Nepal, one of which is Nepali. The western group is comprised of Bengali, Bihari, Oriya (of Orissa), and Assamese in India proper. The Sinhalese of Ceylon, spoken by the descendants of seaborne immigrants from northeast India, probably belongs in this group also, and the aboriginal Veddas of Ceylon speak a form of Sinhalese.

Dravidian

THE DRAVIDIAN LANGUAGES, spoken by about one fifth of the people of Greater India, are patently older than Indo-European in India, but we do not know how old, or whether they were spoken by the Indus Valley Bronze Age people. Attempts have been made to relate them to other families, particularly Finno-Ugrian and the extinct Elamite, but without notable success. The Dravidian languages may be divided geographically into three groups; southern, northeastern, and northwestern.

In the southern two thirds of the peninsula, four languages spoken by people of all castes from Brahmins on down, and by tribal groups as well, share a single terrain. These are Kannada (Kannarese), Telugu, Malayalam, and Tamil. the last-named being spoken also in parts of Ceylon. In the forested mountains between Kerala and Madras states and on the coast between the Malayalam and Kannada speech areas, a number of other, relict Dravidian languages are spoken by the Todas, the Tulu, and others.

The northeastern Dravidian languages are, on the contrary, fragmented, scattered, and surrounded by languages of other families. Their speakers are casteless, remnant peoples, like the Gonds and Oraons. Northwestern Dravidian consists of only one language, Brahui, spoken in Baluchistan by people who live among the Baluchis.

In historic times Dravidian has been yielding ground to Indo-European. Marathi has pushed Kannada southward, and the Gonds who dwell on the plains have adopted Indo-European, whereas those clinging to existence in the wooded hills still speak Dravidian.

Munda

THE MUNDA languages which constitute a subfamily of the Austro-Asiatic phylum, are spoken by about 5 million tribal people scattered in small groups along the northern edge of the Deccan plateau. The most numerous and geographically unified are the Santal, the Ho, and the Munda. Smaller groups live in linguistic islands elsewhere.

In pre-Aryan times, Munda-speakers may once have reached the foothills of the Himalayas. Pressed between Indic and Dravidian, these languages have lost ground, but are in no immediate danger of extinction. That they were already spoken in India when the Aryans arrived is indicated by the presence of Munda loan words in Sanskrit. Some writers believe that they were brought to India from the east by the Neolithic settlers whose axe types have been traced to Indochina, and a remote connection with Mon-Khmer has been postulated.

Mon-Khmer, Burushaski, and Sinitic Languages

MON-KHMER LANGUAGES, which constitute an Austronesian subfamily, are spoken by the Khasis of the Khasi Hills of Bengal, south of the Brahmaputra River. This region is a cool, wet plateau. These languages are also spoken in the Nicobar Islands, which are administered by India, as are the Andamans.

There remain for consideration here only Burushaski of Hunza in northernmost West Pakistan, which was discussed in Chapter 3, and a considerable number of Sinitic languages spoken along the southern slopes of the Himalayas in northwestern India, Nepal, Sikkim, the Northeast Frontier Area, the Garo Hills, and eastern

Assam. They all belong to the family usually designated as Tibeto-Burman, and to four of the nine Sinitic families postulated by T. Sebeok: Bodo-Naga$_1$-Kachin; Naga$_2$-Chin, Gyarung-Misir, and Tibetan.

The Living Peoples of Greater India[8]

GREATER INDIA is the meeting point of the three Eurasiatic subspecies: the Caucasoid, the Australoid, and the Mongoloid. Its variety of terrain and climate has offered opportunities for peoples of many economies, languages, religions, and social classes to pursue separate lives for millennia, and many of them still do so. In the absence of fossil skeletal material that might serve as a racial guide, we can only divide the peoples of India, for purposes of study, into a combination of economic and geographical groups.

The most numerous and the latest to enter the subcontinent are the Indo-Iranian-speaking peoples of the north. The next oldest are probably the Dravidian-speaking Indians of caste, who except for the Brahui, whom we mentioned in Chapter 3, live in the south. Both the Indo-Iranian speakers and the Dravidian speakers are primarily Caucasoid, and the Dravidian speakers resemble ancient Southwest Asians such as the Natufians.

Mongoloids of Tibetan origin have been living in the Himalayan borderlands for a long time—we do not know how long—because they have been kept from moving into the lowlands by their

8 Guha: *Racial Affinities of the Peoples of India.* G. T. Bowles: "Linguistic and Racial Aspects of the Munda Problem," PMP, Vol. 20 (1943), pp. 81–101. N. D. Wijeserka: *The People of Ceylon* (Colombo: M. D. Gunasena & Co.; 1949). D. N. Majumdar: *Races and Cultures of India,* 2nd ed. (Lucknow: Universal Publishers; 1950). A. K. Mitra: "Physical Anthropology of the Muslims of Bengal," BDAI, Vol. 1, No. 2 (1952), pp. 79–104; "The Riang of Tripura," BDAI, Vol. 5, No. 2 (1956), pp. 21–120. S. S. Sarkar: *The Aboriginal Races of India* (Calcutta: Bookland; 1954). Sarkar, ed.: *A Physical Survey of the Kadar of Kerala,* Memoir No. 6 (Calcutta: Dept. of Anthropology, Government of India; (1959). Chatterjee and Kumar: "Racial Affinities of the Urali of Travancore and Cochin States," *Anthropologist,* Vol. 3, No. 1–2 (1956), pp. 1–22; "Somatometric and Somatoscopic Observations and Their Affinities of the Manuans of Travancore-Cochin," JASC, Vol. 28, No. 2 (1957), pp. 1–18; "A Comparative Study of the Somatometric and Somatoscopic Observations and their Racial Affinities of the Paliyans and the Malapantarams of Travancore-Cochin," JSAC, Vol. 28, No. 2 (1957), pp. 19–42. Coon: "An Anthropogeographic Excursion Around the World." Olivier: *Anthropologie des Tamouls du Sud de l'Inde* (Paris: École Française d'Extreme-Orient: 1961). H. W. Stoudt: *The Physical Anthropology of Ceylon,* CNMES, Pub. No. 2, 1961. Gates: "The Asurs and Birhors of Chota Nagpur," in T. N. Madan and G. Sarana, eds.: *Indian Anthropology* (Bombay: Asia Publishing House; 1962), pp. 163–84; *The Totos, a Sub-Himalayan Mongoloid Tribe,* MM, No. 5 (1963).

vulnerability to tropical heat and tropical diseases. Their presence in India goes back at least to Harappa.

A fourth element in the population is that of the Munda-speaking peoples of the Chota Nagpur Hills, and other tribes who resemble them physically but speak languages of other families. These people are patently descended from migrants from Southeast Asia who came bearing Neolithic slash-and-burn agriculture probably during the second millenniun B.C. According to the Vedic literature, they seem to have been there when the Aryans arrived, but whether they preceded the Dravidians in the south is open to question. The Khasis of Assam are also part of this group.

There remains a fifth element for which no antecedents or connections can be postulated. They are the hunters and gatherers, the true primitives pushed and driven into deep forests and hilly country both in the Indian Peninsula and in Ceylon. Knowing the tortoise-like pace of ethnic and cultural change in India in the past, we have every right to suppose that these people inhabited India long before any of the others arrived.

The Food Gatherers

IN SURVEYING all these various ethnic layers of peoples, we shall begin with the hunters and gatherers and with the Veddas in particular. Only a few hundred unmixed Veddas are left in Ceylon, and of them even fewer are still hunters. Four hundred years ago the Veddas were the sole inhabitants of much of the forested interior of the northern half of the island and conducted travelers through their territory from one tribal boundary to another.[9] Early Sinhalese accounts state that there were two kinds of aborigines in Ceylon, who differed in skin color. Even now, the living Veddas are divided into clans, some of which have paler skins than the others.[1]

The Veddas are small, slender people, with a mean stature for adult males of 157 centimeters (5 feet 1½ inches). They are as lithe and mobile as African Pygmies and equally adept at gliding through the jungle. But they are in no sense dwarfs. Racially they are primarily Caucasoid, but some of them have a partly Australoid

[9] C. G. and B. Z. Seligman: *The Veddas* (Cambridge: Cambridge University Press; 1911).
[1] Coon: "An Anthropogeographic Excursion Around the World."

appearance, particularly in the upper nasal region. Some physical anthropologists have invented a race in their name, the Veddoid, and have seen it as a major substratum in Indonesia, Southeast Asia, and southern Arabia. In our opinion the Veddas represent an ancient mixture of Caucasoid and Australoid peoples who have been subjected to local environmental influences, but the Caucasoid traits are the more evident of the two.

On the mainland, "Veddoid" tribes are legion. Few have been studied anthropometrically. The Uralis of Kerala are primarily Australoid. The Birhors of Chota Nagpur lean more to the Caucasoid side. None of these peoples merit the name Negrito in any sense. Yet, because of the existence of the Kadar,[2] the term Negrito has arisen time and time again in the literature of Indian physical anthropology. The Kadar are a refugee people who inhabit the rain forest of the Anaimalai Hills in Kerala State. In 1941 they numbered 566. They are root-diggers, honey-gatherers, and collectors of small game; technologically they are extremely primitive. Their system of marriage is of a rare type, found also among the Arabs, in which a man marries his paternal uncle's daughter. Unlike the Arabs, they practice both polygyny and polyandry. Their genealogies indicate that they are not a single unit genetically but a collection of such units, some of which are so inbred that hands with six fingers are common.

A minority of the Kadar are short, chocolate-skinned, and frizzly-haired. Others are taller, have wavy or curly hair, and are patently Australoid. Still others who claim to be Kadar are largely Caucasoid, like the outcastes living among the caste Hindus of the lowlands. Obviously the Kadar are a composite people who have taken in refugees from time to time but whose original genetic composition has not been obliterated by these additions.

The frizzly hair characteristic of some Kadar has been examined in two laboratories.[3] In both it has been found to be closest to that of the Australian aborigines, and almost Mongoloid in coarseness.[4]

The Kadar are not typical of the tribal peoples of southern India. Mongoloid-Australoid combinations are also found among the Munda-speaking peoples of north-central India, who constitute the second element in the population of the subcontinent.

2 U. R. von Ehrenfels: *Kadar of Cochin* (Madras: University of Madras Press; 1952).
3 A. R. Bannerjee: "Hair," in Sarkar, ed.: *A Physical Survey of the Kadar of Kerala*, pp. 37–49.
4 O. H. Duggins and M. Trotter: "Hair from a Kadar Woman of India," AJPA, Vol. 17, No. 2 (1959), pp. 95–8.

The Austro-Asiatic-speaking Tribes

CONCENTRATED in the Chota Nagpur Hills of southern Bihar State and scattered in small villages elsewhere, live about five and a half million people who speak languages of the Ho-Munda-Santal group, which are related to the languages spoken by the Khmers of Cambodia and the Mons of southern Burma.[5] Some of them are slash-and-burn cultivators; others have taken up paddy-rice farming. Physically they resemble the Cambodians more than any other population so far studied. The men have a mean stature of 159 centimeters (5 feet 2½ inches). These people are dolichocephalic, have small heads, and are generally dark brown in skin color. Their hair form ranges from straight to very curly, but is for the most part wavy. They have broad nasal roots; alveolar prognathism is usually present; their beards are scanty and their body hair slight; and a minority have epicanthic eye folds and shovel-shaped incisors. Very few individuals among them look predominantly Mongoloid, and others, with thick lips and curly hair, look almost Melanasian. The majority, however, are a more or less homogeneous blend of Australoid and Mongoloid, with only a minor Mongoloid element visible. Other tribes of this same racial composition are the Asuras, who are hereditary ironworkers; the Oraon, who speak Dravidian; the Marias; and some of the Gonds.

The Khasis, who are the indigenous peoples of the Khasi Hills, speak a language of the same family, practice a similar kind of agriculture, and apparently also came to India from Southeast Asia at some unknown period as Neolithic cultivators. Unlike the Ho, the Munda, and the Santal, they live at an altitude of over 5,000 feet in cloudy, rainy, chilly country. Although they are no taller than the Munda-speakers they have longer trunks and shorter legs, larger heads, longer and broader faces, and longer, narrower noses. Their skin color is light brown with a yellowish or reddish cast; their hair is straight or slightly wavy. Sixty-five percent of them have epicanthic eye folds, and 82 percent have shoveled incisors. They are, in short, predominantly Mongoloid, with a minor Australoid element. Some of them look very much like Formosan aborigines.

We have no reason to believe that the ancestors of the Khasis who migrated to India were any different racially from the ancestors of the Munda-speaking peoples, and it would appear that

[5] Guha: *Racial Affinities of the Peoples of India.* Bowles: op. cit.

climatic influences and diseases had sorted out their descendants
into a primarly Australoid and a primarily Mongoloid population.
To the west of the Khasi Hills are the Garo Hills, at half the altitude
of the former plateau. Their inhabitants, the Garo, who speak a
Tibetan type of language, are also a Mongoloid-Australoid blend,
but they are more Australoid than the Khasis, with darker skins
and curlier hair. The difference between the two peoples may well
be due to the presence or absence of malaria, as will be explained
in Chapter 9.

The Dravidians of Caste

IN SOUTHERN INDIA a little over 100 million people speak
five Dravidian languages: Telugu, Tamil, Tulu, Kannara, and
Malayalam. Most of these people are Hindus, but some are Christians or Muslims. Whatever their religion, they observe the endogamous marital rules of caste. This generalization also includes
the Harijans, or outcastes.

Some 5 million other southern Indians speak Dravidian languages too, but they are aboriginal tribesmen with whose racial
characteristics we have already dealt.

In the judgment of most competent observers, the Dravidians
of caste do not seem to be indigenous to the south. This is quite
apparent, as they are physically different from the aborigines and
lack the abnormal hemoglobins common in the aborigines' blood.[6]

We do not know when the Dravidians came into southern India
or whence, although the presence of the Dravidian-speaking
Brahui in Baluchistan is a suggestion that they came from the
Indus Valley, and both the Brahuis and the Baluchis bear some
physical resemblance to the Dravidians of southern India. Being
Caucasoids, the latter could only have come from the northwest.
That they were already in a Bronze Age or Iron Age cultural level
seems likely, and they may well have been associated in some way
with the Indus Valley civilization, as many archaeologists have
suggested but as yet no one has proven. The racial composition
of the skeletal remains from the Indus Valley sites does no violence
to such a derivation.

When the Aryan ancestors of most of the northern Indians

[6] G. W. G. Bird, E. W. Ikin, A. E. Mourant, and H. Lehmann: "The Blood
Groups and Hemoglobin of the Malayalis," in T. N. Madan and G. Śarana, eds.,
Indian Anthropology (Bombay: Asia Publishing House; 1962), pp. 221–3.

invaded the Indo-Gangetic plain, they stopped short at the Ghats and at the wooded hills of the Deccan. The reason is simple. They were dependent on wheeled vehicles for transportation. Nevertheless, Brahmins went south to convert the Dravidians to Hinduism. Coming mostly without women, the Brahmins at first married into the local population. Only later did they become strictly endogamous. The civilized Dravidians then became Sudras, subdivided into many occupational castes. That is why the two middle castes, the Kshatriya and Vaisya, are mostly lacking in southern India. Both the Muslim and the Christian missionaries who came later followed the same pattern as the Brahmins. Islam and Christianity gave many outcastes an opportunity to form castes of their own.

G. Olivier's study of the living Tamils, presented with comparative data covering the Kannaras, the Telugus, and the Malayalis,[7] is our most complete source of information for these people as a whole, including the Harijans. He found that among the four peoples the mean stature for males ranges from 162 to 164 centimeters (5 feet 4 inches to 5 feet 5 inches). Among the Tamils the range is from 165.4 centimeters (5 feet 5 inches) among the Vellajas to 160 centimeters (5 feet 3 inches) among the Harijans and Shanars. The Vellajas are landlords and farmers; the Shanars are toddy-makers who not long ago were outcastes. The Brahmins and Muslims are nearly as tall as the Vellajas. Comparable differences are found in the body lengths of the babies of these castes at birth.

The mean adult weights of these castes reflect diet as well as stature. The mean weights of male Vellajas and Muslims, who are the best fed, are 56 kilos (123 pounds) and 55 kilos (121 pounds) respectively; the vegetarian Brahmins weigh only 52 kilos (114 pounds); and the three lowest castes weigh between 50 and 47½ kilos (110 to 104 pounds).

The untanned skin color of the Tamils as a whole ranges from a very rare brunette white to a very dark brown, almost black, and the majority have dark brown or medium brown skins. The Telugus, who also live on the eastern side of the peninsula, have equally dark skins; the Kannaras and Malayalis of the western coastal regions are considerably lighter. Among the Tamils, Brahmins and Vellajas differ markedly from the lower castes in skin color; they are for the most part light brown. The darkest skins are found among a caste of fishermen. A similar gradation in skin color is seen among the other Dravidians.

[7] Olivier: *Anthropologie des Tamouls du Sud de l'Inde.*

No mixed or light eyes were recorded in any of these groups. However, among the Tamils the Brahmins for the most part have light brown or medium brown eyes, and the other castes have dark brown or black eyes; the iris color more or less matches the skin color. Among all four Dravidian groups the head hair is generally straight or wavy; no woolly or frizzly hair was found. The castes do not vary in hair form, but they do vary in beard and body hair. The Brahmins, Vellajas, and Muslims are the hairiest.

The head form of the Dravidian also varies, both regionally and from caste to caste. The Kannaras have a mean cephalic index of 81, and their neighbors to the south, the Malayalis, reach the opposite extreme of 73, whereas the eastern peoples, the Telugus and Tamils, are in between, at about 76. Among the Tamils, the Muslims and Vellajas are the roundest-headed, with means of 81 and 79 respectively. The longest-headed are the fishermen, with a mean of 72; and the Brahmins and other castes are in between.

In seeking comparisons to explain these differences, Olivier found a tendency to brachycephaly among the Indo-European-speaking Marathas living immediately north of the Kannaras. The high dolichocephaly of the Brahmins, whose index is 76, is the same as that of the Brahmins of northern India, and the low indices of the Tamil fishermen and of the Malayalis match those of the aboriginal tribesmen.

The Tamil Brahmins have the highest heads, the narrowest faces (except for the Muslims), the longest faces, the narrowest noses, and the lowest nasal indices of all. As elsewhere in India, the nasal index is a sensitive measure of differences between castes. The Brahmins, Vellajas, and Muslims all have an incidence of between 31 percent and 38 percent of convex nasal profiles, and these figures are comparable to those obtained in similar studies of northern Indians, which we shall discuss presently, and of West Asian highlanders and Europeans. Among the lowest castes, nasal convexity is reduced to between 11 percent and 17 percent—figures that suggest a lesser degree of northern influence. The Brahmins also have the highest percentage of loops in their fingertips, 62 percent; the Harijans the lowest, 50 percent. As we shall see in more detail in Chapter 8, this comparison makes the former the most Caucasoid and the latter the most Australoid of all the Tamil castes. Furthermore, the Brahmins have the lowest percentage of blood group B; the lower castes have the highest.

According to Olivier, the Dravidians of caste came to southern India from the northwest in a succession of invasions and have preserved their Caucasoid racial characteristics through endogamy. On the whole, however, he believes that these people constitute a Caucasoid subrace of their own, not clearly identifiable with living Mediterraneans, and that they may well be related to the creators of the high civilization of the Indus Valley. Until we know more about the racial history of India, this conclusion will remain the soundest that has been offered to date.

The Northern Mongoloids

BEFORE MOVING on to study the racial composition of the Caucasoid northern Indians, we shall devote a few pages to the Monogoloid peoples who live along the fringes of the Himalayas. The skeletal material from the Indus Valleys shows that some of them were in parts of Greater India before the arrival of the Aryan invaders. These peoples are found all the way from Afghanistan to Burma, in Pakistan, Nepal, Sikkim, Bhutan, and India. They may be divided into two categories: the Bhotias and the Hill tribes.

The Bhotias are simply Tibetans, whether they are called Sherpas, Bhutanese, or by any other name. They live generally at high altitudes on the borders of Tibet in the countries mentioned. Natives of Tibet itself are also frequently seen, or were before the Chinese occupied their country, in towns like Gangtok, Darjeeling, and Pedong, which lie on the main trade route between Lhasa and Bengal. The Bhotias live for the most part at an altitude of over 9,000 feet and seldom venture below the malaria line, which is at about 4,000 feet, as the following notation will indicate. "Colin Rosser [a British social anthropologist working in Nepal] said that in the West Himalayas he had the choice of two post offices, one down 1,000 feet and only one day's walk down and back, and the other at the same altitude as his station, but five day's walk away and over a 14,000 foot pass. His bearers would not go to the nearby, easily reached one on the grounds that if they did so they would catch malaria. So they took the five day's walk to fetch his mail."[8]

The Bhotias are Mongoloids, generally of short or medium stature, with long trunks; large, mesocephalic or brachycephalic heads; and broad faces. They have an incidence of 60 percent or more of Mongolian eye folds. The Tibetans from across the border, however, are more variable. Some are very tall, with long

[8] C. S. Coon's diary, Feb. 22, 1957.

legs and large hands and feet; their lumbar regions are nearly flat; and they walk like American Indians. Some also have hawk-like faces like those of the Plains Indians. Others have curly hair. This latter trait is said to be concentrated in a dark-skinned population living in the valley of the Tsangpo or Brahmaputra River, north of the Indian border, but as this region is virtually unexplored, except recently by Chinese troops, there is no way of confirming this statement.

The Hill tribes include the Kafirs, mentioned in Chapter 3; the Burushaski, Lahulis, Manchatis, and Kanawris, all living west of Nepal; the Dotials, Magars, Gurungs, Tamangs, Tharus, Rais, and Limbus of Nepal; the Lepchas of Sikkim; and a number of small groups of slash-and-burn cultivators living in the hills of West Bengal including the Totos, whom R. R. Gates studied,[9] the various tribes of the Northeast Frontier Agency of Assam; and the Nagas and other tribes living along the Burmese border.

The hill tribesmen living west of Nepal are Caucasoids, similar in general to other northern Indians, although a few of them show evidence of Mongoloid admixture.[1] They are of anthropological interest principally because they speak non-Indo-European languages. The Nepalese tribesmen, from whom the Gurkha troops of the British, Indian, and Nepalese armies are recruited, are racially clinal between Mongoloids and Caucasoids. Those in western and central Nepal are more Mongoloid than the Limbu and Rai of the eastern part of that country. Some of the Rai in particular are very short and show evidence of thyroid deficiency. As no published anthropometric data are available for any of these people, we must reply for their description on photographs.

In the Katmandu Valley, surrounded by Tamang tribesmen, and with Tharus to the south, live the Newars, an anciently civilized people who constitute most of the urban population of the cities of the valley. They have light yellowish skin and delicate features, and some of them look Chinese. Among them and elsewhere on the flanks of the valley live the Kass, Caucasoids who speak Nepali, an old Indo-European language that has replaced Newari as the official speech of the kingdom. Some of their ancestors were Rajputs who moved northward out of India during the Mogul period, about A.D. 1500, into the valleys of Nepal and even Tibet. In Tibet they established a kingdom at Lhasa, but were soon absorbed. In Nepal, where they live at an altitude habitable by Caucasoids, most of them have not mixed with

---

[9] Gates: *The Totos, a Sub-Himalayan Mongoloid Tribe.*
[1] Bowles: op. cit.

Mongoloids, as witness the portrait of a Brahmin from Sankhu on Plate 98.

Down in the lowlands, in the dense forest of southern Nepal and in adjoining parts of India, the so-called Terai, food-gathering aborigines called Chepang and Kusunda, were reported as late as 1840.[2] They are said to have been short, dark-skinned, and prognathous. This forest, which still harbors rhinoceros, crocodiles, and other large game, is largely uninhabited, although some Munda-speaking people from India have moved into parts of it. On the northern edge of it live another Nepalese tribe, the Tharus.

The native tribesmen of Sikkim are the Lepchas, a light-skinned, largely Mongoloid people noted for the beauty of their women, some of whom have married British tea-planters. In recent decades many Nepalese have immigrated to Sikkim, where they have replaced the Lepchas as the most numerous element in the population.

Short-statured, stocky, and largely Mongoloid tribesmen live scattered in the forest of northern Bengal and the Northeast Frontier Agency, on either side of the Brahmaputra River. They include the Totos,[3] Miris, Apa Tanis, Abors, Daflas, and Mishmis. They are warlike, slash-and-burn cultivators who live in long, communal houses. They have been little studied, and some of them were unknown before the establishment of the Agency about 1940. A picture of an Abor may be seen on Plate 42. For some unknown reason, the Abors have very deep voices. These tribal peoples look very much like Indonesians.

Farther east, in the rugged terrain near the Burmese border, and also on the other side of it, are the Nagas, famous headhunters who have been studied by missionaries. Their skin is reddish brown, and of all the Asiatic Mongoloids they most closely resemble the American Indians in facial features, particularly in their high-bridged, convex noses.

In general these Mongoloid and partly Mongoloid hill peoples of Nepal and points east are of great interest to anthropologists and deserve detailed study. Their distribution and racial characteristics show how closely dependent racial distribution is on geography, as for example in Assam. There the flat valley of the Brahmaputra is densely populated by Bengali Hindus, who disappear as soon as one begins to climb the forested hills on either side, for these hills are Mongoloid territory.

2 B. H. Hodgson: *The Languages, Literature, and Religion of Nepal and Tibet* (London: Trubner & Co.; 1874).
3 Gates: *The Totos, a Sub-Himalayan Mongoloid Tribe.*

The Indo-European-speaking Peoples of India, Pakistan, and Ceylon

ALMOST all of the other inhabitants of India, Pakistan, and Ceylon—numbering over 440 million persons, or nearly 80 percent of the whole—may be treated as a unit from a linguistic point of view and to a large extent in terms of race. The majority are Hindus in religion; others are Muslims, Sikhs, Jains, Buddhists, Zoroastrians, or Christians. They are almost all essentially Caucasoid, however, and a minority are indistinguishable from Western Asians or even Europeans. Most of them are descended in part or wholly from invaders from Western Asia, the plains west of the Caspian Sea, or, more remotely, even from Europe.

According to Thomas W. Clark, a distinguished British specialist in Indic languages who worked in Nepal in the 1950's, there were probably two Aryan invasions.[4] The first consisted of people accustomed to herding at moderately high altitudes and on broken ground. They were mainly shepherds who came out of Western Asia across Afghanistan into Kashmir and the Western Himalayas, into the valleys of Nepal, long before the Rajput invasion mentioned earlier, and thence into Bengal. Some may have reached the northwestern part of the peninsula. The Kafiri language, Old Nepali, and Bengali are related languages, along with Gujarati, which is spoken in the state of Gujarat in western India, southeast of West Pakistan. All these languages, taken as a unit, differ profoundly from Hindi, Punjabi, Rajasthani, and the other widespread Indic languages.

According to this interpretation, the second invasion was that of the Sanskrit-speaking peoples, who were related to the Scythians and Sarmatians. They were cattle breeders who crossed the mountain passes in covered wagons, like the American pioneers and the Boer Voortrekkers. Arriving in massive invasions with their women and children, they slowly expanded until they reached the edges of the hills, where grazing was poor and their large-wheeled wagons could not be easily hauled, and there they stopped. That they did this is very evident, for example, in the Brahmaputra Valley in the region of Gauhati, where the area of Indian settlement is a thin flat ribbon cut sharply from the territory of the hill tribes as if with a knife.

4 Personal communication to C.S.C.

They brought with them the old class distinctions seen in northern and central Europe, of earls, churls, and thralls, with a fourth or priestly class superimposed. The initial division of the population into Brahmins, or priests; Kshatriyas, or warriors; Vaisyas, or farmers and merchants; and Sudras, or craftsmen, was elaborated in India into many subcastes, with Outcastes, Untouchables, or Sweepers added, but the basis of the caste system was imported. Originally men of the upper castes were allowed to take wives from lower castes, just as Homeric heroes took captive women as concubines, but by the time modern Hindu society had assumed its historic form, the castes had become more tightly endogamous.

In regions of massive settlement, hypergamy, as this practice is called, made relatively little genetic difference. On the peripheries, and particularly in regions settled by the first wave of invaders, it was more influential from a racial standpoint, just as it was later in southern India, as we have previously noted. Even as late as the eighth century A.D. the Parsis, Zoroastrian refugees from Iran, practiced hypergamy when they first settled in western India, but soon afterward became endogamous. Now they have several castes of their own, headed by one of priests.

From time to time religious movements have arisen in India which promised to level castes. They began with Buddha, included the introduction of Islam and the formation of the Sikh people, and culminated, most recently, in the teachings and influence of Mahatma Gandhi. So far none of these movements has succeeded in wiping caste out completely.

As physical anthropologists, we are interested in the caste system principally because it has created a tangled network of small genetic isolates, as several studies of blood-group distributions and fingerprint patterns have indicated. On the other hand, both Indian and foreign anthropologists have shown much more interest in the aboriginal tribes of the south and in the Dravidians than in the Indo-European-speaking majority in the north. For a study of the latter we must rely chiefly on B. S. Guha's *Census of India* (1931); on the earlier *Census* (1901) by H. H. Risley;[5] and on the work of A. K. Mitra on the Bengali Muslims.[6]

We have a smaller amount of detailed information for the Northern Indians than we do for Western Asians, Europeans, or Dravidians, but we need it less. As we have already described these other peoples in detail, all we need say here is that the

[5] H. H. Risley: *Census of India* (Calcutta: Government of India; 1908).
[6] Mitra: "Physical Anthropology of the Muslims of Bengal."

Northern Indians resemble Western Asians, Europeans and Dravidians in different ways and degrees, with a few exceptions. For
example, about 400,000 hunting people called the Bhils, who
speak an Indo-European language, live in Gujarat and neighboring
states. They are relatively dark-skinned and resemble in certain
respects the aborigines of southern India. They represent some
kind of aboriginal stratum not clearly related to any other aboriginal people. Also, a slight Mongoloid element may be observed
among some of the Bengalis.

The Sinhalese, the most numerous people of Ceylon, are said
to be descended from invaders from Bengal who arrived by sea.
Today most of them are slender, dark-skinned, Caucasoid-looking
people. But as one leaves the coastal plain and climbs the central
mountainous core, up to Kandy and on to Nuwara Eliya, they
grow shorter, stockier, and somewhat lighter in skin color, and
some of them are actually partly Mongoloid. Hookworm and malaria, which sorely plague the lowlands, vanish above 4,000 feet,
and that is precisely where one begins to find Mongoloid-looking
people. This is reminiscent of the situation in the foothills of the
Himalayas.

Returning to northern India, we find that despite all the genetic
fragmentation seen by modern geneticists in blood groups, fingerprints, and other genetic markers, in anthropometric and morphological traits the northern Indians are much alike. As in the case
of the Dravidians, the higher castes are lighter-skinned and have
narrower noses than the lower ones.

The mean stature of males ranges from about 164 centimeters
(5 feet 4½ inches) to 172 centimeters (5 feet 8 inches). The
tallest people are found in Rajasthan and the Punjab. Cephalic
indices range from 72 to 80. The highest are found along the
coast, as in Arabia and parts of Europe, and the lowest in the
interior. For the most part, hair form is straight or wavy, body
hair variable, and beards are fullest among the warrior castes and
the Sikhs.

Most of these people have glossy black hair, although brown
hair is not uncommon. Reddish and blond hair are extremely rare.
Almost all of them have brown eyes of various shades, but one
sees light and mixed eyes in rare individuals, particularly among
the Sikhs. The highest proportion of mixed and light eyes reported
is 12 percent, found in one caste in Maratha. Convergent eyebrows and convex nasal profiles, typical of Western Asians, are
particularly common in the upper castes.

The physical attribute Indians are most keenly aware of, and about which they are very sensitive, is skin color. Without doubt there has been some intentional selection on this basis. Pinkish white skins are extremely rare, and brunette white skins are also in a minority. Most of the light skins have a yellowish or reddish cast. Light brown skins are commonest in the western part of northern India, and dark brown skins in the east, particularly in Bengal, where the climate is both hot and damp. As among the Dravidians, the castes differ in skin color; the Brahmins are the lightest.

Despite these social correlations, it would be unsound, for several reasons, to attempt to measure the quantity of Western Asian or European genes in any individual or group in northern India on the basis of skin color. The dry climate of the plains bordering the Thar Desert favors a brunette white or light brown skin that is capable of tanning, just as the similar climates of the Arabian and Sahara deserts do. A sheltered life in shaded temples and offices also favors a relatively light skin color, whereas life out of doors in a wet hot climate favors the darker shades of pigmentation. Several millennia of environmental selection have undoubtedly influenced the distribution of skin color among the peoples of India, and the Indo-European speakers are no exception, despite endogamy and social selection. If persons of European descent remain in the hottest, sunniest, and dampest parts of North America and Australia as long as the Aryans have been in India, we may end up as dark as they are.

Conclusion

IN DIA is the easternmost outpost of the Caucasoid racial region. It is climatically variable. We do not know what kind or kinds of people lived there during the Pleistocene, only that they made the same kinds of tools that were made in Europe, Africa, and Western Asia through the Lower and Middle Paleolithic phases of the Pleistocene. As in Africa, there is no evidence of a true Upper Paleolithic culture before the end of the Pleistocene. A Mesolithic culture or cultures preceded the Neolithic, but we are not sure whether it developed locally or was brought in from elsewhere. Neolithic agriculture was introduced from both the West and the East, probably first from the West. Bronze- and iron-working both came from the West, and at a fairly late date.

From this evidence, from the few skeletons we have of postglacial age, and from the ethnic stratification and geographic distribution of living peoples, we may make the following very tentative reconstruction of the racial history of the peoples of Greater India. The earliest peoples who have left recognizable survivors were both Caucasoid and Australoid food gatherers. Some of the survivors are largely Caucasoid; others are largely Australoid. No evidence of a Mongoloid element has been found among any of them. The Dravidians are Caucasoids related to the Brahuis and Baluchis and possibly to some of the Mesolithic peoples living farther to the west, such as the Natufians.

The Neolithic peoples who came in from Southeast Asia were an Australoid-Mongoloid mixture, probably more or less like the modern Khmers. Their descendants who stayed at low altitudes and in damp hot climates remained mostly Australoid, but those who went up to high altitudes became mostly Mongoloid. The Mongoloids of Tibet and Upper Burma have been prevented from settling on the plains of northern India in numbers because they are cold-adapted and easily fall victim to malaria and other lowland diseases.

The Indo-European-speaking peoples of northern India are the descendants of at least two waves of invaders from the west and northwest. They have retained most of their original racial characteristics except for skin color, which has become darker in varying degrees, partly through natural selection out of the range of skin colors that their ancestors brought with them, and partly through local admixture, particularly in the earliest period. The problem of climatic selection in skin color is not uniquely Indian, but global. It will be discussed in general terms in the next chapter.

8

Racial Differences in Adaptive Characters

Introduction

Now that we have considered the geographical distribution of the living races, from Lapland to the Cape of Good Hope and Cape Horn, the moment has come to cast our eyes back at some of the generalizations made in Chapters 1 and 2, to elaborate on them a little, and particularly to try to explain why human populations vary regionally as much as they do. Our principal observation will be that anatomically and physiologically the races of man react differently to a number of environmental stresses.

We shall also discuss some of the differences between races which result from exposure to culture, including the loss of traits no longer needed. And finally we shall mention a few racially variable genetic traits which we cannot even attempt to explain, but for which some explanation may one day be found.

On Races and Clines[1]

BEFORE we start relating races to climate, it may clear the air to discuss in some detail a matter mentioned in Chapter 2: the

[1] This section is a close paraphrase of a few pages in Coon's "The Taxonomy of Human Variations," PNYAS, 1965 (in press). With permission.

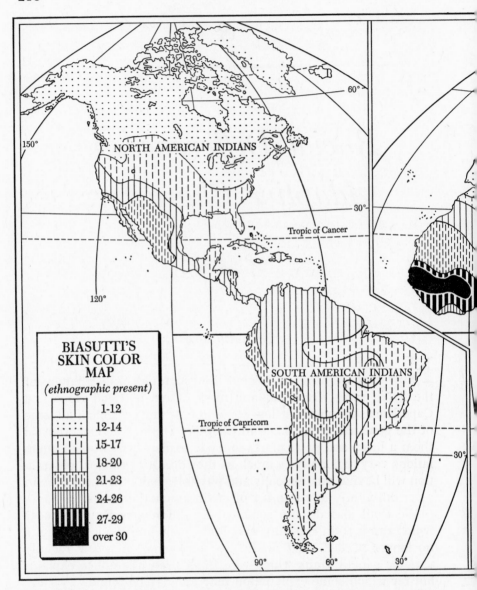

BIASUTTI'S
SKIN COLOR
MAP
(ethnographic present)

	1-12
	12-14
	15-17
	18-20
	21-23
	24-26
	27-29
	over 30

NORTH AMERICAN INDIANS

SOUTH AMERICAN INDIANS

Tropic of Cancer

Tropic of Capricorn

60°

150°

30°

120°

90°

60°

30°

30°

relationship between races and clines. This discussion is particularly needed at this time because the concept of race is currently unpopular in certain quarters, largely as a result of ideological or emotional motivation, or both. Various authors, two of whom were cited in Chapter 1, have substituted for it the concept that races do not exist, only clines. The usual rationalization for this iconoclastic notion is that variations in the frequencies of inherited characters run continuously from continent to continent like the isobars of a weather map.

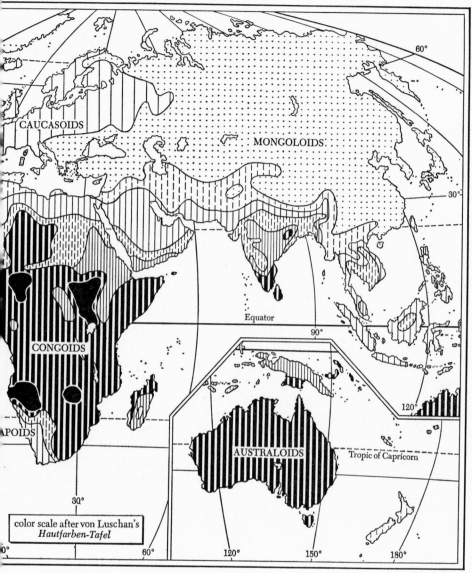

CAUCASOIDS

MONGOLOIDS

60°

30°

CONGOIDS

Equator

90°

120°

AUSTRALOIDS

Tropic of Capricorn

POIDS

30°

color scale after von Luschan's
Hautfarben-Tafel

60°

120°

150°

180°

Proponents of this view like to copy a map of the world distribution of skin color from R. Biasutti's monumental *Razze e Popoli della Terra* without checking either his method or his sources. Professor Biasutti, who died at an advanced age in 1965, just as this chapter was being written, was an eminent and highly respected Italian geographer who firmly believed in the existence of races. He drew his skin-color map before 1940, using a technique that is employed to make weather maps. He plotted points where information on skin color existed, and then drew concentric lines

between and around these points across intervening undocumented terrains. The absence of published data on the Arabian
Peninsula, Iran, and Afghanistan—to cite but three examples—
did not deter him from carrying out his orderly scheme. In all
fairness to Biasutti's memory, it must be said that he could not
have anticipated that a quarter of a century later persons trying
to disprove the existence of races would take the details of his
map literally.

Another much copied and equally eminent and innocent cline-
maker is A. E. Mourant, who has created lively curvilinear maps
of distributions of blood groups throughout the world.[2] He did not
hesitate to draw bold sweeping concentric circles around the land
of the exotic Basques, dramatizing their supposedly polar position
in the ABO blood-group genes. H. V. Vallois and P. Marquer later
mapped the distribution of these genes in France by departments,
producing an entirely different effect.[3]

Wholly aside from the fallacy of using weather-map techniques
to depict human variations, for genes do not float in the air like
rain clouds, several other serious objections may be raised to the
theory that there are no races, but only clines. As defined in
zoology, the word *cline* refers to a single character alone. Taxonomy based on single characters has long been abandoned. To
create one map showing clines which cover a multiplicity of
characters would be an ordeal, with or without a computer. Even
if such a map could be drawn, how could it accommodate the
complexities of mixed populations, and human mobility? Where
on such a map would a cartographer plot the Qashqai of southern
Iran: in their verdant and lofty summer pasture in the Zagros
Mountains, or several hundred miles away in their dreary winter
quarters on the coastal plain?

How could one draw such a map of Kerala State in India, which
is inhabited by several ethnic groups differing widely in skin
color, hair form, stature, nose form, and many other characters,
although many of them live in the same communities? How could
one make a skin-color map of New York City?

Even if these technical difficulties could be overcome, more
serious objections would arise after the technically perfect map
had been drawn. If we compare existing maps depicting such
environmental phenomena as mean winter temperature, cloud
cover, and days of sunshine, we find that the peoples of separate

2 Mourant, A. C. Kopec, and K. Domaniewska-Sobczak: *The ABO Blood Groups*
(Oxford: Blackwell Scientific Publications; 1958), Maps 1, 2, and 3, pp. 265–7.
3 Vallois and Marquer: op. cit. Maps are on pp. 171–80.

parts of the world respond differently to similar pressures. In Europe fair skin and light eyes are commonest in zones of least sunlight and greatest cloud cover. On the other hand, in Negro Africa, the deepest pigmentation is also found in the most dimly lit

Fig. 2. – THE ABO BLOOD GROUP GENES IN FRANCE.

after A. E. Mourant (1958)   after H. V. Vallois & P. Marquer (1961)

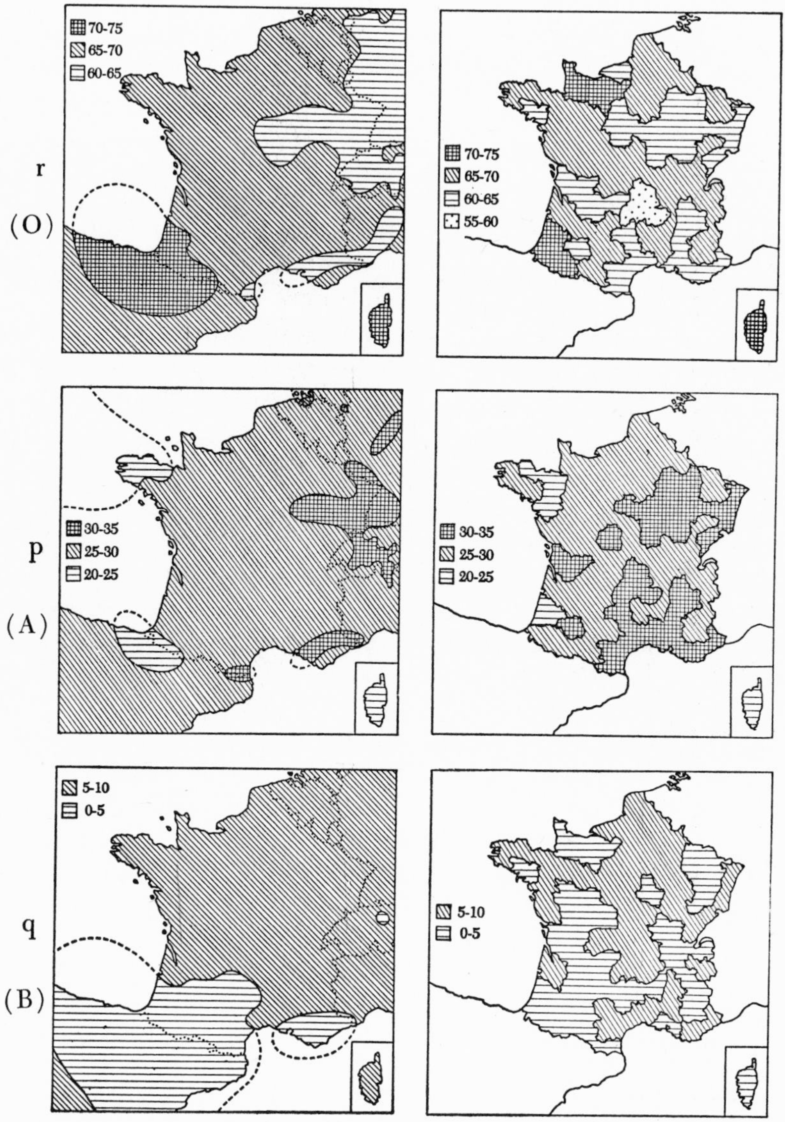

With permission of H. V. Vallois

regions. The critical difference is one of absolute—not relative—humidity in terms of water vapor pressure. And in Eastern Asia skin color is only very slightly correlated with any of these natural phenomena.

As for stature, we find that Europeans are tallest along the +25° F January frost line, whereas in some parts of Eastern Asia the Mongoloid peoples are tallest where it is in fact a few degrees colder in winter. In Negro Africa the tallest people live in the hot humid swamps of the Upper Nile, whereas, as we have indicated, the tallest Pygmies live at a high elevation in Rwanda and Urundi. The tallest Australian aborigines inhabit the hottest, dampest part of the continent, in the very north, and stature decreases as one goes southward to Tasmania. In other words, each subspecies has its own clinal system with regard to both skin color and stature, and some systems are the exact opposite of others. As we shall discuss presently and in more detail, each race achieves its own measure of cold tolerance by its own distinct combination of possible physiological processes. Only one subspecies, the Mongoloid, has produced populations adapted to living and reproducing at high altitudes.

If we carry the study far enough, we find that it supports exactly the opposite conclusion from that claimed by those who disapprove of the concept of race. It shows not only that races indeed exist, but also that each race has its private set of clines, by which it may be defined.

The Interpretation of Weather Maps

WHATEVER we have said about weather maps, we find them excellent for depicting global variations in climate, such as temperature, light, and moisture, to which human beings are adapted.

Map 18, which indicates the winter temperatures of the land surfaces of the world, was made by combining the January means for the northern hemisphere with the July means for the southern. Because of the size of the pages of this book, it had to be drawn with intervals of no less than 20° F.

It shows that the northern hemisphere is the colder one. Siberia, Tibet, Canada, Alaska, and Greenland are—except for Antarctica—the winter iceboxes of the world. Most of Europe and the Western Asian highlands lie during winter in a zone within 8° to 12° of the freezing point, and all the low-lying lands between the two

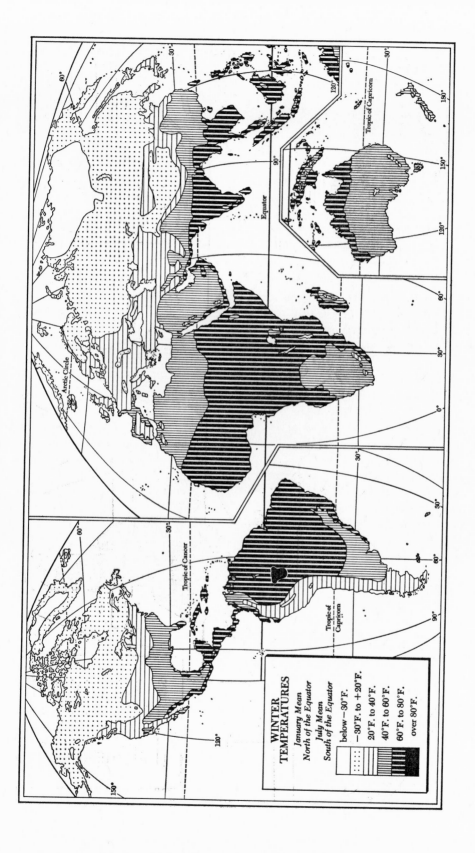

WINTER
TEMPERATURES
January Mean
North of the Equator
July Mean
South of the Equator

below −30°F.
−30°F. to +20°F.
20°F. to 40°F.
40°F. to 60°F.
60°F. to 80°F.
over 80°F.

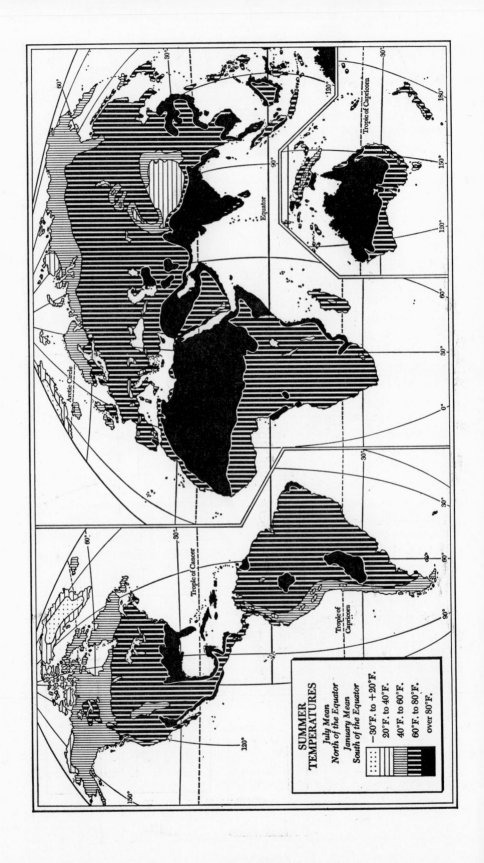

**SUMMER
TEMPERATURES**

*July Mean
North of the Equator
January Mean
South of the Equator*

−30°F. to +20°F.

20°F. to 40°F.

40°F. to 60°F.

60°F. to 80°F.

over 80°F.

tropics are warm. Adaptation to winter cold is primarily a Mongoloid problem; it is only secondarily a Caucasoid one.

Summer temperatures (See Map 19, p. 216) are much more uniform. Only Tibet, Greenland, portions of the Arctic coasts of North America and Siberia, and high spots in the mountains of Europe and South America are below +40° F. Heat stress is concentrated in Africa north of 10° N. latitude, in the lands encircling the Persian Gulf, in India, and in Australia. Adaptation to summer heat is a problem principally for Mediterranean Caucasoids, the Bushmen, the peoples of India, Australian aborigines, and some of the Southeast Asians, many of whom are partly Australoid.

Although winter and summer temperatures show seasonal ranges for the different parts of the world, the total amount of global radiation that strikes the surface of the earth per year may be a better measure of total heat. This is shown on Map 20 (p. 218). The global mean is about 150 kilogram calories per square centimeter of surface. The regions that receive the most radiant heat are situated on or near the Tropics of Cancer and Capricorn. Most of the world's land area which receives over 200 kg. cal./cm.^{2} per year lies in the Kalahari Desert, central Australia, the southwestern United States, and the Atacama Desert of northern Chile. The equatorial regions of the world, which are warm throughout the year, receive much less radiant heat annually, between 100 and 160 kg. cal./cm.^{2} The world's largest area of low radiation in the tropics is in the Amazon and Orinoco valleys. Western Indonesia, New Guinea, and a sizable patch of equatorial Africa also receive relatively little radiation. An excess of radiant heat is therefore a problem affecting principally the Mediterranean branch of the Caucasoids, the Bushmen, the Australian aborigines, and a few of the American Indians. Reduced radiant energy, below the level of 120 kg. cal./cm.^{2} per year, is largely confined to the lands occupied by Europeans, Northern Asiatic Mongoloids, Eskimos, and some American Indians.

The last three maps have to do primarily with heat. Map 21 (p. 220) is chiefly concerned with light, as measured in terms of the total annual hours of sunlight. This map then reflects a balance between radiation, cloud cover, and humidity, and it matches the radiation map more nearly than it does the ones showing winter and summer temperatures. It shows that the sunniest parts of the world are, as expected, those occupied by Mediterraneans, Bushmen, Australian aborigines, Indians of the Southwestern United States and whoever is foolish enough to be found on the Atacama Desert. The most dimly lit places, except for certain regions in the far north, are Northwestern Europe, the foggy Northwest Coast of North America, the region of fjords and inland channels of southern Chile, equatorial South America, Tasmania and the southern tip of New Zealand, parts of West Africa, and, surprisingly enough, much of southern China. Negroes, northwestern Europeans, the extinct Tasmanians, Amazonian Indians, and southern Chinese all inhabit or inhabited places where the sun shines on their faces less than three hours seventeen

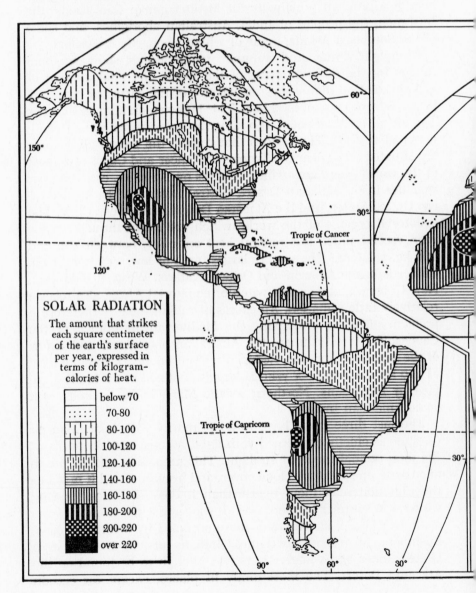

SOLAR RADIATION

The amount that strikes each square centimeter of the earth's surface per year, expressed in terms of kilogram-calories of heat.

below 70
70-80
80-100
100-120
120-140
140-160
160-180
180-200
200-220
over 220

minutes and thirteen seconds a day; yet they have the fairest, the blackest, and the yellowest skins in the world.

Sunlight is reduced by rainfall which creates shady forests, and by water vapor pressure plotted independently of temperature. The latter is more useful than a map of relative humidity. As Map 22 (p. 222) indicates, with minor exceptions the greatest mean annual precipitation is found in the tropics: in Central and South America, West Africa and the Congo, Madagascar, India,

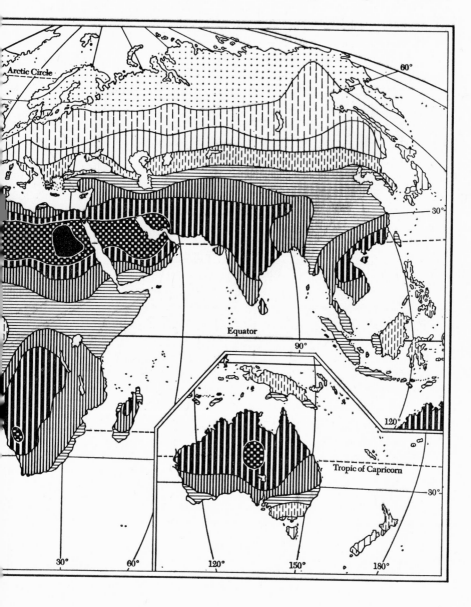

Southeast Asia, Indonesia, and New Guinea. The exceptions are the Northwest Coast of North America, the archipelago of southern Chile, parts of Norway, Scotland, Iceland, Japan, Tasmania, and New Zealand. The driest part of the world is a great zone that stretches from the Atlantic coast of the Sahara Desert, across Arabia, down into Somalia, around the Zagros into Iran, and then northward and eastward all the way to Manchuria. It is broken only by the spine of Asia, the Tien Shan and Altai mountains,

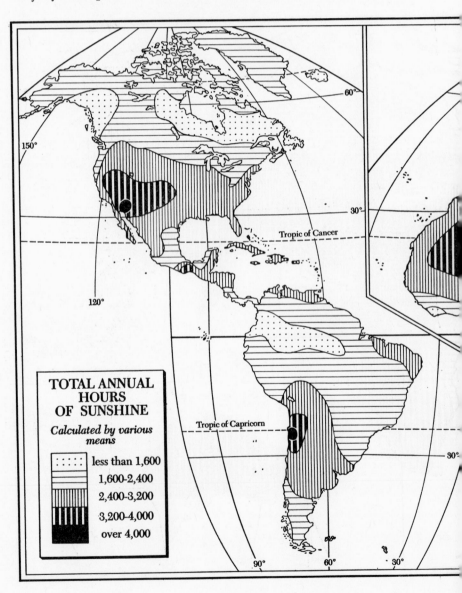

TOTAL ANNUAL
HOURS
OF SUNSHINE
Calculated by various means

::::::	less than 1,600
	1,600-2,400
	2,400-3,200
	3,200-4,000
	over 4,000

which long separated the Caucasoid and Mongoloid regions. Smaller areas of little rainfall are found in North America, South America, southern Africa, and Australia.

Map 22 coincides to a considerable extent with Map 20, which shows global radiation. But the resemblance holds only for the parts of the world lying between 40° N. latitude and 40° S. latitude. Once we go polewards from the forties, it ends. In the latter regions, radiation is low with or without much rainfall.

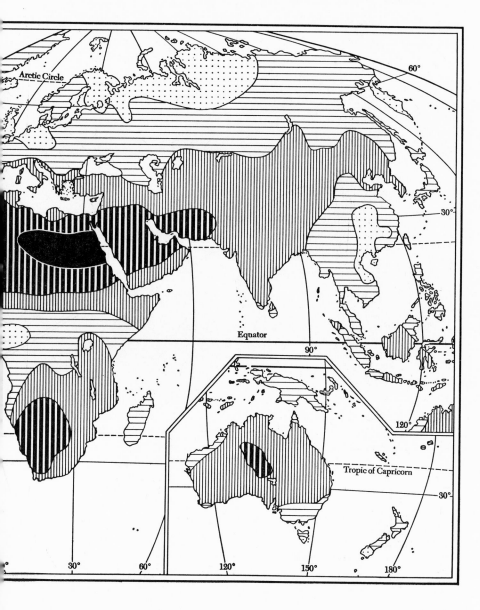

Our last maps in this series are 23 and 24 (pp. 224, 226), which show the mean water vapor pressures for winter and summer. They are constructed by the same technique as Maps 18 and 19 (pp. 215, 216), the temperature maps.[4] Water vapor pressure, measured in millbars, indicates the total amount of moisture in the air at a given point. It is independent of rainfall and cloud cover. For

[4] H. E. Landsberg: "Die Mittlere Wasserdampfverteilung auf der Erde," MR, Vol. 17, No. 4 (1964), pp. 102–3.

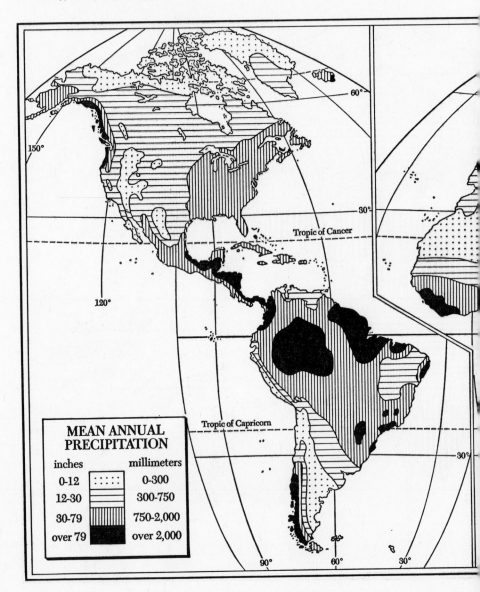

MEAN ANNUAL PRECIPITATION

inches		millimeters
0-12		0-300
12-30		300-750
30-79		750-2,000
over 79		over 2,000

example, in the ring of land around the shores of the Persian Gulf, water vapor pressure reaches a world peak in summer. Yet this region is also one of the driest and sunniest on the earth. When high pressure is combined with a high temperature, as it is in the Persian Gulf, the heat load becomes almost insufferable.

In the damp tropics, where the thermometer seldom rises above 80° F., the high water-vapor content of the air intensifies small changes in temperature. One seldom feels completely comfortable,

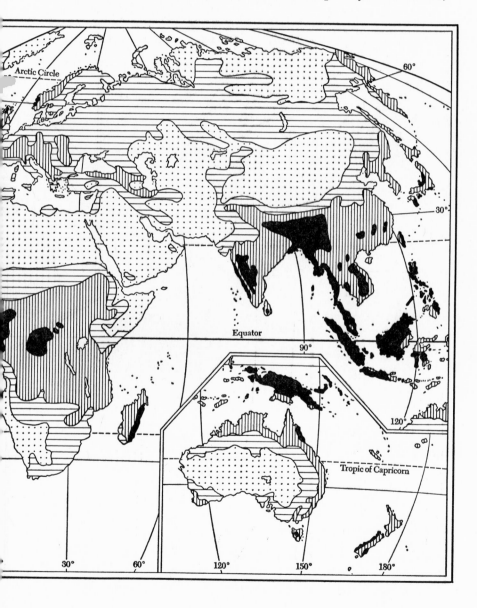

for a rise of two or three degrees brings on sweating, and an equally slight fall may make one shiver.

As Maps 23 and 24 indicate, it is always damp near the Equator, except in the Andes and the highlands of East Africa and New Guinea. In summer the dampness spreads to the Gulf Coast of the southern United States, the coasts of the Indian Ocean, and to China and the Philippines. The Sahara Desert, and to a lesser extent the Arabian Desert, have dry air the whole year; the deserts

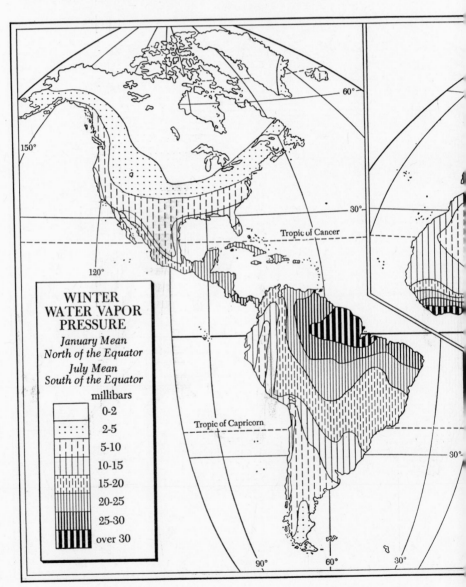

WINTER
WATER VAPOR
PRESSURE

January Mean
North of the Equator

July Mean
South of the Equator

millibars

	0-2
	2-5
	5-10
	10-15
	15-20
	20-25
	25-30
	over 30

of Central Asia, from Iran to Manchuria, are more humid. In this respect the Australian and Kalahari deserts resemble the Sahara. Northwestern Europe, although cloudy, rainy, and cool, does not have damp air. In China, where there is also much cloud cover and considerable rainfall, the air is damp in summer.

The effective thickness of the earth's atmosphere is about 30 kilometers, or 14 miles. Through this protective skin the sunlight that reaches the earth is screened. The atmosphere is 14 miles

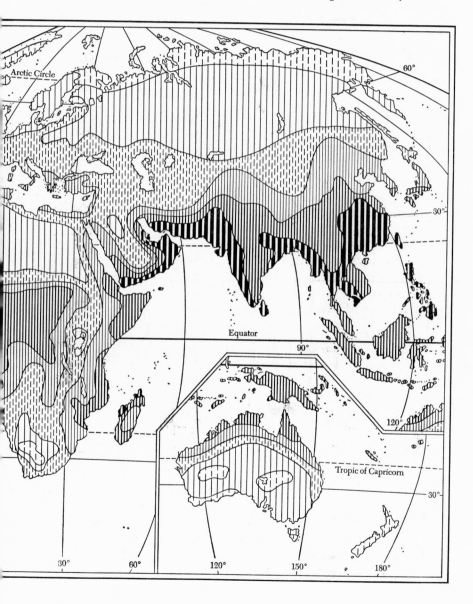

thick when the sun stands exactly overhead, as on the Equator
during the equinoxes and on the Tropics of Cancer and Capricorn
during their particular solstices. During the equinoxes, at a latitude of 54° north, which is just south of Scotland and Scandinavia, the sun's rays have to pass through one and a half times as
much atmosphere as they do at the Equator, and at the Arctic
Circle they pass through twice as much.

On a global average, 50 percent of solar radiation is absorbed

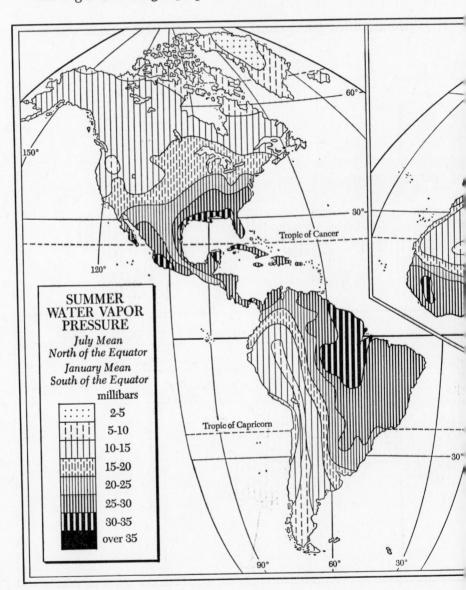

SUMMER
WATER VAPOR
PRESSURE
*July Mean
North of the Equator*
*January Mean
South of the Equator*
millibars

::::::	2-5
¦¦¦¦¦	5-10
	10-15
	15-20
	20-25
	25-30
	30-35
▓▓	over 35

at the earth's surface; 16 percent is absorbed by atmospheric gases and clouds; and 34 percent is reflected back into space. Where the sun is nearly overhead and the land is covered with vegetation, nearly 70 percent is absorbed, but the ratio falls to 30 percent on a cloudy day.

If the air is saturated, much of the infrared radiation is trapped in it, making the air hot and sultry. But if the air is dry, as on deserts, only the air close to the ground, the private atmosphere

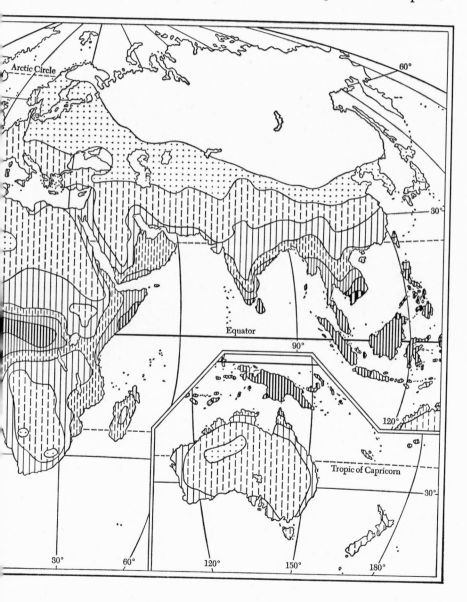

of lizards and snakes, is excessively hot. Most of the infrared radiation bounces back into space. This is why maritime and continental climates are different, and why the equatorial lowlands of the world, being excessively humid, receive no more infrared radiation than do many places forty degrees of latitude to the north or south.

Ultraviolet radiation is more efficient at penetrating the atmosphere than infrared radiation is, and that is why a person can be severely sunburned on a New England beach on a hazy June day, and why hand-line fishermen on the foggy Grand Banks get lip cancer from glare off the water.

The maps we have looked at and the information just reviewed concerning the role of the atmosphere indicate quite clearly that the subspecies of man have been moulded into different shapes and hues by a variety of special climatic combinations. The Caucasoid region is divided into two parts, the northern and the southern. In the northern part, and particularly in Northwest Europe, winters are chilly to cold, summers are mild or cool, and there is little sunlight, plenty of rain, and the air is relatively dry. The southern part, which includes the Sahara and the Arabian deserts, has cool winters, extremely hot summers, bright sunlight, and, except for southern and eastern Arabia, dry air. What both the northern and the southern Caucasoid regions have in common is a combination of at least one cool season and low humidity. Conditions in the deserts of North Africa and Arabia are very similar to conditions in Bushman country in South Africa, and in much of Australia. Thus Mediterraneans, Bushmen, and Australian aborigines are faced with similar environments.

On the other hand, the home of the Pygmies and Negroes is warm the year round, has little sunlight, heavy rainfall, and the air is saturated with moisture. There is very little seasonal change. Much the same conditions prevail in coastal New Guinea, most of Melanesia, and parts of Indonesia. In Polynesia and Micronesia the air is warm and moist, there is a medium amount of sunlight, the rainfall is abundant, and offshore breezes cool the air on the windward sides of the islands, where most of the people live.

The Chinese and other northern Asiatic Mongoloids are faced with great seasonal changes in temperature, little sunlight, and variable rainfall, and in China the air is very humid in summer. Of all the major regions of the Old World, except for the deserts, theirs is the most subject to seasonal change. The Americas, which have all climates, were first settled by people already adapted to climatic differences; like other Mongoloids, the American Indians can tolerate much environmental variation.

We did not draw an eighth map, one of altitude, because the reader can find it in any atlas. Only two parts of the world have altitudes high enough to be of importance in racial differentiation, Tibet and the Andes, and both are inhabited by Mongoloids.

Skin Color

CLIMATIC INFLUENCES are evident in many of the organs and systems of the body, but none is as conspicuous as the effect of climate on skin color, and no other human trait is more variable. So easily perceptible are variations in skin color that many racial classifications have been based on it, and many peoples of the world who have never heard of anthropology classify themselves and each other in terms of this single trait.

One would think that after nearly a hundred years in which physical anthropology has existed as a field of study someone would have invented an accurate method of measuring skin color, and that others would have adopted it, but such is not the case. The most commonly used scale, and the one on which Biasutti's global map of skin color is based, is von Luschan's *Hautfarbentafel*. This is a rectangle of thirty-six colored lozenges of glass, ranging from pale pinkish white to black, and with three yellowish tones, Nos. 4, 5, and 6, interrupting the pinkish to brunette white sequence. The scale does not match all skin colors very closely, primarily because its lozenges are glossy. R. R. Gates has produced a table of nine colors—printed on paper—which he copied from the skins of white and colored Americans, and which comes closer to reality, but this has been little used.[5]

Back in the 1920's several anthropologists used a color top in an effort to measure skin color accurately. The essential part of the top was a rotating disc on which were attached pie-shaped slices of paper of different colors. A certain proportion of colors would be set up so that, as the top spun, a uniform blend would be produced which would be compared with the skin color of the person being studied. Unless the experimenters got it right the first time, they would stop the top and change the proportions of colors several times, until they hit on the matching shade. This procedure often

[5] Gates: *Pedigrees of Negro Families* (Philadelphia: The Blakiston Co.; 1949).

took more time than a complete anthropometric study of the individual.

A recent and more successful method is to record the light reflected by the skin, tanned and untanned, at different wave lengths. Because this tells us to a certain extent what the skin does with light, the procedure is functional. J. S. Weiner and his associates[6] have shown that, when measured through a filter at a light level of 6850 angstroms (an angstrom is one ten-millionth of a millimeter), Bushman skin reflects 43 percent of light, as compared to 24 percent in the case of Yoruba Negroes in Nigeria, and 64 percent in the case of Europeans. In other words, black Negro skin absorbs 76 percent of light; yellowish Bushman skin absorbs 56 percent; and untanned European skin only 36 percent. And in many Europeans the absorption is even less. The difference of 40 percent between Yorubas and Europeans may be the greatest in the world. Although we have no comparable data on the reflection of light by Mongoloid skin, it is probably near the figure for Bushmen.

Exactly why the skin colors of different races range all the way from black to almost white is not fully known. Much research has been done on this complex subject, and the literature on it is voluminous. We can only summarize it briefly here. The principal differences seem to be in the ways that the layers of the epidermis react to sunlight filtered through the atmosphere and reflected from the sky.

The skin consists of two main layers, the dermis and the epidermis. The dermis is made up of a mat of protein fibers that contains the apocrine, eccrine, and sebaceous glands, the hair follicles, and a network of capillaries. It is innervated by branches of the sympathetic nervous system and sensory fibers. The epidermis contains four layers. The deepest of these is the *stratum germanitivum,* or Malpighian layer. It contains melanocytes—cells capable of producing granules of melanin, which migrate toward the surface.

Next comes the *stratum granulosum,* which carries melanin and also produces granules of a horny substance called keratin. The third is the *stratum lucidum,* a thin layer seen distinctly only in palms and soles; and the fourth and last is the *stratum corneum* or horny outer layer, built up of dead keratin and interspersed in some cases with broken-down hemoglobin and particles of melanin. These three inert substances give the skin some of its yellowish, reddish, and brown chromatic elements. Blood in the dermis and

6 Weiner et al.: op. cit.

melanin in the *stratum granulosum* also contribute to skin color in various degrees in different races.

Racial differences are also found in the thickness of the *stratum corneum* and in the amount of melanin produced by the melanocytes. There is no difference, however, in the number of melanocytes, which are present even in albinos.

The unfiltered light that strikes the human skin is divided into three segments. The waves between 2400 and 3900 angstroms are called ultraviolet; those between 3900 and 7700 angstroms are visible light; and those from 7700 to 30,000 angstroms are infra-

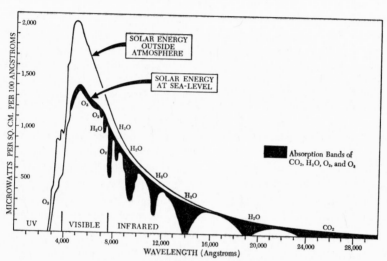

Fig. 3.–Solar Radiation Reaching the Earth
(after M. Luckeish, 1946)

red.[7] (See Figure 4.) Even on a very clear summer day at Cleveland, Ohio, water vapor and carbon dioxide in the atmosphere cut out much of the infrared radiation, particularly at wavelengths above 14,000 angstroms. Visible light is reduced to a lesser degree, mostly by oxygen, while ultraviolet radiation is affected by ozone.

The ultraviolet rays that penetrate the human skin have three principal effects. Wavelengths composing a narrow band centered around a peak of 2967 angstroms irradiate ergosterol (Provitamin D_2) in the *stratum granulosum,* producing Vitamin D_2 through the action of intermediate chemical substances. At the same wavelength they cause erythema, which is a capillary congestion, a severe sunburn. These two effects are rapid. A few days after ex-

[7] M. Luckeish: *Applications of Germicidal, Erythemal, and Infrared Energy* (New York: D. Van Nostrand; 1946).

posure, tanning is caused by wavelengths of a band between 3000 and 4000 angstroms, with a peak at 3400 angstroms. It may be added that heat stroke, which may accompany erythema, is influenced by the chloride content in sweat. If the chloride level is high, you faint.

Sweat also helps protect the skin against infections by bacteria and fungi, but in the cloudy countries of Northern Europe skin infection is far less critical to health than a failure to synthesize Vitamin D_2. This is particularly true in winter, when very little if any ultraviolet radiation penetrates the atmosphere. The presence or absence of clothing is unimportant in this respect because the *stratum granulosum* contains enough Provitamin D_2 to provide the daily requirement of Vitamin D_2 if only a few square inches of skin are irradiated. A deficiency of Vitamin D_2 can cause rickets, and rickets can so deform the pelves of infant females that they will die in childbirth later.

In cloudless as well as cloudy regions the ultraviolet radiation that reaches the earth's surface is too weak to make Vitamin D_2 where the sun is less than 20° above the horizon. This threshold is reached in winter at about 40° of latitude, and at 87° in summer.[8] Because sunburn and Vitamin D_2 are produced by a peak on the ultraviolet scale close to that for tanning, most people at these latitudes lose their tan. When spring arrives they are crocus-white and ready to absorb as much as 10 percent of ultraviolet radiation. As the sun rises higher and higher above the horizon, the amount of ultraviolet radiation increases, but the production of Vitamin D_2 will level off as the pigment released into the epidermis by tanning screens the rays.

The amount of radiation at the 2,967 angstrom peak which Negro skins absorb in the wet tropics is enough to supply their Vitamin D_2 needs, because despite the humidity the sun is still nearly overhead. But in higher latitudes, where the ultraviolet radiation is reduced, the pigment in the skins of Negroes may block too much of the little ultraviolet light that penetrates the atmosphere and may cause rickets. In the northern United States, before the days of vitamin additives, Negro children used to suffer more from rickets than white children did.[9] Up until the present century, if

8 F. Daniels: "Man and Radiant Energy: Solar Radiation," in D. B. Dill, E. F. Adolph, and C. G. Wilber, eds.: *Handbook of Physiology. Section 4: Adaptation to the Environment* (Washington, D.C.: American Physiological Society; 1964), pp. 969–88.

9 P. R. Peacock: "Quantitative Data in Skin Reactions to Ultra Violet Rays," *Lancet*, Vol. 2 (1925), pp. 367–72. F. G. Murray: "Pigmentation, Sunlight, and Nutritional Disease," AA, Vol. 36, No. 3 (1934), 438–45.

black-skinned people were incorporated into any population living either north or south of the fortieth degree of latitude, their descendants would eventually have been selected for skin color on the basis of this vitamin factor alone.

But ultraviolet radiation is not the only part of the scale that can influence skin color. Both visible rays and infrared diffuse heat. The Negro's skin, which reflects less light than the skin of Bushmen or Europeans, absorbs more radiation in general, including infrared. These rays have a warming effect, which is probably the principal reason why Negroes are at a disadvantage in comparison to tanned or yellow-brown-skinned people in deserts, where Negroes absorb 40 percent more calories per hours than do Caucasoids.[1]

In the humid forests and swamps of Negro Africa, high temperatures approaching those of deserts are never reached. When the air is saturated and the temperature has risen above the sweating point, a fire makes people of all races more comfortable because although the fire may raise the temperature it also lowers the humidity. Under the same conditions, a slight drop in temperature below the sweating point can cause marked discomfort from cold. A skin that can derive warmth from the longer waves of the spectrum gives its owner an advantage, particularly if he lacks the defenses against cold found in some races. We therefore suggest that one function of deep pigmentation in Negroes is to keep them warm, and that the same observation may apply to the dark-skinned peoples of Bengal, the Munda-speaking tribesmen, and the dark-skinned Dravidians of the peninsula of India, the Melanesians, and particularly to the natives of Bougainville Island, whose skins are very black and whose climate is cloudy, rainy, and very humid.

Recent experimental work has begun to explain how, if not why, Negroes and other dark-skinned peoples become heavily pigmented. We now know that melanocytes are activated and melanin is released into the epidermis by a hormone called MSA (melanocyte-stimulating-hormone), which has been synthesized. When it is injected into human beings, their skins darken temporarily. The skins of Negroes respond to these injections more markedly and more rapidly than do the skins of whites.[2]

More than 130 years ago, C. L. Gloger showed that subspecies of animals and birds that inhabit damp shady places are more

---

[1] E. F. Adolph et al.: *Physiology of Man in the Desert* (New York: Interscience Publishers; 1947). N. A. Barnicot: "Human Pigmentation," *Man*, No. 144 (1957), pp. 1–7.

[2] A. B. Lerner: "Hormones and Skin Color," SA, Vol. 205, No. 1 (1961), pp. 98–108.

darkly pigmented than those that live in drier, sunnier regions.[3] Other biologists have demonstrated that these changes may take place rapidly, as in the case of the English sparrows cited in Chapter 2.[4] We cannot yet demonstrate why natural selection favors the prevalence of very dark skins among otherwise unrelated populations living in the wet tropics, but the answer may not be far away.

So far we have concerned ourselves only with the world's extremes of skin color as determined principally by differences in melanin production. Although melanin is the principal pigment found in human skin, however, it is not the only one. Disintegrated hemoglobin may add a reddish undertone to the effects of melanin; and keratin, the substance from which nails, claws, hoofs, and horns are formed, gives the skins of some races a yellowish tinge. In the *stratum granulosum* at the base of the epidermis are found keratohyalin granules, from which keratin is formed, and whence it migrates to the *stratum corneum*, or horny layer.

Skins containing little melanin and a dense *stratum corneum* packed with keratin appear yellowish or yellowish brown, as among Bushmen and Mongoloids. As J. S. Weiner and his associates have shown, such skin reflects light efficiently in deserts. H. F. Blum has further stated that a thick, horny *stratum corneum*, densely packed with discs of keratin, resists the penetration of ultraviolet radiation much more efficiently than the thinner skin of a European. In the case of Negroes, whose *stratum corneum* is no thicker than that of Europeans, what resistance occurs is produced mainly by the melanin in the *stratum corneum* itself.[5]

In Eastern Asia Mongoloid skin does not vary greatly with latitude, partly perhaps because Mongoloids have other physiological mechanisms for thermal regulation, and partly because cloud cover in the territory they inhabit is greatest in the south and decreases toward the north. In the New World the skin color of the American Indians varies regionally much more, for reasons still to be discovered. Like that of Caucasoids, it is darkest where radiation is at its peak. In the dimly lit tropical forests of South America skin color is quite light, as it is in the interior of Borneo. That the skin of American Indians is more efficient than European skin in resisting the deleterious effects of bright sunlight is obvious in

3 C. L. Gloger: *Das Abändern der Vögel durch Einfluss des Klimas* (Breslau, 1833).

4 Johnstone and Selander: "House Sparrows: Rapid Evolution of Races in North America," pp. 548–50.

5 H. F. Blum: "Light and the Melanin Pigment of Human Skin," NYAS-Sp, Vol. 4 (1948), pp. 388–98. Barnicot: op. cit.

Latin America, where glossy yellowish skin is characteristic of mestizos.

Eye Color

E Y E   C O L O R varies geographically with light and the vapor content in the atmosphere, but it does not vary to the same degree of sensitivity as skin color, because the cornea of the eyeball blocks ultraviolet radiation completely, whereas some ultraviolet rays penetrate the outer horny layer of the skin. There is thus no question of sunburn, and eye color changes little if at all during the individual life cycle. The only radiational danger to the eye is glare, which is as much of a hazard in the Arctic, where bright light is reflected from snowfields, as it is on deserts or over water.

Eye color is correlated in general with skin color, but in some parts of the eye more than in others. Pigment is found in four parts of the eyeball: the sclera, the deep layers of the iris, the outer layers of the iris, and the retina. In persons with light skins the sclera, or "white" of the eye, is bluish white except when reddened through irritation, as by smoke or dust. In persons with very darkly pigmented skins, like Negroes or Australian aborigines, it may be streaked or spotted with superficial granules of melanin.

The color of the iris, which is what most of us mean by eye color, depends on the effect of light on variations in the location and amount of pigment in the two layers of the iris, and in some cases between these two layers. Melanocytes like those in the deep epidermal layers of the skin are present in the inner layer of the iris in all normal human eyes. If there is no pigment in the front or in intervening layers, or if the front layer of tissue is lacking, the light reflected from the iris appears blue, like deep-lying blood vessels in an unpigmented skin. Pigment in the front of the eye is clustered around the radial and circular muscles which dilate and contract the diaphragm. A dilated diaphragm then may look darker than a contracted one.

Mixed eyes are those in which the pigment cells in the front of the iris do not completely mask the pigment behind it. Irises in which the pigment of the back layer is entirely masked may appear light brown, dark brown, or black, depending on the amount of pigment in front, and some eyes show a mixture of dark and light brown comparable to the mixed-light eyes. East of Movius' Line, light and light-mixed eyes are virtually nonexistent, because they are a peculiarity of Caucasoids and of other peoples with whom Caucasoids have mixed. The correlation between iris color and skin color is general, but not complete, as we have seen in our study of the peoples of Europe and Western Asia, and there are even blue-eyed, black-skinned Negroes in Nigeria.[6]

The fourth pigmented area, the retina, which requires optical instruments to measure, shows a much closer relationship to skin color than iris color does. Insofar as this pigmentation has been studied, it indicates that albinos and other persons with unpigmented skins have unpigmented retinas; brunette white skins go with a light melanin deposition in the retina; and so on along the line to chocolate skins and chocolate retinas. And, according to W. H. Wilmer, yellow and reddish skins go with retinal pigments of the same hues.[7] This line of research will require much more work before the relationship between the pigmentation of the retina and that of the skin is firmly established. Yet new information on this subject has already been obtained by experimental research on rats. In these rodents, which resemble man in many ways, the neural pathway by which information about lighting reaches the pineal gland involves the eyes and is independent of the actions of the pituitary body or gonads.[8]

This evidence would indicate that environmental selection for eye color is related to a certain extent to selection for skin color, at least as far as retinal pigment is concerned. It has been further shown that lightly pigmented persons can perceive the violet-blue end of the visual spectrum more accurately than darkly pigmented persons can.[9] It may thus be true, after all, as observers have long claimed, that blue-eyed persons can distinguish distant objects more accurately than dark-eyed persons can in dim, misty light. Such a capacity would have been useful to hunters in Western Europe during the Pleistocene.

---

[6] In 1928 Gates concluded that one of the genes controlling skin color also influences iris color. Gates: "A Pedigree Study of Amerindian Crosses in Canada," JRAI, Vol. 58 (1928), pp. 511–32.

[7] W. H. Wilmer: *Atlas Fundus Oculi* (New York: The Macmillan Co.; 1934). E. Dodt, R. M. Copenhaver, and R. D. Gunkel: "Electroretinographic measurement of the spectral sensitivity in albinos, Caucasians, and Negroes," AMAAO, Vol. 62, No. 5 (1959), pp. 795–803. Daniels, Jr.: op. cit.

[8] R. J. Wurtman, J. Axelrod, and J. E. Fischer: "Melatonin Syntheses in the Pineal Gland: Effect of Light Mediated by the Sympathetic Nervous System," *Science*, Vol. 143, No. 3612 (1964), pp. 1328–9.

[9] G. Wald: "Human Vision and the Spectrum," *Science*, Vol. 101, No. 2635 (1945), pp. 653–8. I. G. Ishak: "The Photopic Luminosity Curve for a Group of fifteen Egyptian Trichromats," JOSA, Vol. 42 (1952), pp. 529–34.

Hair

HUMAN HAIR varies in some respects as much as skin color, and its racial variation is greater than that found in most other species of mammals. It varies in distribution, abundance, form, and color, and these variations give environmental protection in a number of ways. Hair color is correlated with skin and eye color to a greater degree among Caucasoids than in other races, largely because these three pigment systems vary more in this race than in others.

Hair is a specialized growth of dead cells, composed mostly of keratin, like the *stratum corneum* of the skin, and grows out of cuticles in the dermis. The number of cuticles in the skin does not vary greatly, but the number that produce terminal hair, which is what we are talking about, varies considerably. This hair is composed of three parts: cuticle, cortex, and medulla.[1] The cuticle is a single layer of unpigmented cells. In coarse hair the margins of these cells do not interlock, nor are they raised very high. In fine hair the free edges of the cuticle cells are raised so high that the hairs can interlock and become matted, particularly if the hair is crimped or tightly curled. The cortex, which forms the bulk of most hairs, consists of keratinized cells between which lie air spaces, called fusi. These fusi are most numerous and are largest in coarse hair.

Except in white hair, the cortical cells contain pigment. In black- and brown-haired individuals this consists of flattish, elongated melanin granules aligned lengthwise in the cells. When these granules are large and numerous, they produce the visual effect of black or dark brown hair. Spherical or slightly oval granules are seen as red. A red-haired person is therefore one whose hair contains mostly spherical pigment granules. Many apparently black-haired persons have the spherical pigment also, although its effect is masked. Blond hair is produced by a low rate of pigment-granule formation and its granules are small. Thus golden-blond hair contains both the red and the blond pigment components, and ash-blond hair contains the blond component alone. This simple explanation of the whys and wherefores of differences in the color of human hair, particularly of red hair, had to await the invention of

[1] W. Montagna: *The Structure and Function of Skin* (New York: Academic Press; 1956).

the electron microscope.[2] It makes us wonder whether some of the reddish appearance of certain human skins may not also be due to the presence of spherical melanin granules. White hair is a product of the aging process, but among peoples with unspecialized hair, particularly among Caucasoids and Australian aborigines, it may appear before they reach senility.

The medulla of the hair may be continuous, discontinuous, or absent. It is made up of large, loosely connected, keratinized cells, with large intercellular spaces which reflect light if it reaches them. Mongoloid hair has large medullas and large air spaces, whereas tightly curled Pygmy or Negrito hair has either small medullas or none at all, like the hair of infants.

Hair form depends to a certain extent on the angle at which it comes out of the scalp, and this angle is a function of the thickness of the dermis. The thicker the dermis the greater will be the angle,[3] and the greater the angle the rounder the hair will be in cross section. The cross section of the hair, in turn, is related to its degree of straightness and curliness, the curliest hair being the most oval.

Mongoloid hair is the thickest and straightest, as well as the stiffest. Its cuticle has the smoothest surface, its medulla the largest dead air pockets. Of all human hair, it is the one that most closely resembles the hair of the deer family,[4] which affords a maximum of thermal insulation per unit of bulk or weight.

Thermal insulation is also achieved among frizzly- or woolly-haired peoples by matting and thus forming a dead-air pocket over the scalp. A parallel to this is found in the merino sheep of northern Australia. Although the surface of their wool may have a temperature of 190° F in the sun, their body temperature remains well within the limits of normal function.[5] Because human hair of this type rarely falls below the hairline, its presence does not prevent the neck from losing body heat through sweating. Uncut Mongoloid and Caucasoid hair, however, covers the back of the neck completely. And the beards of Caucasoids may also protect the front of the neck. Bald Caucasoid men retain a fringe of hair around the lower zone of the scalp, which bears enough hair to afford the neck some protection.

2 M. S. C. Birbeck and N. A. Barnicot: "Electron Microscope Studies on Pigment Formation in Human Hair Follicles," in M. Gordon, ed.: *Pigment Cell Biology* (New York: Academic Press; 1959), pp. 549–61.

3 E. Upham and W. Landauer: "The relation of thickness of cutis and subcutis to hair slope in human skin," AR, Vol. 61, No. 3 (1935), pp. 359–66.

4 F. M. Brown: "The Microscopy of Mammalian Hair for Anthropologists," PAPS, Vol. 85, No. 3 (1942), pp. 250–74.

5 W. V. Macfarlane, R. J. Morris, and B. Howard: "Water Economy of Tropical Merino Sheep," *Nature*, Vol. 178, No. 4528 (1956), pp. 304–5.

Variations in human hair make some sense in terms of what we have just learned. The concentration of reddish and dark hair in the foggiest, rainiest parts of Western Europe follows Gloger's rule, as explained in the section on skin color. Blond hair in general, and in particular that kind of blond hair which lacks red-pigment cells, reflects 32 percent of light at a 7000 angstrom wavelength, compared to 18 percent reflected by light-brown hair, 15 percent by reddish-brown hair, 12 percent by red hair, 8 percent by dark red, and 1 percent by black hair.[6]

Persons with straight or wavy blond hair have no other substantial protection against the sun's rays to compare with the air chambers trapped in individual Mongoloid hairs and the collective mats of Negroid hair. In Europe the zone of blond hair reaches far eastward from the Baltic to the steppes of southern Russia and even beyond in regions of hot summer sun. In Australia blond hair is concentrated in the hottest deserts.[7] This distribution does no violence to Gloger's Rule, which states that populations of a species living in humid regions tend to have black or red hair, or feathers, whereas those living in arid, open country tend to have tawny hair or feathers. In this as in other respects human beings are just as subject to the laws of nature as other animals.

Fat

THE PRINCIPAL function of head hair is to maintain the precise thermal equilibrium of the brain, including, in cold climates, that of the blood vessels which feed the brain through the neck. Fat serves a similar purpose for many other parts of the body. Fat is a substance formed from the reaction of one molecule of glycerol with three molecules of fatty acids. The body stores it in various tissues and draws on it in time of need. It also serves as an insulator. Without a thick layer of fat, sea mammals, such as whales, seals, and dugongs, would be unable to maintain the core temperatures of their bodies in their aquatic medium.

Most of the fat in human beings is deposited beneath the skin, where it can be measured more or less precisely by skin-fold calipers at a number of critical sites: the cheek; the chin under the mandible; the chest at the axillary border of the *pectoralis*

[6] B. B. Gardner and D. L. MacAdam: "Colorimetric Analysis of hair color," AJPA, Vol. 19, No. 2 (1934), pp. 187–201.

[7] A. A. Abbie and W. R. Adey: "Pigmentation in a central Australian tribe with special reference to fair-headedness," AJPA, Vol. 11, No. 3 (1953), pp. 339–60.

major muscle; the side, over the lower ribs; the waist, between ribs and iliac crest; the abdomen, at the right of the umbilicus; the triceps, on the back of the upper arm halfway between shoulder and elbow; the front of the thigh; the knee, just above the kneecap; the calf, at the back of the level of greatest girth. These measurements are usually taken on young adult males in good health, and the coverage is nearly world-wide.[8] Specialists in body constitution can calculate from these measurements the approximate proportion of the body's mass which consists of subcutaneous fat.[9]

Data on fat folds in females are much scarcer. What there is shows that young women are fatter than men and that they vary less racially in this respect than men do. The average young white woman's body probably contains about 29 percent of measurable fat[1] in terms of her total body weight, and the male percentage is about half this figure. In young adult Chinese living on Taiwan the figures are 27.55 percent for women and 9.94 percent for men.[2] Although we cannot speak for peoples of other races, common observation suggests that this sexual difference may be widespread.

Among Europeans and Americans, from late fetal life on, the average female adipose layer is thicker than that of the male, and in females adipose deposits thicken conspicuously at the nape of the neck and in the breasts, belly, and thighs at adolescence.

[8] R. W. Elsner: "Skinfold Thickness in Primitive Peoples Native to Cold Climates," ANYAS, Vol. 110 (1963), pp. 503–14. A. A. J. Jansen: "Skinfold Measurements from Early Childhood to Adulthood in Papuans from Western New Guinea," ANYAS, Vol. 110 (1963), pp. 515–31. Chen et al.: "Body Form, Composition, and Some Physiological Functions of Chinese in Taiwan." Hertzberg et al.: *Anthropometric Survey of Turkey, Greece, and Italy.* Edward I. Fry: "Subcutaneous Tissue in Polynesian Children," HB, Vol. 32 (1960), pp. 239–48. C. E. French, M. K. R. Siddiqui, J. B. Youmans, and A. F. Schafer: "A Nutritional Survey of the Armed Forces of Pakistan," *Journal of Nutrition* Supplement 2 (1959), pp. 1–69. Russell W. Newman: "Skinfold Measurements in Young American Males," AB, Vol. 28, No. 2 (1956), pp. 154–64.

[9] Four investigators found a correlation of from .79 to .85 between the fat of young adult males as estimated by skin-caliper measurements and the results of X-ray studies. One investigator obtained a correlation of only .69 for females. K. R. Stitt: *Skinfold Measurement: A Method of Determining Subcutaneous Fat,* Department of Foods & Nutrition, School of Home Economics, University of Alabama, 1962.

[1] This figure does not include omental fat, which pads the viscera in the abdomen and produces a potbellied appearance. No one has succeeded in measuring omental fat, which appears only with obesity and later in life than the fat we are concerned with.

[2] B. Škerlj, J. Brožek, and E. E. Hunt: "Subcutaneous Fat and Age Changes in Body Build and Body Form in Women," AJPA, Vol. 11 (1953), pp. 577–600. Chen, Damon, and Elliot: op. cit. C. M. Young, J. Blondin, R. Tensuan, and J. H. Fryer: "Body Composition Studies of 'Older' Women, Thirty to Seventy Years of Age," ANYAS, Vol. 110 (1963), pp. 589–607.

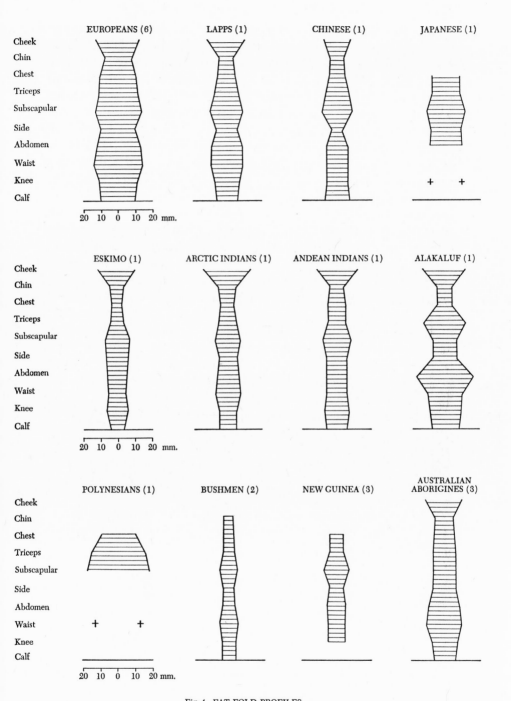

Fig. 4.—FAT FOLD PROFILES.

The numbers in parentheses refer to the numbers of series used
in each case. "Europeans" means Europeans other than Lapps.

Except for a very temporary breast development in early adolescence, the adipose layer in males shows few changes. At later ages, changes in the regional distribution of subcutaneous fat on the body, and in the total amount of body fat, are so markedly dependent on nutrition and health that racial patterns of changes are difficult to discern, particularly since they are little documented. It would be interesting to know about them. Anthropologists working in the field have noticed that among the Bushmen, the Australian aborigines, and some American Indians, for one reason or another, old women are characteristically emaciated.

The relationship of climate and insulation through fat has been clearly indicated in a study made by R. W. Newman on some 2,000 American Army men.[3] He made comparisons of the January and July temperatures of the states in which the men had been born and also of the two components of each man's total body weights. These were the weight of each man's measurable fat and the weight of the rest of his body, which is called his fat-free weight. Newman found that the fat-free weights of these men increased with low winter temperature and decreased with high summer temperature, whereas the weights of their fat varied in the opposite direction; the men were fattest where it is coldest in summer and leanest where the summers are hottest.

Because the continental United States covers a large area and a wide range of temperatures, this is an important discovery. It means that fat is of indifferent value as an insulator in extreme winter cold, and it is an impediment to the loss of body heat in hot summer weather. In moderate cold, however, it is a good insulator. If we apply these findings to the peoples of other parts of the world, some of whose fat profiles are shown on Fig. 4, the indication is that the same principles apply globally, with modifications that will be explained presently.

Europeans are fat in many parts of their bodies because they live in places that are cool in the summer. And Upper Paleolithic representations of women indicate that European women have been fat for a long time. Polynesians and Önges are fat because they spend much time in the water. The Bushmen are lean because their homeland is very hot in summer, and what reserve fat they have is lumped in their buttocks. The fat pattern of the Alakaluf Indians, whose climate is chilly the year round, and who used to go about naked, comes closest to that of the Euro-

3 R. W. Newman: "The Relation of Climate and Body Composition in Young American Males," AJPA, Vol. 13 (1955), pp. 386–7.

peans. Both the Eskimo and the Arctic Indians, who wear adequate clothing out of doors, have special fatty deposits only on parts of the body that are exposed when they are outdoors, particularly on their faces, including their eyelids.[4] Except for the Alakalufs, the Mongoloids are leaner on the whole than Europeans are, and the Nomadic Lapps are intermediate between other Europeans and Mongoloids.

The Nilotic Negroes, who live in extreme heat, particularly in summer, may turn out to be the world's leanest people.[5] The West Africans, whose country is not very hot in summer although it is damp, are sometimes fat, but judging from tests made on their relatives in the United States, their fat insulates them less than a comparable amount insulates other peoples.[6]

On the whole, a general distribution of fat some 7 millimeters or more thick is a good insulator in regions where the summer temperature rarely rises above 80°F but an inadequate one where winter temperature falls below +20°F. Racial differences which serve as defenses against cold have to do largely with the vascular system.

The Vascular System: Blood

THE VASCULAR SYSTEM consists of the heart, which is a pump; the blood vessels, which keep blood circulating throughout the organs of the body; the lungs, which put oxygen into the blood and take carbon dioxide out; and the blood itself. In its function of humidifying and warming incoming air, the nose may also be considered as a part of the vascular system.

The functions of blood are to supply the body with nutrients and oxygen, to prevent infectious diseases, to remove carbon dioxide and certain other waste matters, and to help maintain the heat balance of the body needed in a warm-blooded animal. Owing to our reduced hair cover and to the limited usefulness of body fat as an insulator, most of the work of keeping the body

4 Experiments on rabbits have shown that even without a Mongoloid fat pad, eyelids keep the eyeball warm. See S. Oppenheim-Lautrach: "Metrische und deskriptive Merkmale des menschlichen und tierischen Auges," TB, Vol. 22 (1947), *Oculus*, I, pp. 54–153.

5 D. F. Roberts: "Contribuzione alla etnologia dei pre-niloti," RA, Vol. 44 (1957), pp. 319–24.

6 P. T. Baker: "American Negro-White Differences in Thermal Insulative Aspects of Body Fat," HB, Vol. 31, No. 4 (1958), pp. 316–24.

warm falls on the blood and on the routing of the vessels which carry it. Blood carries out its function of heating and cooling through the skin, which in man, as compared to other mammals, has a prodigious blood supply far exceeding the metabolic requirements of the dermis and epidermis. On a hot day, as much as 10 percent of the blood in the body may circulate in the dermis during the hotter hours, and up to 23 percent of the total volume of blood, which averages a little less than six quarts in a normal, average-sized adult male, may be lost in a single hour through sweating.

Sweating is the principal mechanism for removing water from the blood. However, it is not the only one. When the body is at rest and not sweating, it loses about 16 grams (about 12 ounces) of water per square meter of skin per hour—which is roughly between one half and two thirds of the total skin area of an adult male—by simply seeping through the skin. At the same time about 6 grams (.06 ounce) escapes from the lungs. These amounts vary with the humidity in the air. In dry air the skin loses about 10 percent more water than it does in damp air, and the lungs about 80 percent more. The total loss is thus greatest when the air is dry, and if a man is exercising in hot dry air, the loss from the lungs is even greater. These circumstances impose a burden over and above the sweating requirements of the human body in people living on deserts.[7]

The amount of sweat that a human being can exude depends less on racial differences in the number of his sweat glands than it does on how many of them are stimulated into action before he reaches the age of two and a half. For example, Japanese children born and raised in the tropics have a greater number of active sweat glands than those confined to Japan.

Blood, Sweat, and Wet Heat

IN ALL RACES, adaptation to damp, tropical heat depends to a certain extent on behavior. Any sensible person relaxes in the shade in the heat of the day, and part of the difficulties that Europeans have in the tropics stem from their attempt to keep the same working hours they keep at home. Nevertheless, even when Europeans behave sensibly, their body temperatures may

7 Y. Kuno: *Human Perspiration* (Springfield, Ill.: Charles C. Thomas Co.; 1956).

still be slightly higher than those of Negroes or other persons adapted to tropical heat. Particularly if they are pink-skinned and plump, Europeans living in the damp tropics are likely to suffer from prickly heat. This painful affliction is caused by an irritation of overworked sweat glands. Pimply areas rise and the skin temporarily loses its capacity to sweat, making matters worse. The only immediate relief is to immerse the body in cool water, but if the ailment becomes chronic, the best remedy is to go home or to some other, cooler place.

Prolonged, strenuous exertion in the damp heat may lead to a loss of as much as five pounds of water per hour, or, as previously stated, about 23 percent of the normal volume of blood in the body. Such a loss may deplete the body of both water and salt, bringing on cramps or fainting. Natives of tropical Africa are more resistant to these reactions than even acclimatized Europeans are. They both eat and sweat less salt than Europeans do. Even when Europeans consume more salt and drink more liquids, they still sweat more and lose more salt. The answer of course is to avoid strenuous exertion, and when in Africa, do like the Africans, or perhaps a little less.

More serious than prickly heat, or even cramps or fainting, is heat stroke. This follows when sweating fails and fever sets in, and may lead to death. In their own countries Negroes are rarely if ever subject to this hazard, but out on the desert, largely because of their pigmentation, they suffer more than white people do.

Blood, Blood Vessels, and the Cold[8]

AS STATED EARLIER, fat insulation plays an important role in protecting the human organism against cold, but there are limits to the amount of fat a healthy person can carry around and still be able to do his work. Vascular adaptation to cold, however, requires no added weight or bulk and does not entail any interference with muscular movements, or the hazard of heat stroke in summer.

Before we go into details, two points should be made. In the first place, physiologists who study cold adaptation experiment on each other to establish norms. These men are almost all of British, Scandinavian, or German descent. Northwestern Europeans are adapted to temperatures hovering about the frost line

[8] An extensive bibliography on this subject will be found in Elsner: op. cit.

in winter, and to cool summers. In no sense can they represent the mean adaptive values for the races of man as a whole; it is not certain that such a mean can be calculated, or if it were, that it would help us understand the adaptation of different races to either heat or cold.

In the second place, archaeological evidence indicates that human beings have probably lived in the extreme cold of the Arctic, and in that of the continental subarctic regions, for no more than 13,000 years, or about 600 generations. They could not have begun to live in these places at all if they had not already known, or immediately learned, how to provide themselves with adequate environmental protection, particularly clothing.[9] Their principal need for vascular protection was therefore in parts of the body that had to be exposed at least part of the time while they were out of doors, notably the face and hands, and also the feet when wet. Although we have no measurements of fat on the hands, we know that peoples who are habitually exposed to extreme cold have a certain amount of fatty protection on the cheeks and feet. Experimental studies on some Siberian peoples, Manchurians, Japanese, Eskimo, and Alaskan Indians show that when the hands of peoples of the far north are exposed to prolonged immersion in cold water, they experience an increase in the flow of metabolic blood. Because they must keep their hands bare while working out of doors, this adaptation has a distinct survival value. It is limited to Mongoloids and may be considered a Mongoloid adaptation to extreme cold. Comparable studies of the cheeks have shown the same thing in northeastern Asiatic peoples, as reported by the Japanese.[1]

Not all of the American Indians have adequate environmental protection against the cold. This is particularly true of the Canoe Indians of Tierra del Fuego and the Magellanic archipelago. Their climate is like that which may have prevailed in Western Europe during glaciated episodes of the Pleistocene. We have already seen that the pattern and amount of fat deposition of the Alakalufs is comparable to that of Europeans. But Alakalufs also have an adaptation which Europeans lack. It is a high basal metabolism which requires a high consumption of calories, particularly fats, and helps keep the entire body in thermal equilibrium under conditions which few persons of other races could tolerate.

9 This generalization need not apply to the earliest ancestors of the American Indians, for reasons stated in Chapter 4.

1 H. Yoshimura and T. Iida: "Studies on the Reactivity of Skin Vessels to Extreme Cold. Part II. Factors Governing the Individual Difference of the Reactivity, or the Resistance Against Frostbite," JJP, Vol. 1 (1950–51), pp. 177–85.

A third type of vascular protection against cold has been found among Australian aborigines, African Bushmen, and nomadic Lapps. In essence this adaptation consists of a heat exchange between cool, incoming venous blood and warm, outgoing arterial blood in the arms and legs. It is anatomical in nature rather than metabolic, because it requires the blood vessels concerned, or connecting branches of them, to lie close enough together to make the heat exchange. In this operation the veins are involved more than the arteries. Each of the principal arteries of the arm and lower leg—brachial, radial, ulnar, tibial, and peroneal—is accompanied, as a rule in the same sheath, by a pair of companion veins called *venae comites*. At various places, particularly near the elbows and other joints, neighboring arteries are connected by short blood vessels, called *anastamoses*, so that under certain circumstances one can replace the other, and they can exchange blood.[2]

This type of adaptation allows small or very slender people, whose physiological economy cannot afford great bulk, much fat, or a high basal metabolism, to survive moderate cold, comparable to that experienced by the Alakalufs. In the case of the Lapps, it is really an additive to the warmth of their clothing and their tents. Because it is found among populations of three of the five subspecies, the chances are that it was independently acquired in each. Its presence among the Bushmen is only one more nail in the coffin of the current idea that they are racially a part of the Congoid subspecies. Negroes have no known adaptation against severe cold and suffer from frostbite when exposed, for their hands and feet are large, bony, and lean,[3] being adapted rather for damp heat.

Physiologists working in the field of cold adaptation try always to find subjects living as nearly as possible under the environmental and cultural conditions of their ancestors, because adaptations to environmental extremes may be lost, when conditions are changed, or at best reduced to a minority of the gene pool of the population. Later, through mechanisms of genetic heterogeneity and balanced polymorphy, which save us the remnants of a once useful attribute until it is needed again, it may someday return. This seems to be the case with the Lapps, for those who dwell in heated houses and do not wander afield with

[2] Coon: *The Origin of Races*, pp. 66–8.

[3] J. P. Meehand: "Body Heat Production and Surface Temperatures in Response to a Cold Stimulus," JAP, Vol. 7, No. 3 (1954), pp. 537–41. P. F. Iampietro, R. F. Goldman, E. R. Buskirk, and D. E. Bass: "Response of Negro and White Males to Cold," JAP, Vol. 14, No. 5 (1959), pp. 798–803.

reindeer seem to lack the thermal adaptation of their nomadic brethren, although the ancestors of all of them were presumably nomadic reindeer herders. By the same token, the Upper Paleolithic Europeans may have possessed some adaptations which their descendants have lost, or which lie hidden as minor elements in polymorphisms in their genetic makeup. Adaptations to the cold are not genetic fixtures, like the dimensions of the parts of the inner ear, but factors that come and go with use.

Adaptations to Altitude

ADAPTATION to altitude is a simple matter. It involves principally the ability of the body of a pregnant woman to move enough oxygen from the placenta into the fetus to ensure its survival. In Wyoming and Colorado, at altitudes above 10,000 feet, there is an incidence of 20 percent to 30 percent more miscarriages than in lower-lying parts of the United States. In Lake County, Colorado, infants are small at birth, and shortly after birth 30 percent more of them die than is the case with children born at lower altitudes.[4] For the Mongoloids, however, 10,000 feet is no hazard. Some of them live normal lives and produce healthy children even at an altitude of over 14,000 feet. They do this in the only two available places on the earth, the Andes and Tibet. During the colonial period the Spanish Conquistadors made many attempts to acclimatize both Europeans and Negroes to the heights, but without success. Negroes who were imported to work in the mines died. Individual Europeans were able to adapt, but for over fifty years none of their children lived past infancy. Hybrids of European fathers and Indian mothers did better, and the reproduction rates improved with further addition of Indian genes.[5] As a result, the highlands of Ecuador, Peru, and Bolivia are still largely inhabited by Indians.

The secret of the Indians' success at reproduction in the Andes is well known.[6] Their chests, lungs, and hearts are large. Their arms and legs are short. The volume of their blood is greater than that of most other people. And their blood is thick and very

4 D. Grahn and J. Kratchman: "Variation in Neonatal Death Rate and Birth Weight in the United States and Possible Relations to Environmental Radiation, Geology and Altitude," AJHG, Vol. 15, No. 4 (1963), pp. 329–52.

5 C. Monge: *Acclimatization in the Andes* (Baltimore: John Hopkins Press; 1948).

6 Newman: "Mankind and the Heights," NH, Vol. 67, No. 1 (1958), pp. 9–19.

red, with a high proportion of red corpuscles. Although each individual corpuscle carries no more oxygen than those of other races at this altitude, their sheer number provides the amount of oxygen needed for success in reproduction. Until the Chinese Communists drove thousands of Tibetans into India, we had no way of knowing whether their ability to reproduce at comparable heights was due to the same combination of factors. This problem is now being studied among Tibetan exiles, and preliminary reports indicate that the same factors are at work.

Blood, Breath, and the Shape of the Nose

I N F I V E previous chapters we frequently mentioned racial differences in the shape of the nose. We noted that the nose tends to be long and narrow, and often beaky, in people who live in dry or cold places, or both, whereas among the inhabitants of the wet tropics the nose is usually short and wide. The shape of the nostrils also varies from parallel slits to funnel-shaped holes.

In India and elsewhere these variations in the form of the nose are often regarded as status symbols. Whatever the social implications, these variations are functional. The principal function of the nose, aside from smelling odors wafted in the air, is to moisten and heat the air inhaled by the lungs. This processing is done almost instantaneously and very efficiently by tissues and capillaries lining the nasal passages,[7] and is thus one more function of the vascular system. The task of the nasal passages is to bring the air in the lungs to a temperature of 95°F and a relative humidity of 95 percent. The critical factor is not the temperature but the humidity, but the air has to be warm because colder air will not carry that much water vapor.

The average daily amount of air breathed by a human being is about 500 cubic feet. The moisture in it which is needed for the proper functioning of the lungs is about 19 ounces. This moisture must come from both the atmosphere and the nasal passages, the relative proportions depending on the climatic conditions. Cold air carries little water. At a temperature of 0° F, 500 cubic feet of air is saturated when it contains one half of

[7] A. W. Proetz: *Applied Physiology of the Nose* (St. Louis, Mo.: Annals Publishing Co.; 1954). V. E. Negus: "Humidification of the Air Passages," AOL, Supplement 100 (1952), pp. 74–83. G. Macdonald: *On the Respiratory Functions of the Nose* (London: Alexander Watt; 1889).

an ounce of water. Usually it contains less. Hot dry air in the Libyan Desert, at a temperature of 122°F in the shade, contains 5.2 ounces of water. Table 6 shows the quantities of water sup-

TABLE 6

DAILY SUPPLY OF WATER REACHING THE LUNGS FROM TWO SOURCES, IN TERMS OF THE TEMPERATURE AND HUMIDITY OF THE ATMOSPHERE

Kind of Air	Oz. of H_2O taken from air	Oz. of H_2O supplied by nose	Total
Cold dry	.16	18.8	19
Cool moist	1.8	17.2	19
Hot dry	5.2	13.8	19
Warm moist	7.0	12.0	19
Hot moist	14.4	4.6	19

plied in a day by the air itself and by the blood vessels lining the nasal passages. The principal difference indicated in this table is that between hot moist air and all others, but the other differences are significant also.

Obviously, in order to perform its air-conditioning function, the surface area of the nasal lining has to be proportionate to its work load. A high, narrow nasal opening can warm and moisten air more efficiently than a short, broad one. This is why, as A. Thomson and L. H. F. Buxton discovered over forty years ago,[8] nasal indices vary in terms of zones of climate, with the lowest indices in the coldest and driest places and the highest indices in the hottest and most humid regions. A correlation can also be shown between nose form and altitude because the air at high places is both cool and thin.

The individual range of the width of the nasal opening on the skull is small, from about 20 to 30 millimeters, and the differences between racial means are even smaller. The variation in this measurement is limited because the lines of stress in the maxillary bones produced by the mechanical requirements of chewing run upward from the roots of the upper canines on either side of the nasal opening, and the distance between the canines depends on the size of these teeth and on the sizes of the four upper incisors between them. Among living races these six teeth do not

[8] A. Thomson and L. H. F. Buxton: "Man's Nasal Index in Relation to Certain Climatic Conditions," JRAI, Vol. 53 (1923), pp. 53–92.

vary greatly in size. Substantial differences in the area of the nasal passages, therefore, have to come from the height of the opening, which has no particular mechanical limitation. In all races, the height of the nasal opening is about 60 percent of the height of the upper face.[9] People living in dry and/or cold climates then have long faces, and those living in wet and/or hot climates may have short faces.

The forward projection of the bridge of the nose is also involved, to a limited extent, in this air-conditioning process in that it extends anteroposteriorly the surface area of the nasal tissues that heat and moisten the air. Whether a nose adapted for dry air has a convex profile depends on the general architecture of the skull. An Eskimo may have a flattish nose in which much of the functional surface is internal, where it is well protected, whereas a Sioux Indian, a Tibetan, an Arab, a highland Papuan, or a desert-dwelling Australian aborigine may have a beaky nose that serves the same purpose as efficiently as is needed. A Negro living in the highlands of Kenya may be expected to have a longer, narrower nose than a Negro living in the Congo basin.

Now that we know why noses differ from race to race and within races, there is no further need for anyone to postulate fabulous migrations involving the Lost Tribes of Israel or the Phoenicians to explain these differences. Furthermore, if an anatomist examines carefully the facial skeletons of people of different races all of whom have convex noses, he will find differences in the ways the bones contributing to the form of the nose fit together.[1] In any race, when needed the nose grows longer and higher through the usual evolutionary mechanisms.

Of Human Size and Form

THE SIZES of the human body and its various shapes are composite dimensions and composite ratios that are influenced by a myriad of factors, a few of which have been explained in this chapter. In 1847 Carl Bergmann, a German physiologist interested in the relationships of body mass, surface area, and heat production in warm-blooded animals, observed that within a species animal populations living in the colder parts of its range

[9] Most of this information regarding variations in the nasal opening of the skull come from a personal communication from Lucille Hoyme.

[1] Personal communication with Georg Neumann.

tended to be a larger and heavier than those living in the warmer parts. This is the essence of Bergmann's Rule,[2] announced only fourteen years later than Gloger's Rule on pigmentation.

Thirty years after Bergmann's pronouncement, J. A. Allen, an American zoologist who had never heard of it,[3] not only discovered it independently but further stated that the animals with the largest bodies might be found not in the coldest part of the range of their species, but somewhere nearer its center. To this he added that the protruding parts of the body such as tails, ears, beaks, limbs, and wings tend to be relatively shorter in the cooler part of the range than in its warmer regions. This last observation constitutes Allen's Rule,[4] which is better known than his modification of Bergmann's Rule. They are of equal validity and importance, as can be clearly seen in the case of man.

Allen's Rule explains the lean body build of desert folk, be they Tuaregs or Turkomans; the beanpole physique of the Nilotic Negroes; and the squat, short-limbed, and short-necked physique of peoples who dwell in cold regions. Allen's modification of Bergmann's Rule reflects the fact that beyond the point where winter cold ceases to be stimulating and becomes a hazard—a point beyond which no people went earlier than 13,000 years ago—bodies grow shorter and more globular, and weight fails to increase. It may even decrease.

In every species of animal there are functional limits to the sizes and proportions of its members because the different parts of the body do not increase or decrease in concert. Otherwise the Eskimo would be eight feet tall and have stilt-like legs that they could not keep warm. Other animals that survive in the temperatures which the Eskimo, Chukchi, and Tungus face every winter do so not so much because of increases in size as because of increases in efficiency of environmental protection. The human animal does the same thing by wearing the furs of other animals out of doors and by heating his habitations.

The peaks of stature and of weight found in different races have been indicated elsewhere. They reflect to a certain extent differences in kinds of adaptation and also differences in humidity as well as temperature. The maximum stature of Europeans

2 C. Bergmann: *"Uber die Verhältnisse der Wärmeökonomie der Thiere zu ihrer Grösse,"* GS, No. 3 (1947), pp. 595–708.

3 We are reminded of Morgan's rediscovery of Mendel's Law. Such scientific hiatuses would be almost impossible today thanks to *Science, Nature,* and comparable periodicals.

4 J. A. Allen: "The Influence of Physical Conditions in the Genesis of Species," RR, Vol. 1 (1877), pp. 108–40.

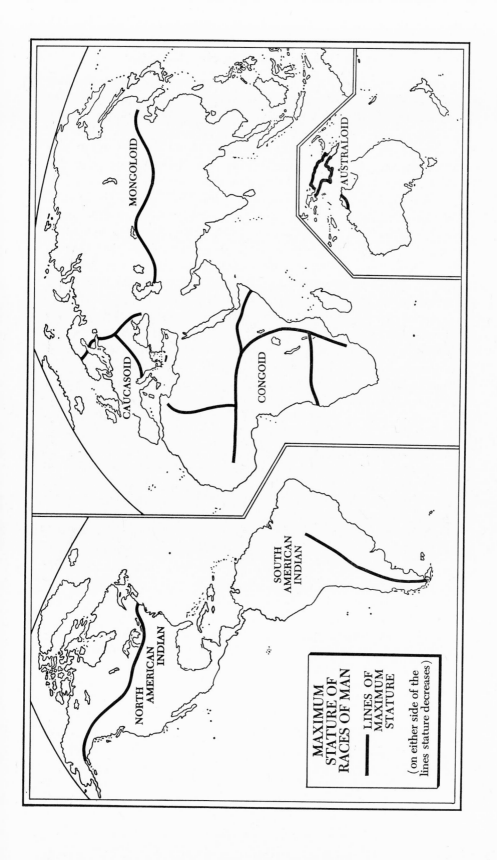

MAXIMUM
STATURE OF
RACES OF MAN

— LINES OF
MAXIMUM
STATURE

(on either side of the
lines stature decreases)

MONGOLOID

AUSTRALOID

CAUCASOID

CONGOID

NORTH
AMERICAN
INDIAN

SOUTH
AMERICAN
INDIAN

follows more or less the 25°F winter isotherm, between 14° and 32°. In Asia the Mongoloids are tallest in the east at about the +10°F line, but as one approaches the Pacific, one finds that their stature dips to the level of Europeans. This is so because the human body, however insulated or warmed, suffers less from dry cold than from wet cold.

In North America the peak stature is the same for American Indians and for Americans and Canadians of European origin. In Africa the situation is complicated by the elaborate mixture of races, the dwarfing of Pygmies and Bushmen, and the north-south axis of the highlands. The tallest Caucasoids are found in the desert, the tallest Negroes in the steamy swamps. In New Guinea the tallest people live along the coast, and stature falls to the Pygmy level in the highlands. In Australia the tallest aborigines live in the north, and stature goes down in the direction of the south pole; among white Australians the progression is exactly the opposite. Again we are reminded that because of wide distribution and isolation from each other over long periods, the subspecies of man have behaved as if they were separate species—which of course they are not.

Racial Differences of Uncertain Significance

EVERY DIFFERENCE between races which is great enough to be of statistical significance and which can be shown to be hereditary must have a reason. Either it is due to environmental selection, like those we have just discussed, or it has something to do with cultural differences, or it is the result of relaxation of selection in organs or systems of the body whose functions are no longer very important.

A good example of a trait of unknown significance is the dental pearls found among the Ainu and others in the northern periphery of both the Old and New World. As stated in Chapter 5, the distribution of this trait has genetic implications suggesting remote relationships between certain Caucasoid and Mongoloid peoples. Other examples are variations in type of earwax, in size of the eyeball, in the muscles of facial expression, in dermatoglyphics, in color blindness, and in the ability to taste phenylthiocarbamide (PTC).

Earwax

IN 1955 E. Matsunaga discovered that the cerumen, or wax that exudes from human earholes, comes in two forms, sticky and crumbly or dry.[5] We have already mentioned this in reference to the Ainus, but will discuss it in a more general way here. Dimorphism in earwax type is controlled at a single genetic locus, where an allele for wet wax is dominant over an allele for dry wax. Having determined this fact, Matsunaga proceeded to calculate the gene frequencies for peoples of many regions and races, as shown on Table 7.

TABLE 7

FREQUENCIES OF THE GENE FOR DRY EARWAX

Northern Chinese	.98
Koreans	.96
Tungus	.95
Mongols	.94
Japanese	.92
Southern Chinese	.86
Ryukyu Islanders	.79
Li of Hainan	.67
Micronesians	.61
Formosan aborigines	.53
Melanesians	.53
Ainus	.37
Germans	.18
American whites	.16
American Negroes	.07
Maya Indians*	.02

* 296 Indians of the Tzotzil, Zinancatec, and Tzeltal linguistic groups living near the border of Guatemala, reported in H. Kalmus, A. L. de Garay, U. Rodarte, and L. Cobon: "The Frequency of PTC Tasting, Hard Ear Wax, Colour Blindness, and Other Genetical Characters in Urban and Rural Mexican Populations," HB, Vol. 36, No. 2 (1964), pp. 134–45. The other figures are from Matsunaga: "The Dimorphism in Human Normal Cerumen."

Dry earwax is found in nearly all of the northern Asiatic Mongoloids. Its frequency decreases gradually as one moves southward to Micronesia, Formosa, and Melanesia. The Ainu turn out to be essentially Caucasoid in this respect, as previously stated.

[5] Matsunaga: "Polymorphism in Ear Wax Types and Its Anthropological Significance"; "The Dimorphism in Human Normal Cerumen," AHG, Vol. 25, No. 4 (1962), pp. 277–86.

No figures are available for Australian aborigines, but judging from the direction of the cline running from China to Melanesia, they should be low. Europeans have very little dry earwax, and African Negroes have even less. The figure for unmixed Maya Indians is amazing; if they were mixed with Europeans their percentages would be higher, as is the case with the mestizos studied by the same investigators. These figures appear to drive a thick wedge between Asiatic Mongoloids and American Indians, but we shall have to wait for more information on other tribes before trying to interpret this isolated finding.

Matsunaga realized that a polymorphism must have a function to exist, but he could find no correlation with blood groups or the tasting of PTC. He suggests that the condition is associated with the Caucasoid-Negroid type of body odor which the Japanese loathe. Cerumen is formed in a modified sebaceous gland, but so is milk, and the Maya Indians have no odor offensive to anyone. The problem is still unsolved.

Eyeball Size

THE SIZE of the human eyeball has been shown to vary from race to race. Because no figures on eyeball dimensions are available except from one Japanese source, we are obliged to express these differences in eyeball weight, measured in grams, as shown on Table 8.[6] As it is unlikely that the specific gravity of eyeballs

TABLE 8
EYEBALL WEIGHTS (IN GRAMS)
Right eyeballs only

	Males	Females
American Negroes	(37) 8.51 ± .10	(39) 7.95 ± .11
American whites	(52) 7.85 ± .05	(64) 7.29 ± .10
Japanese	(46) 7.42 ± .05	(19) 6.61 ± .15

differs very much racially, these weight measurements should reflect differences of absolute size. We have given figures for the right eyeball only, because it is heavier than the left eyeball in

6 T. W. Todd, H. Beecher, G. H. Williams, and A. W. Todd: "The Weight and Growth of the Human Eyeball," HB, Vol. 12, No. 1 (1940), pp. 1–20. Y. Tamaru: "On the Weight and Size of Human Eyes" (in Japanese), AOMA, Vol. 41 (1929), pp. 551–68.

all series by from .01 to .04 grams, an insignificant difference. To pool the two would be to count each individual twice, complicating the probability statistics.

It is clear from these figures that Negroes have significantly heavier eyeballs than do American whites and that the eyeballs of white Americans are significantly heavier than those of Japanese. Moreover, in all three races the eyeballs of males are heavier than those of women.

We have no idea how large the eyeballs of Australian aborigines and Bushmen are, but if those of the Bushmen turned out to be as large as those of Negroes, we would be surprised. Nor do we know what these racial differences mean. In general, nocturnal primates have larger eyeballs than diurnal primates, but no human race is nocturnal, only individuals.

The Muscles of Facial Expression

LIKE certain other primates, human beings sometimes express their feelings nonverbally, by facial grimaces. No one can express anguish more convincingly by his facial expression than an Italian. A Negro's facial expression, on the other hand, consists largely of exposing his eyeballs and his teeth. There is a good reason for this difference: the Italian's mobile and moving communication would be lost, under most lighting conditions, on a black face.

Communication through facial expression, a commonplace among baboons, has reached its peak among two racial groups, the European and Western Asian Caucasoids, and the Mongoloids of China and Japan. It depends upon the specialization of certain bundles of thin muscles derived from the platysma—the subcutaneous muscle sheath of mammals which permits them to shake their coats. Although Caucasoids and Eastern Asian Mongoloids have the most complicated and differentiated muscles of facial expression, the muscles are not the same in both groups.[7] In each race, separate sets of fibers of the platysma became segregated to take over this function, and the patterns are completely different from race to race. Furthermore, the muscle fibers in the Mongoloid faces are much coarser than in the European faces. In sum, light-skinned Caucasoids and Mongoloids independently

[7] E. Loth: *Anthropologie des Parties Molles* (Warsaw: Fondation Mianowski; and Paris: Masson et Cie.; 1931).

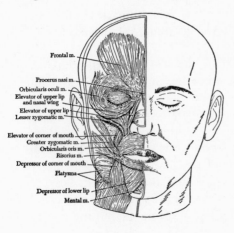

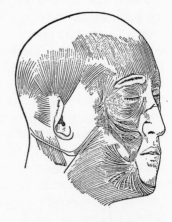

A European, from H.Sicher, *Oral Anatomy*,
(The C. V. Mosby Co: St. Louis, 1960).

A Chinese, from E. Loth, *Anthropologie des Parties Molles*,
(Warsaw: Fondation Mianowski, and Paris: Masson & Cie., 1931).

Fig. 5.—The Muscles of Facial Expression.

developed the same capacity for nonverbal communication through a change in the expression of their faces.

Dermatoglyphics[8]

DERMATOGLYPHICS is an inclusive term covering the study of the patterns of epidermal ridges seen on the grasping surfaces of the fingers and palms of the hands, and on the toes and soles of the feet. Like the tread of an automobile tire, these ridges keep us from slipping as we grasp things and as we walk. They also excrete moisture through the pores of sweat glands running along the crests of the ridges.

When hands, feet, fingers, and toes are inked and pressed on paper, these ridges make prints. They are particularly useful for genetic studies because they are formed in the eighteenth week of fetal life and are not influenced by environment afterward. Moreover, the measurable degree of similarity in certain characteristics of closely related individuals accurately reflects genetic distance. The most commonly taken and the only ones we shall discuss here are fingerprints, or, more accurately, fingertip prints.

[8] The standard work on this subject is Cummins and Midlo: *Finger Prints, Palms, and Soles.*

Specialists in dermatoglyphic studies, including members of the F.B.I., classify fingerprints in two ways, by patterns and by ridge counts. The patterns of fingerprints form a continuum from simple to complex, and are classified as arches, loops, and whorls. The simplest patterns are arches, which are wavy lines cresting upward. A loop is an oblique, U-shaped configuration that is cut off at its base by a transverse line. On one side of the finger the loop remains open. On the other side it joins its base line by a triangular junction known as a triradius. (See Figure 6.) A whorl

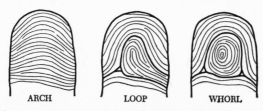

ARCH   LOOP   WHORL

Fig. 6.–Three Basic Types of Fingerprints.
(after H. Cummins & C. Midlo, 1961)

is an enclosed circular area joined to its base line by two triradii. In the comparison of fingerprint patterns of different populations it is customary to tabulate the percentages of arches, loops, and whorls in all the fingers. This is the basis for the first method of comparing fingerprints.

The second method is dependent on the first. It consists of counting the number of ridges between a triradius and the central point of a loop or whorl on all fingers which have them. In the case of a loop there is no choice, but in the case of a whorl, one selects the triradius that yields the higher count. Lacking triradii, arches cannot provide ridge counts.

From the genetic standpoint, counting ridges is a more sensitive tool than counting the numbers of arches, loops, and whorls. It is less complicated and can be more easily traced in studies of families. The total number of ridges found on all ten fingers ranged from 0 to 285 in one English sample.[9] The counts are almost but not exactly the same in identical twins, which suggests some disturbance before or at about the eighteenth week of fetal life. Total ridge count seems to have a polygenic basis of inheritance and to be little subject to selection.[1] We do not have enough data

[9] S. B. Holt: "Genetics of Dermal Ridges: Sib Pair Correlations for Total Finger Counts," AHG, Vol. 21, Part 4 (1957), pp, 352–62.
[1] L. Van Valen: "Selection in Natural Populations: Human Fingerprints," *Nature*, Vol. 200, No. 4912 (1963), pp. 1237–8.

as yet to use ridge counts for global racial studies, but they have already been employed to show genetic distance between neighboring castes in India.[2]

On the other hand, an extensive literature is available on the world-wide distribution of percentages of arches, loops, and whorls. A table giving the percentages of arches, loops, and whorls in 312 populations may be found in I. Schwidetzky's *Die neue Rassenkunde*,[3] on pages 37–49. As this book is readily available, we have reduced its massive contents to small compass in Table 9, which gives the regional ranges of percentages of fingerprint patterns throughout the world. Its message is simple and clear.

No population living east of Movius's Line, not even of Negritos, has an incidence of more than 8 percent of arches. To the west, there is an incidence of arches of from 10 percent to 16 percent in Pygmies other than Kivu potters, and in one other related group; in Bushmen; and in a few Negro tribes that have probably recently mixed with Pygmies. With a very few exceptions, Caucasoids have an incidence of no more than 8 percent of arches.

In all of Europe, Western Asia, Africa, and among the peoples of caste in India, there is a prevalence of loops of from 52 percent to 75 percent. One cannot distinguish Caucasoids, Negroes, Pygmies, or Bushmen from each other on this basis. In this sense the Ainu and the Gilyaks are Caucasoid too, and so, essentially, are most of the Eskimo. To the east of the half of the world dominated by loops, and with the exceptions noted, whorls reach maxima of over 50 percent among all Mongoloids, including American Indians. Among Australian aborigines and Negritos the minimum percentages of whorls are over 50 percent.

In sum, arches are unimportant as racial criteria, except that dwarfed African populations have an incidence of over 10 percent. A majority of loops characterizes the Caucasoids and all the Africans; Mongoloids have more whorls than loops, and Australoids have the most of all. A few local problems are illuminated by new information. The Ainus and Gilyaks are basically Caucasoid, as stated in Chapter 5, and the Eskimo seem to have a Caucasoid component. We have no data on the Lapps. As for the Basques, the Spanish Basques resemble neighboring Spaniards more than they do French Basques, who in this respect resemble other French citizens.

Even if we do not know as yet what differences in fingerprint

2 R. P. Srivastara: "A Quantitative Analysis of the Fingerprints of the Tharus of Uttar Pradesh," AJPA, 1965. In press.

3 Stuttgart: Gustav Fischer; 1962.

TABLE 9
REGIONAL RANGES OF FINGERPRINT PATTERNS

	Arches	Loops	Whorls
Europe	0–9[1]	63–76	20–42
Western Asia	2–8[2]	52–75	32–44
North Africa	1–7	54–62	28–43
India: Caste	2–4	55–63	33–42
Negroes	3–12	53–73	20–40
Pygmies	10–16[3]	52–70	16–42
Bushmen	13–16	66–68[4]	15–21
E. Asia, Mongoloids[5]	1–5	43–56	44–54
Ainu	2–7	63–70	26–35
Gilyaks	1	57	42
Eskimo[6]	1–5	49–63	34–47
Am. Indians[7]	2–8	46–61	35–57
S.E. Asia + Indonesia	1–5	44–64	32–55
India: tribal	0–2	38–60	37–48
Negritos	0–1	40–44	55–60
Australian abor.	0–1	28–46	52–73
Papuans + Melanesians	1–2	41–60	37–59
Micronesians	2	49	49–50

[1] Plus one Frisian series with 10.2%, one German series with 11.8%, and one Polish series with 12%.

[2] Plus one Turkish series with 14.3%.

[3] Excluding the potters of Lake Kivu (8.1%) and the Bakola Pygmies (7.2%). Six series are in the 10–16% range.

[4] The Hottentots have a 76% incidence of loops, the highest figure recorded anywhere.

[5] Excluding a small and aberrant series of 18 Orochs.

[6] Excluding the aberrant isolate in east Greenland, with a 1% of incidence of arches, 27% of loops, and 72% of whorls.

[7] Excluding a small and aberrant group of 40 Guyaki Indians from South America.

patterns mean, dermatoglyphics is a potent tool in racial classification, as it shows no discernible relationship to the physical or social environment.

Color Blindness

RACIAL STUDIES are always complicated by the coexistence and interaction of these two areas of selection, environmental and behavioral. Environmental selection is what makes races differ from each other in most of the anatomical details that easily meet the eye, such as the color of the skin and the form of the nose. Behavioral selection is the mechanism by which the living races of man evolved from their ancestral species. Either area of selection can have both positive and negative aspects, as we gain one trait or capacity and lose another.

If the pruning by natural selection of deleterious or nonadaptive variants should become less efficient than before, through changes in the physical or cultural environment, then these variants—like loose sails luffing in the wind—would begin to accumulate in the population. In 1962 R. H. Post suggested that high frequencies of color blindness illustrate relaxed selection. This handicap is due to genetic defects in both the green and the red ranges of color vision. Green color blindness is about three times as common as red, and more men are color-blind than women.[4] Another illustration is myopia.[5]

Post divided the numerous populations tested for these defects into three groups: people who still live primarily by hunting and gathering; those who have fairly recently begun to grow crops, raise domestic animals, or both; and those whose ancestors were engaged in food production for thousands of years. Among the hunters, only about 2 percent of the males are color-blind. Among the intermediate group the toll rises to about 3.3 percent, and in the third it varies from about 6 percent to 10 percent. These differences have nothing to do with race except, and only by coincidence, that those Caucasoid and Mongoloid peoples whose ancestors gave up hunting the earliest have the highest percentages of color blindness.

Post reasoned that hunters need accurate color vision to succeed in the chase, or even to survive, that farmers and herdsmen are less dependent on color vision, and urban populations are the least dependent on it. Elizabeth Marshall Thomas has cited the example of a Bushman who was not allowed to marry because he had never killed a buck, who was dependent on his sister for food, and who was nearly blind at the time she photographed him. What kind of eye defect he had we do not know, but it is not unreasonable to suppose that his poor vision and his bachelorhood were interrelated.[6] In Minnesota, during the 1953 deer-hunting

4 R. H. Post: "Population Differences in Red and Green Color Vision Deficiency: A Review and a Query on Selection Relaxation," EQ, Vol. 9, No. 3 (1962), pp. 131–46; "Selection against 'Colorblindness' among 'Primitive' Populations," EQ, Vol. 12, No. 1 (1965), pp. 28–9. J. V. Neel: "Mutations in the Human Population," in W. J. Burdette, ed.: *Methodology in Human Genetics* (San Francisco, Calif.: Holden-Day; 1962), pp. 203–24. Neel and R. H. Post: "Transitory 'Positive' Selection for Colorblindness?" EQ, Vol. 10, No. 1 (1963), pp. 33–5.

5 R. H. Post: "Population Differences in Visual Acuity: A Review, with Speculative Notes on Selection Relaxation," EQ, Vol. 9, No. 4 (1962), pp. 189–212.

6 E. M. Thomas: *The Harmless People*, p. 150 and Plate 15b.

season, 60 percent of the hunters who shot other hunters, mistaking them for deer, were color-blind, and all of their victims wore red.[7]

J. V. Neel has pointed out that the changes brought about by mutations in the frequencies of the genes controlling both types of color blindness are too high to be accounted for by relaxation of selection alone, and that there should be some positive selection in their favor.[8] Basing his calculation on Post's assumption that agriculture had begun in all the populations of his third group by about 4,000 years ago, Neel postulated a mutation rate of one out of 10,000 per locus per generation for green color blindness and one of three out of 10,000 for red. As mutation rates go, these are extremely high. If we place the onset of agriculture at 8,000 years ago, which in several parts of the world is a likelier date than 4,000 years ago, the mutation rates quoted would be halved, but they would still be too high to account for without selection. Neel and Post have therefore suggested that with the rise of a division of labor, creating crafts, a priesthood, and the like, color-blind men may have been drawn into these visually uncritical occupations, which in many cultures are endogamous. With the growth of cities and of industry, and the relative decrease of the rural population in many countries, the incidence of color blindness may be expected to have increased even more.

While Post's hypothesis is still open, his contribution to methodology is beyond question. The association of archaeology, cultural anthropology, and genetics which he has made creates a new dimension in physical anthropology that may help us solve some other problems which, unlike color blindness, are racial.

Tasters and Nontasters

O V E R thirty years ago a chemist spilled a synthetic compound in a laboratory, and during the mopping-up process he and his coworkers had the temerity to taste the substance. An argument arose at once as to whether it was bitter or tasteless.[9] The substance was phenylthiocarbamide, or PTC, a substance that does not exist in nature. Since then the laboratory argument has grown into a global tasting match in which thousands of people of many countries and races, and even a number of apes and monkeys,

---

[7] D. E. Foltz: "Boobs in the Woods," SEP, Oct. 13, 1962, p. 8.
[8] Neel: op. cit. Neel and Post: op. cit.
[9] Hulse: *The Human Species* (New York: Random House; 1963), p. 319.

have had slips of paper saturated with this compound thrust into their mouths. Geneticists fancy this test because it is easy, the trait is genetically simple, and it has no implications of superiority or inferiority.

Ilse Schwidetzky, with her usual painstaking breadth of coverage, has listed 141 populations tested for tasting and the percentages of tasters and nontasters found in each.[1] When her table is broken down into regional and racial units, and the data for both sexes is pooled, the following distributions appear. Unfortunately we have no data for Pygmies or Bushmen.

TABLE 10

PERCENTAGES OF INDIVIDUALS ABLE TO TASTE PTC

	Tasters
Europeans other than Lapps, Western Asians, Egyptians, Indians of caste	59%–83%
Lapps	93%
Ainus	94%–96%
Eskimo	59%–74%
Negroes	91%–97%
Eastern Asian Mongoloids, American Indians, Indonesians, Polynesians	83%–100%
Micronesians	72%–82%
India: tribal	63%–82%
Önges (Andamans)	68%
Papuans, Melanesians, Australian aborigines	49%–67%

Unlike color blindness, the ability to taste PTC has no circumstantial association with the level of cultural complexity, but it is associated, in a curious way, with race. The Mongoloids and the Negroes have the highest percentage of people with the ability to taste PTC, and the Australian aborigines, the Papuans, and the Melanesians have the fewest. Thus, in this respect, the east-west division of the world found in so many genetic characters breaks down. Obviously, tasters and nontasters have been selected for something different from either cultural or physical environment in the broad sense. Three associations with disease have been reported—as yet without confirmation—but none of them seems important enough to explain the world distribution of tasting. Caucasoid nontasters over forty years old are particularly likely to have glaucoma.[2] Nontasters of several races have been found

1 *Die neue Rassenkunde*, pp. 63–7.
2 B. Becker and W. R. Morton: "Taste Sensitivity to Phenylthiourea in Glaucoma," *Science*, Vol. 144, No. 1624 (1964), pp. 1347–8.

to be more susceptible than tasters to certain thyroid difficulties, including goiter.[3] Among a triracial isolate in southern Maryland, the nontasters had the most dental caries.[4]

Although PTC is an artificial product, related substances that taste much like it have been found in certain nonpoisonous wild plants, including edible roots. Among a large minority, the inability to taste PTC would permit food gatherers like Australian aborigines, who depend on wild vegetable products as much as on game, to enjoy an ampler menu than they might if all or nearly all of them found an abundant, bitter-tasting plant repulsive. Since Bushmen eat many wild vegetable products, it would be interesting to know how many of them are able to taste PTC.

These observations and suggestions only serve to emphasize the fact that the more we learn about race the more avenues of research are opened to us, and the more we realize that human beings may adapt themselves to most of the visible and invisible selective forces that they face in the world, and not just the most conspicuous ones. This will become particularly evident in our study of the blood groups.

[3] K. D. Kitchen, W. Howell Evans, C. A. Clarke, R. B. McConnell, and P. M. Sheppard: "PTC taste responses and thyroid disease," BMJ, Vol. 1 (1959), pp. 1069–74. E. Azevêdo, H. Krieger, M. M. Mi, and N. E. Morton: "PTC taste sensitivity and endemic goiter in Brazil," AJHG, Vol. 17, No. 1 (1965), pp. 87–90.

[4] C. S. Chung, C. J. Witkop, and J. L. Henry: "A Genetic Study of Dental Caries with Special Reference to PTC Taste Sensibility," AJHG, Vol. 16, No. 2 (1962), pp. 231–45.

9

Race, Blood, and Disease

How Infant Mortality Accelerates Natural Selection

T HE MAJORITY of the morphological variables of the human organism which we have studied in the last chapter should not, if left to their own selective resources, be expected to change the gene frequencies of populations very rapidly because their selection rates are low and few of them completely prevent reproduction. Selection for altitude is an exception, as it has to do with the transfer of oxygen between mother and fetus and may prevent the baby from being born.

It would take a relatively long time for most of the characters unfavorable under certain conditions of light, temperature, and humidity to be removed from a local gene pool by natural selection if they were not associated in one way or another with some other genetic factor or factors limiting the effects of diseases that destroy fetuses, babies, and small children. Where such an association exists, these morphological traits may be reduced rapidly, or even be eliminated. In the past, diseases of infancy have killed off a high proportion of all babies born, in some cases well over fifty percent, as they still do in unsanitary regions. Natural selection favoring disease-thwarting genes is therefore rapid. Most of these genes that have so far been identified are carried throughout the various organs of the body in its fluids. They are found in or on red blood cells, in serum, or both.

Some of them have been shown by clinical study, which is as close as we can come to experimenting with human beings, to resist the lethal or debilitating impact of certain diseases. Others have been associated with specific diseases through geographical coincidence, a biological equivalent of guilt through association. A third group of blood factors vary geographically with or without apparent racial significance, and although they may turn out to be part of the body's weaponry against disease, so far their individual targets, if they have them, are unknown. At present these last are, from our point of view, simply racial markers, as all blood groups were thought to be before the roles of some of them in thwarting individual diseases were discovered.

But the new discoveries that some blood-group substances protect people against disease does not destroy the usefulness of the blood groups as a set of tools in studying races. Instead it makes them comparable to other inherited characters long known to be affected by natural selection. Also, it would be surprising if resistance to disease should turn out to be the only function of the substances carried by the blood because it is a commonplace of genetics that a gene which helps produce one effect is likely to be involved in others. This phenomenon is known as *pleiotropy*.

How the Genes for the Blood Groups Are Associated with Morphological Traits

S O F A R, however, the genes governing the blood groups have not been linked to any of the morphological traits studied in the last chapter, such as skin color, hair form, and nose form. In fact, attempts to discover such linkages have uniformly failed.[1] The only thing that has been found is instances of geographical coincidence, as where a high frequency of blood group O coincides with a high frequency of blue eyes. An individual from that particular population has a good chance of transmitting the genes for both conditions. It is another case of guilt by association, which is good enough for our purposes.

Let us anticipate what is to follow by an example. A certain African people who have black skins live in a region sorely beset by several forms of malaria. Over generations their ancestors have been selected and reselected in favor of a number of genes that together manage to keep malaria from wiping them out. At one point in history a group of invaders gallops in off the desert

[1] Schwidetzky: "Neuere Entwicklungen in der Rassenkunde des Menschen," in *Die neue Rassenkunde,* pp. 92–4.

and conquers these malaria-resistant Negroes. In the desert both malaria and malaria-resisting genes are absent. The invaders have light skins. Infants born to invaders by the women they have brought with them perish in great numbers from malaria. Infants born to invaders by local women have a better chance of survival, and those born to the unmixed local people have the best chance of all. The invaders may remain as a local aristocracy, but most of them will soon be as black as their subjects, and they will possess about the same frequencies of local blood-group genes that provide protection against malaria.

Mechanisms like the one just cited help explain why W. C. Boyd's classification of races, as outlined in Chapter 2, closely coincides with the classification based mostly on morphology which is used in this book. They also help to explain certain differences between these two classifications. Despite the morphological differences of Bushmen and Negroes, Boyd includes them in a single race because of their similarities in the information on blood groups available to him. This is to be expected. Being African races, both have been exposed to African diseases. Boyd separates the Asiatic Mongoloids from the American Indians, classifying them as two races. Morphologically both are basically Mongoloid. The American Indians have a simpler and more nearly uniform blood-group pattern. There are several possible reasons for this, among them the fact that their ancestors crossed Bering Strait, where the cold may have screened out the genes for resisting diseases common in warmer places, which operate through mechanisms to be explained later in this chapter.

The Critical Diseases and How They Are Thwarted Genetically

THE CHILDHOOD DISEASES with which we are chiefly concerned are malaria, plague, smallpox, bronchopneumonia, and infant diarrhea. These are by no means all the killers that have depopulated islands and parts of continents, but they are the only ones for which specific genetic defenses may even be suggested at the present state of our knowledge.[2] To this list may be tenta-

---

[2] No comparable defenses have been discovered, or even postulated on the basis of geographical coincidence, for yaws, hookworm, cholera, tuberculosis, bacillary dysentery, amoebic dysentery, measles, scarlet fever, typhoid, the paratyphoids, undulant fever, Malta fever, or trachoma. Some of these diseases are certainly as important from our point of view as any of the others listed above except malaria.

tively added syphilis, which affects persons of all ages and is not as great a baby killer as those listed above; rheumatic diseases; some forms of cancer; and pernicious anemia. The last two destroy older people much more than they do children, and therefore their influences must move at a relatively sluggish pace. But they will change the genetic constitution of the population in the long run. It seems to be part of the strategy of nature that the principal genetic factors that soften the blows of infant diseases are other diseases. It is a matter of a private disease killing a public one. We are reminded of a shepherd's dog who eats more than his share of his master's food, but who protects his master's sheep against wolves.

In the interplay between genetic and infectious diseases, the victim of both may be weakened, but he may survive to reproduce. The victim of either disease alone might not survive. The reason is to be sought in the mechanism of polymorphism. We have mentioned it elsewhere in this book, and shall now explain it briefly.

The Importance of Polymorphisms in Resisting Diseases

A s i t s Greek etymology implies, a polymorphism is a condition characteristic of populations which have more than one form for any genetic character. Any one of two or more alleles may be found on either or both of a pair of chromosomes. (Alleles are alternative genes which may be found on a single position on a chromosome. Actually, an allele is a molecule of protein, like all other genes.) If the same allele is found on both chromosomes, the individual of whom the chromosome is a part is homozygous for that character. If different alleles are found on the two chromosomes, he is heterozygous; he is not polymorphic, but the population of which he is a part is.

When a population is polymorphic for a given trait which depends on a single genetic locus and the frequencies of the two alleles are known, then it is possible to calculate the expected percentage of heterozygotes.[3] If the heterozygotes significantly exceed the expected number, one suspects that some selective force is pruning one or perhaps both of the homozygotes. Some of the homozygotes were perhaps never born, or if they were, they died young so that the sampling studied did not include them.

The heterozygote is favored by the selective forces—as for

[3] By the Hardy-Weinberg, formula, $p^2 : 2 pq : q^2$, when p and q represent the frequencies of the two alleles.

example in the case of the sickle-cell trait versus malaria—which we cited in Chapter 4 and will now deal with at greater length. If you happen to be a homozygous sickler you may die of anemia in childhood, and if you are a homozygous non-sickler, malaria may fell you at an early age. If you are a heterozygote for sickling, however, you may suffer somewhat from your hereditary defect, but not be weakened enough not to be able to reproduce, having resisted malaria at least to an age suitable for that purpose.[4]

As long as a group of people who have acquired genetic defenses against endemic local diseases remain in their disease-ridden location, and no one eliminates the diseases' hosts by means of DDT, drainage, or other sanitary precautions, the polymorphisms that protect the people will continue to be balanced. In other words, the frequencies of the allelic combinations will remain at the optimum level to cope with both the invading and the protecting diseases at the same time. But if some organization like the Peace Corps reduces the local disease organisms by means of public health measures, or if the people themselves move to a new region where the disease against which they have been genetically battling is not found, then the balance will become upset as the selective advantages of the heterozygotic individuals vanish, and the genetic defect which once insured their survival will become scarcer and scarcer and may eventually disappear.

The Three Factors in the Blood That Influence Diseases, Mark Races, or Both

THREE CATEGORIES of blood substances are known to offer, or thought to offer, resistance to diseases. These are the hemoglobins, the blood-group antigens, and the globulins. The first of these, the hemoglobins, are effective only in their abnormal forms. The hemoglobins as a whole, normal and abnormal, are substances inside the blood cells. Their function is to transport oxygen to the tissues of the body. A hemoglobin has two parts, the *heme* or iron-containing portion, which does not concern us here, and the *globin*, which consists of four chains of amino acids folded in a complex pattern. The latter provides the hemoglobins's defense

---

4 We are aware that this paragraph is an oversimplification of the rather complex mechanism involved, as anyone can discover who goes to the original literature on the subject.

against disease in its abnormal form. In normal hemoglobins the order of the molecules in each strand, and the chemical composition of each molecule, are invariable.

Variations in either the order or the chemical composition of one or more molecules in any of the four strands may inhibit the functioning of the hemoglobin as a whole and at the same time give rise to a disease of its own making, one which resists a second disease brought in by infection from outside the organism. Because the technical details of the manner in which one disease fights another have little to do with anthropology, they do not warrant description here.

Substances of the second category are macromolecules which ride loosely on, or are imbedded in, the surfaces of the red blood cells, or float in the serum, or all three. These macromolecules are the antigens of the well-known ABO and Rh blood groups and of other less famous blood factors. That they are involved in some way in the destruction of disease organisms is suggested by the way they act when hostile blood is transfused. They have not yet been caught in the act of attacking the organisms of smallpox, plague, and the like, but if they do so, they may eventually be apprehended.

Their resistance to specific diseases has been indicated by three methods: clinical association, geographical association, and chronological association. In the third case, polymorphisms wax and wane in concert with the relative severity of the diseases which they are suspected of combatting.

We have voluminous data on the geography of blood groups and of diseases, but very little clinical information, and even less data on the periodic fluctuations of polymorphisms. Chronological data is scarce because the first blood groups were discovered only in 1901, and few records go back more than forty years.

Another feature of some of the blood groups, most notably ABO and Rh, is the failure of certain categories of marital partners to reproduce. The Rh-negative hazard is well known. The ABO one is as important, if not more so. In both systems, when a man and a woman of certain combinations of blood types beget and conceive a child, antigens which agglutinate each other may pass between the pregnant woman's blood and that of her fetus, causing abortion. The resulting loss imposes a certain genetic load on the populations affected. Large, healthy populations may afford it. In a population that is small and already overloaded with diseases, however, an overly great degree of blood-group incompatibility might tip the scales and bring about extinction. But this does not always happen, as we know from the study of some populations of this kind. When the disease load is critical, the genes responsible for incompatibility tend to disappear. In this sense the frequency of these expensive polymorphisms is inversely proportional to the severity of the diseases that afflict them.

The third category of blood substances of interest to anthropologists embraces those showing geographical variations which help define races genetically, but which have no clear association, geographical or otherwise, with particular diseases. This may simply mean that we know less about them than about the other two. Some of them are rare blood-group alleles which are usually named after the first person known to have reacted to them, like Duffy. Others are the *globulins*, which are proteins carried in the plasma. Three of these have been studied enough to show variations of anthropological interest.

The *transferrins* transport iron throughout the body and help protect it against the loss of iron ions. The *haptoglobins* remove exhausted hemoglobin from the blood after the red cells have disintegrated. The gamma globulins are believed to perform a similar function for the Rh substances, and are also involved in protecting the body against diseases. Genetic variations in each of these three have been detected by electrophoresis, a technique that measures their speed in movement on an electric field. In all three the variations so detected have begun to show geographical variations of anthropological significance.

Primatologists have successfully used haptoglobins in measuring the genetic distances between primate species. If this technique can be sufficiently refined, it may become a new tool in classifying the races of man as accurate as dermatoglyphics and earwax are.

Diseases and Their Protectors, Known or Suspected

OUR NEXT STEP in trying to determine the relationship between diseases, blood, and race will be to study each of the small number of diseases known to be or suspected of being influenced by factors in the blood. The order in which they will be treated is that listed in Table 11. We have tried to make it reflect a balance between the probable importance of each such disease in the history of human races and the soundness of its relationships with the blood types named. Only the first is considered sound. The rest remain, in varying degrees, *sub judice*.

TABLE 11
DISEASES, BLOOD TYPES, AND MEANS OF VALIDATION

Diseases	Blood Factors	Validation		
		Clinical	Geogr.	Chronol.
Malaria	Alpha thalassemias	+	+	
	Beta thalassemias	+	+	
	Hemoglobins S, C, E	+	+	
	G6PD deficiency	+	+	
Infant diarrhea	ABO	+		+
Bronchopneumonia	ABO	+		
Rheumatic diseases	Rh (Gene D)	+		
	MN (Gene N)	+		
	Gamma Globulin (Gm (a+))	+		
Smallpox	ABO		+	
	MN (Gene N)		+	
Plague	ABO		+	
Cancers	ABO	+		
Ulcers	ABO, Secretor	+		
Pernicious anemia	ABO		+	
Syphilis	ABO	+(?)	+	
	Diego		+	

Malaria

MALARIA, a prime killer of mankind and particularly of infants and children, is concentrated in the tropics of the Old World, from West Africa to Melanesia, and is especially prevalent in wet forests. It was probably nonexistent, before the advent of Europeans, in the New World,[5] Australia, Micronesia, and Polynesia. It rarely extends into regions above an altitude of 6,000 feet or above the winter frost line.

In man four species of plasmodium parasites cause it: *Plasmodium falciparum*, *Plasmodium vivax*, *Plasmodium malariae*, and *Plasmodium ovale*. The first, and the most widespread, produces subtertian fevers; the second, tertian fevers; and the third, quartan fevers. The fevers that result from the fourth resemble those brought about by *Plasmodium vivax*. In parts of West Africa

---

[5] Marston Bates: "Man as an Agent in the Spread of Organisms," in W. L. Thomas, Jr., ed.; *Man's Role in Changing the Face of the Earth* (Chicago: University of Chicago Press; 1956), pp. 788–804. T. D. Stewart: "A Physical Anthropologist's View of the Peopling of the New World," SWJA, Vol. 16, No. 3 (1960), pp. 259–73.

where both *Plasmodium vivax* and *Plasmodium ovale* are found, the local inhabitants are virtually immune to *P. vivax*.[6]

The mosquitoes that infect people with these plasmodia consist of several dozen species of the genus *Anopheles*. Apparently these species are local rather than specialized in the particular parasite carried. In West Africa, for example, *Anopheles gambiae* is the chief agent of *Plasmodium falciparum* in open country. In the shade of the forest, however, *Anopheles funestis* carries the same parasite.

As indicated in Table 11, genetic defenses against malaria are provided, as far as we know, only by polymorphisms in the hemoglobins. These polymorphisms are caused by individual abnormalities in one or more of the globin chains. The biochemical details need not concern us here.[7] All we need to know is that each abnormality has arisen independently by mutation, and that they affect the life cycles of the red cells, cause anemia, and, in at least some cases, reduce the amount of oxygen carried to the tissues of the body from the lungs.

The thalassemias, because they were first identified in the Mediterranean countries, bear a name containing the Greek word for "sea." Four of the so-called alpha thalassemias which concern us are Thalassemia H, Barts' Thalassemia, Thalassemia E, and Lepore's Thalassemia.[8] Each is biochemically unique. They are concentrated in Southeast Asia, but have also been reported to exist in Nigeria.[9] Both regions are characterized by intense falciparum malaria.

The principal beta thalassemia is the classic "Mediterranean thalassemia," or Cooley's anemia, endemic not only in the region

6 S. Adler: "Remarks on the Host Range of Some Malarial Parasites," in E. Goldschmidt, ed.: *The Genetics of Migrant and Isolate Populations* (Baltimore: Williams and Wilkins; 1963), pp. 114–17.

7 Walter E. Nance: "Genetic Control of Hemoglobin Synthesis," *Science*, Vol. 141, No. 3576 (1963), pp. 123–9. F. Jacob and J. Monod: "Genetic regulatory mechanisms in the synthesis of proteins," JMB, Vol. 3 (1961), pp. 318–56. D. L. Rucknagel and J. V. Neel: "The Hemoglobinopathies," in A. G. Steinberg, ed.: *Progress in Medical Genetics*, Vol. 1 (New York: Grune and Stratton; 1961), pp. 158–260.

8 Lie-Injo Luan Eng: "Haemoglobinopathies in East Asia," AHG, Vol. 28, Part 1 (1964), pp. 101–11. S. H. Boyer, D. L. Rucknagel, D. J. Weatherall, and E. J. Watson-Williams: "Further Evidence for Linkage Between the Beta and Delta Loci Governing Human Hemoglobin and the Population Dynamics of Linked Genes," AJHG, Vol. 15, No. 4 (1963), pp. 438–48. S. Tuchinda, D. L. Rucknagel, V. Minnich, U. Boonyaprakob, K. Balankura, and V. Suvatee: "The Coexistence of the Genes for Hemoglobin E and Thalassemia in Thais, with Resultant Suppression of Hemoglobin E Synthesis," AJHG, Vol. 16, No. 3 (1964), pp. 311–35.

9 R. G. Hendrickse, A. E. Boyo, P. A. Fitzgerald, and S. R. Kuti: "Studies on the Haemoglobin of Newborn Nigerians," BMJ, Vol. I, No. 5172 (1960), pp. 611–14.

for which it is named but also in the malarial regions of Africa and Southern Asia, and all the way to China, the Philippines, and New Guinea. An incidence of at least one of the beta thalassemias has also been reported in West Africa, the world's focal point of diversity and concentration of antimalarial genes.

Earlier in the book we referred to sickle-cell anemia caused by hemoglobin S. This malady is characterized by a shriveling of those red cells affected by it into a fancied sickle shape. In addition to providing defense against malaria to heterozygotes, sickling also reduces the oxygen in the blood and may limit the ability of persons with this trait to live at high altitudes.[1]

Negroes living in the highlands of East Africa have little sickle-cell anemia, probably due to a combination of relaxation of selection for it in the absence of malaria, and selection against it because of the thin air. In the New World, which Negroes have lived in for only a few centuries, they are not found in any great numbers on the Andean altiplano. Among North American Negroes, sickling seems to be on the wane, probably as a result of the virtual elimination of malaria where they live, and because of admixture with persons of other races, or either of the two. A comparable relaxation of selection has been observed among the Negroes living in the interior highlands of Dutch Guiana, where malaria is rare,[2] but among the Black Caribs of British Honduras, where malaria is still active, the gene frequency of the sickling trait remains in a stable polymorphic balance with the incidence of malaria.[3]

The sickle-cell trait is concentrated in West Africa, but is also found elsewhere. It runs up the west coast of Africa to Morocco and Algeria and is also present in Sicily, Greece, Cyprus, Syria, southern Anatolia, along the Arabian coast, and in southern Iran, and in restricted parts of India and Burma. In most of these places, except tropical Africa, the people who have it are not Negroes. Although Negroes may have been the first to spread it, it is also possible that it has arisen through independent mutations in different regions where it has a selective advantage. We sus-

---

[1] It is particularly hazardous for heterozygous sicklers to fly in unpressured airplanes. R. H. Kampier: "Splenic Infarction Due to Sicklemia and Air Travel," SoMJ, Vol. 50 (1957), pp. 277–8.

[2] J. H. P. Jonxis: "The Frequency of Haemoglobin S and Haemoglobin C carriers in Curaçao and Surinam," in Jonxis and J. F. Delafresnaye, eds.: *Abnormal Haemoglobins. Symposium Organized by the Council for International Organizations of Medical Sciences* (Oxford: Blackwell; 1959), pp. 300–6.

[3] Firschein: "Population Dynamics of the Sickle-Cell Trait in the Black Caribs of British Honduras, Central America."

pect that this latter may be true in some cases, since in Africa itself there is more than one gene for sickling.[4]

Another antimalarial gene, that for Hemoglobin C, is local to West Africa, whence it seems to have spread to North and South Africa and to the New World, but only in small amounts. It produces only a mild anemia and seems to take the place of the sickling gene where malaria is less critical. If this interpretation is correct, Hemoglobin C may possibly be regarded as a tapering-off gene—though this has not yet been demonstrated clinically—a gene that offers protection from a plasmodium less lethal than *Plasmodium falciparum*.

So far we have concentrated on West Africa, the world's greatest arena of malarial organisms and of genetic defenses against them, but we must not forget that Southeast Asia, Indonesia, coastal New Guinea, and its neighboring islands constitute another tropical forest region with severe malarial problems. In this setting, a local antimalarial mutation, Hemoglobin E, seems to have arisen. Just as several antimalarial mechanisms act in concert or even in equilibrium with each other in Africa, so in the extended Southeast Asiatic world Hemoglobin E is mutually entangled with the alpha thalassemias.

In addition to the thalassemias and Hemoglobins S, C, and E, another foe of malaria has been discovered in the form of a hereditary deficiency in a chemical compound bearing the awesome name of glucose-6-phosphate-dehydrogenase. The whole concept—deficiency, chemical, and all—has been abbreviated into G6PD. This genetic defect depends upon a mutation in the female sex chromosome, X. If a woman inherits it, she may or may not be somewhat anemic, depending on whether she carries the defect on both chromosomes or on one only. If a man inherits it, it may be expected to give him a more severe anemia because he has only one X chromosome. Thus men are the most numerous sufferers, and healthy women the principal carriers.

Long before its relationship to falciparal malaria was even suspected, G6PD deficiency had been recognized as being responsible for a disease called favism, because of its relationship to *favas* (*Vicia faba*), or the broad bean. Affected persons who eat the seeds of this plant or even inhale its pollen suffer severe allergic reactions, including hemolytic anemia, jaundice, fever, and diarrhea. Although this genetic defense against malaria is

[4] M. Hall-Craggs, P. D. Marsden, A. B. Raper, H. Lehmann, and D. Beale: "Homozygous Sickle-cell Anemia Arising from Two Different Haemoglobin S," BMJ, Vol. 2 (1964), pp. 87–9.

concentrated in the swampy lowlands of the Mediterranean basin, it reaches its peak—an incidence of 60 percent—among Kurdish Jews, whose home is in the highlands. Like nearly all other antimalarial polymorphisms, it is present in West Africa. It has also been found as far afield as the malarial lowlands of New Guinea.

According to F. B. Livingstone,[5] in areas where a number of antimalarial polymorphisms coexist and all are engaged in combat with malaria, a balance arises between them. The most powerful polymorphisms become most numerous where the disease is most severe. When the disease has begun to relax, the guardians of medium strength rise to the fore, and so on down the line until they all eventually disappear, the least effective being the last to leave. This all makes excellent sense because a defense is always a burden, to be reduced by natural selection as it is needed less and less.

To a student of racial distribution and racial origins, Livingstone's study of malaria and of its blood-borne antagonists is of great interest. It indicates that the various species of plasmodia which cause malaria and the genetically independent defenses against it are not paired as individual plasmodium against individual human gene, but by rank of severity and of effectiveness as a defense.

In West Africa and the Southeast Asia focal area, the two principal malarial centers of the world, we find more or less the same diseases and the same genetic defenses, but in different balance. It would seem that in each area local mutations originally provided the needed curbs to malaria, then some of them were diffused from each center to the other, and each center has since achieved its own antimalarial equilibrium. Despite these diffusions, some of which may be quite recent, the Old World is still divided in half, in this respect as in so many others, by Movius's Line.

Malaria has been important racially in a related way, in that it has permitted the black-skinned peoples of Africa and the Southeast Asian focal area to survive the onslaught of Caucasoid and Mongoloid expansions and invasions which have been taking place during the last 10,000 to 15,000 years. As we have stated in previous chapters, we believe the Negroes and Melanesians to be new races created by these invasions and absorptions, by selective

[5] F. B. Livingstone: "Aspects of the Population Dynamics of the Abnormal Hemoglobin and Glucose-6-Phosphate Dehydrogenase Deficience Genes," AJHG, Vol. 16, No. 4 (1964), pp. 435–50; "Anthropological Implications of Sickle-Cell Gene Distributions in West Africa," AA, Vol. 60, No. 3 (1958), pp. 533–62.

screenings for climate and disease, and particularly by screening for defenses against malaria. In both regions malaria may have been less of a burden during the food-gathering stage of culture than it became after the introduction of agriculture, which, as Livingstone has shown, lets sunshine into clearings in the forests, makes puddles for mosquito larvae to mature in, and keeps people from moving about and thus lets filth accumulate.

Malaria, in sum, destroys some individuals and weakens others. However, the individual's genetic defenses against it, themselves also somewhat debilitating, preserve, or help create, his race.

Infant Diarrhea

IN EUROPE and America many babies used to die of infant diarrhea, and in unsanitary parts of the world many still do. According to F. Vogel and his associates[6] one of several organisms involved in the mixed infections leading to this disease is *Escherichia coli*. Several strains of this microorganism have been identified. At the peak of his illness, a child may have several of them, but a different proportion of these strains may be found in the stools of infected babies from year to year.

It so happens that the *Escherichia coli* organism contains antigens so similar to those of the ABO blood types that human blood reacts to the former as if they were the products of a person's own genes. Under these circumstances it is not surprising that during different epidemics babies are selected in terms of different ABO genes. In Heidelberg it was found by clinical study that in 1956, and again from 1960 to 1963, the sickest infants were mainly of blood group A, whereas in 1957 to 1959 the pendulum swung to group O.

Vogel's clinical findings, which to the present stand alone, suggest that infant diarrhea favors the survival of blood groups B and AB, or the gene for B. But more works needs to be done elsewhere to confirm or to refute his discovery. The only general conclusion that can be drawn from this evidence is that the ABO blood groups are so sensitive to some selective forces that their frequencies can change rapidly within a population. We have further evidence of this in the chronological study made by Vallois

6 F. Vogel, J. Dehnert, and W. Helmbold: "Ueber Beziehungen zwischen den ABO Blutgruppen unter der Säuglingsdyspepsie," HG, Vol. 1, No. 1 (1964), pp. 31–57.

and Marquer, which was geographical but not clinical. They reported that the frequency of the gene for B had gone down in France during the preceding forty years, possibly as a result of improving sanitation.[7]

Both these studies give us a theoretical basis on which to explain why peoples who first settled previously uninhabited continents and islands, and who no longer needed protection against diseases left behind them, began to lose first the gene for B and then that for A. Or, possibly, the Asiatic Mongoloids once had blood-group frequencies like those of the living Indians and built up their A and B frequencies after their populations had become dense.

Bronchopneumonia

ANOTHER common baby-killer which has been studied clinically is bronchopneumonia. Like infant diarrhea, it was studied in a single region only, in this case eastern Scotland.[8] There it was found to be least dangerous to children of blood group O. Children of groups A and AB were most vulnerable. It would therefore seem that the particular variety of pneumococcus organism involved in this disease produces an antigen like that of group A, against which a child of group A or AB would have no protective antibody.

Rheumatic Diseases

THE TERM "rheumatic diseases" covers a wide range of disorders, from arthritis to gout to rheumatic fever. Only the last-named is comparable to the last three diseases discussed, in that it attacks children. It particularly affects their hearts. All of these diseases which we have discussed have significant associations with the frequencies of three blood systems: Rh, MN, and gamma globulin. In a number of independent clinical studies it has been shown that persons with the allele D of the Rh series—a gene found in most Rhesus positives—and persons with the allele N of the MN series are particularly susceptible to rheumatic diseases.[9]

[7] Vallois and Marquer: op. cit.

[8] D. Struthers: "ABO Groups of Infants and Children Dying in the East of Scotland (1949–1951)," BJSM, Vol. 5 (1951), pp. 223–8.

[9] A. S. Cohen, W. C. Boyd, S. Goldwasser, E. S. Cathcart, and M. Heisler: "Correlation between Rheumatic Diseases and Rh Blood Groups," *Nature,* Vol.

In 1957 and 1958 several European investigators had meanwhile discovered that the gamma globulin known as Gm (a-1) agglutinates the incomplete red cells of Rh-positive individuals suffering from rheumatic diseases.[1] Since then the blood of rheumatics has been tested, with this relationship in mind, in various parts of the world.

Among nine series of Europeans from different countries the gene for gamma globulin Gm (a-1) has frequencies ranging from 23 percent in Italians to 43 percent in Lapps. Every other population which is not European, or mixed with Europeans,[2] has an incidence of 100 percent of this negative gene. These include Negroes from Dakar, American Indians, Indian Indians, and Javanese. Only the first of these four groups tested numbered more than 100 individuals.

The combination of clinical and geographical information reported above suggests some sweeping conclusions that cannot be confirmed until more data on the distribution of the Gm gene is at hand. One possible conclusion is that the Rh-negative and Gm-positive genes help each other maintain relatively high frequencies in Europe. Another is that the vulnerability of people of blood group N to rheumatic diseases helps counteract the curious over-production of N sperms by MN heterozygotes,[3] as we shall explain later.

Smallpox

SMALLPOX is a well-known Old World disease caused by the virus *Variola*. It apparently originated in Asia and was brought to Western Europe by the Crusaders and to America by the Spanish Conquistadors and the English settlers. Smallpox, more than any other agency, is believed to have opened North America to settlement by Europeans.[4] Of racial importance is the fact that

---

200, No. 4912 (1963), p. 1215. C. A. Clarke: "Blood Groups and Disease," in A. G. Steinberg, ed.: *Progress in Medical Genetics*, Vol. 1 (New York: Gruen and Stratton; 1961), pp. 81–119.

[1] H. Walter: "Die Bedeutung der serologischen Merkmale für die Rassenkunde," in Schwidetzky, ed.: *Die neue Rassenkunde*, pp. 135–232.

[2] In this category we have tentatively included a series of 74 Eskimo, whose gene frequency is 78 percent. Four of these Eskimo could conceivably have European ancestors.

[3] Y. Hiraizumi: "Are the MN Blood Groups Maintained by Heterosis?" AJHG, Vol. 16, No. 3 (1964), pp. 375–9.

[4] E. W. and A. E. Stearn: *The Effect of Smallpox on The Amerindian* (Boston: Bruce Humphries; 1945).

this disease has changed the distribution of peoples in certain parts of the world, and in others it has influenced the frequencies of ABO and MN blood groups.

The evidence for its possible association with the ABO blood groups is purely geographical. Where the disease is endemic, the O gene is at a minimum and both the A and B genes are high. Its most severe effects have been noted among populations which were exclusively or predominantly of group O before the impact of the disease was felt. It clinical validation is *sub judice*.[5]

Evidence for the relationship between smallpox and the MN system is both geographical and clinical. In centers of the Old World where smallpox is endemic, frequencies of the M gene run about 20 percent higher than the world average of 44.4 percent as determined by Mourant.[6] In the New World, among tribes of American Indians decimated by smallpox, the frequency of M is higher, and reaches a peak of 90 percent among one tribe of Indians in the Amazon. Among tribes of Australian aborigines and Papuans which had not been exposed to the disease, N runs between 70 percent and 90 percent.

Clinical evidence comes from both Nigeria and Brazil. In both countries it has been found that persons suffering from smallpox show the most severe symptoms if they belong to group N, and the least if they belong to group M.[7]

Plague

P L A G U E exceeds even smallpox in its destruction of human life. It has endemic foci in Central Asia, Iraq, southwestern Arabia, and Uganda.[8] The bacillus *Pasturella pestis* which causes it produces an antigen similar to the H substance, the antigen of blood group O. This H substance is also found in smaller quantity in the people of group A_2.

It has been stipulated, but as yet has not been shown clinically, that persons of the blood types OO, A_2O, and A_2A_2 are relatively

[5] Livingstone: "Natural Selection, Disease, and Ongoing Human Evolution, as Illustrated by the ABO Blood Groups," HB, Vol. 32, No. 1 (1960), pp. 17–27. Vogel et al.: "Ueber die Populationsgenetik der ABO-Blutgruppen." Azevêdo, Krieger, and Morton: "Smallpox and the ABO Blood Groups in Brazil," AJHG, Vol. 16, No. 4 (1964), pp. 451–4.

[6] Mourant: *The Distribution of the Human Blood Groups.*

[7] Azevêdo et al.: "Smallpox and the ABO Blood Groups in Brazil."

[8] F. P. Gay: *Agents of Disease and Host Resistance* (Springfield, Ill.: Charles C. Thomas; 1935).

susceptible to plague because they cannot carry anti-H antibodies in their sera.[9] According to this theory, populations long subject to plague should have high frequencies of the groups which have anti-H, namely A_1, B, and A_1B, and so they do. The theory is logical and the geographical association close. All that we need now is proof.

Cancers, Ulcers, and Pernicious Anemia

TURNING NOW from diseases of infancy to those of maturity and old age, we note that persons of different ABO groups are susceptible to different degrees to a number of degenerative diseases. Stomach cancer, cancer of the female genitalia, and pernicious anemia are commonest among persons of group A; gastric and duodenal ulcers tend to affect persons of group O.[1] Among the latter, individuals who secrete the O antigen into their lymph and saliva as well as into their blood are less likely to have ulcers than are those whose O antigen is found in their blood alone. Why the former, known as *secretors*, have this advantage over the latter, or *non-secretors*, we do not know.

Syphilis

WE END this roster of ailments with syphilis, not because of its ill repute but because our knowledge of how it might conceivably be impeded by blood factors stands on even shakier ground than any other on which we have previously stepped. This disease is produced by a spirochete, *Treponema pallidum*. Most but not all authorities think that before the first voyage of Columbus syphilis was confined to the New World.

T. D. Stewart has ventured to suggest that it could have evolved among the natives of the West Indies shortly before that famous voyage, through a mutation in the spirochete of the closely related disease, yaws.[2] In 1492 it would have had only a small geographical range. There is also documentary evidence that a native of the Faroe Islands may have visited the West Indies at some time be-

9 Vogel et al.: "Ueber die Populationsgenetik der ABO-Blutgruppen."

1 J. A. Buckwalter, E. D. Wohlwend, D. C. Colter, and R. T. Tidrick: "Natural Selection Associated with the ABO Blood Group," *Science*, Vol. 123, No. 3202 (1956), pp. 840–1. C. A. Clarke: op. cit.

2 T. D. Stewart: "A Physical Anthropologist's View of the Peopling of the New World," *SWJA*, Vol. 16, No. 3 (1960), pp. 257–73.

tween A.D. 1354 and A.D. 1380.[3] If he brought syphilis back to Europe, he did not spread it.

Certain evidence may possibly relate syphilis to the ABO blood groups and to Diego, the so-called American Indian blood factor. Although persons of any ABO blood group can contract syphilis with equal ease, the blood of persons of group O is rid of the spirochete sooner after treatment than is that of persons of other ABO blood groups. If this circumstance reflects a relative immunity to the severity of the effects of syphilis, in highly syphilitic populations it might lead to the fixation of the O gene, and a frequency of 100 percent of group O, which has actually been found in the majority of American Indians, even many of those living far from the West Indies.

A second candidate for the role of providing a genetic defense against syphilis is the Diego gene, a dominant allele abbreviated in the form Di. Its principal interest lies in that it is so far exclusively a Mongoloid gene and particularly an American Indian one. In Eastern Asia it has turned up among a few Chinese, Japanese, and Sea Dyaks of Borneo, and in China it is geographically associated with a local form of endemic syphilis. It is absent among the Eskimo and Fuegians and reaches its peak of concentration of 34 percent among tribes living on the border between Venezuela and Colombia, far inland.[4] Thirty percent of the Xavantes of the central Brazilian highlands have it.[5]

The alleged association of Diego positive with syphilis stems from the fact that the gene has high frequencies among the South American relatives of the Indians of the West Indies, the Caribs and Arawaks, who are now nearly extinct in the islands. Until this relationship is demonstrated clinically, it is unwise for any Indian to rely on his alleged genetic endowment to protect him from syphilis.

Incompatibility, Differential Fertility, and Race

NOW THAT the list of diseases known to be or suspected of being influenced by blood factors has been exhausted, we turn to

[3] E. G. R. Taylor: "A Fourteenth Century Riddle—and Its Solution," GR, Vol. 54, No. 4 (1964), pp. 573–6.

[4] A. G. de Díaz Ungria: "El Poblamiento Indígena de Venezuela a Través de la Genética," TESA (1963). M. Layrisse, Z. Layrisse, and J. Wilbert: "Blood Group Antigen Tests of the Yupa Indians of Venezuela," AA, Vol. 62, No. 3 (1960), pp. 418–36.

[5] J. V. Neel, F. M. Salzano, P. C. Junqueirâ, F. Keiter, and D. Maybury-Lewis: "Studies on the Xavante Indians of the Brazilian Mato Grosso," pp. 52–140.

two other subjects mentioned earlier in this chapter, reproductive incompatibility and differential fertility.

For several decades it has been known that some of the reproductive difficulties encountered by certain married couples are caused by incompatibility in one or more blood-group systems. The first to be identified was the Rhesus. This system has eight allelic combinations of three pairs of genes,[6] only one combination of which (dce) is Rh negative. Of the other seven the five which contain the allele D produce incompatibility when the mother is Rh negative and the fetus belongs to one of the five groups mentioned.

If the Rh system were completely independent of all others, and had no relationship to diseases or to any other selective factors, then Rh incompatibility would eliminate the Rh-negative gene in every population in which its frequency was originally below 50 percent. This seems to have happened among most peoples living east of Movius's Line, and among the Bushmen. But among Caucasoids and Negroes, Rh-negative is present in all populations studied, and in some parts of Western Europe its frequency rises almost to 50 percent. Some counter-selective factors obviously are keeping it from disappearing in these two subspecies, and we are beginning to find out what they are.

One appears to be the gamma globulin negative gene, Gm, which helps to protect Rh-negatives from rheumatic diseases;[7] another, apparently, is differential fertility. When Rh-negative women are mated with genetically compatible men they bear more children than Rh-positive women do and keep on bearing them later in life.[8]

The ABO blood groups can also cause incompatibility between mother and fetus when the mother belongs to group O and her child to one of the other groups. If there were no diseases in the world against which genes A and B afforded protection, then, being in the minority, A and B would be eliminated everywhere. This may have actually happened in most of the New World.

Two other circumstances besides protection against disease tend to keep ABO incompatibility from eliminating genes A and B.[9]

6 Alexander Wiener believes that there are eight alleles on one locus, whereas R. A. Fisher postulated three pairs on very closely linked loci, D, C, and E. Most serologists today follow the Fisher terminology—as we do here—whether or not they subscribe to Wiener's hypothesis. See R. R. Race and R. Sanger: *Blood Groups in Man* (Oxford: Blackwell Scientific Publications; 1954).

7 Walter: op. cit., p. 217.

8 H. B. Newcombe: "Risk of Fetal Death to Mothers of Different ABO and Rh Blood Types," AJHG, Vol. 15, No. 4 (1963), pp. 449–64.

9 R. L. Kirk: "Blood Group Interaction and the World Distribution of the ABO gene p^2 and the Rh gene r (cde)," AJHG, Vol. 13, No. 2 (1961), pp. 224–33.

Gene A₂ is not incompatible with O, and the ABO and Rh incompatibilities tend to cancel each other out. This second circumstance also helps preserve the Rh-negative gene.

Another red cell antigen, Kell, also causes incompatibility between mother and fetus, and like Rh-negative women, Kell-positive mothers are unusually fertile. This blood type has no known relationship to any disease nor is it linked, as far as we know, to any other system.[1] Its principal interest to anthropologists lies in its geographical distribution.

We have now found three blood-group systems in which incompatibility is balanced by increased female fertility. A fourth, however, shows a different kind of balance. That is the MN system. For some unknown reason, among both Japanese and Europeans, heterozygote males carrying both the M and N genes produce more than 50 percent of N sperm.[2] Were no other selective forces at play, the gene N would eventually rise to a global level of 100 percent and M would be eliminated. Actually the world's range of frequencies of N is from 10 percent to 91 percent. We have already seen that gene N seems to be vulnerable to both rheumatic diseases and smallpox, but female sterility also helps to keep it in balance with M. In a sample of 872 married women over forty years old studied in Michigan, it was found that 13.2 percent of the N women were sterile compared to 6.2 percent of MN women and 1.7 percent of M's. These differences are statistically significant, the MN genes of the womens' husbands were not involved, and the MN system was the only one of seven studied that showed differential fertility.[3]

Blood and Race

AT THIS POINT we can disregard the relationships of blood systems, diseases, incompatibilities, and differential fertility, and return to where we left off in Chapter 1 in our discussion of Boyd's classification of races on the basis of blood. We will now name the blood-group systems involved. To the systems mentioned in connection with protection against disease we will add those as

[1] T. E. Reed, H. Gershowitz, A. Soni, and J. Napier: "A Search for Natural Selection in Six Blood Group Systems and ABH Secretion," AJHG, Vol. 16, No. 2 (1964), pp. 161–79.

[2] Hiraizumi: "Are the MN Blood Groups Maintained by Heterosis?"

[3] Reed et al.: op. cit.

Race, Blood, and Disease

yet unrelated to disease which also show interesting geographical distributions.

These are summarized in Table 12, which does not include the antimalarial genes, rare genes limited to special regions, or alleles with a world-wide range of less than 33 percent. In Table 12, gene

TABLE 12

SOME REGIONAL BLOOD-GROUP FREQUENCIES

	World Range	Cauc.	Cong.	Bush.	E. Asia	America	S.E. Asia Indonesia	Aust. abor. and Oceania
A_1	0–45	5–40	8–30	0–15	0–45	0–20	15–18	8–38
A_2	0–37	1–37	1–8	0–5	0–5	0	0	0
B	0–33	4–18	10–20	2	16–25	0–4	12–22	0–13
O	39–100	46–75	52–70	75–78	39–68	68–100	61–71	51–79
cde	0–46	25–46	4–29	0	0–5	0	0	0
cDe	0–95	1–5	34–82	84–89	0–4	0–7	0–11	1–9
CDe	0–95	39–55	0–21	9–14	60–76	32–68	0–3	68–95
cDE	0–61	6–17	0–19	2	19–31	23–61	8–11	2–20
N	8–78	33–51	39–53	41	37–45	9–35	33–55	73–97
NS	5–74	25–65	22–59	41	38	5–22	21–54	69–74
P	4–84	41–64	50–84	?	17	15–79	46–50	12–67
								Abo. Poly.
Lewis	0–67	34–50	41	?	39	0–34	43–64	0 33–67
Duffy	0–100	37–82	0–6	8	90–100	22–99	?	100
Diego	0–34	0	0	0	0–5	0–35	0–3	0
Gm	23–100	23–37		100	100	100	100	100
Hp^1	9–87	9–44	40–87	29	23–28	32–73	50	46–63

frequencies of special racial significance are italicized.

The Caucasoids are most notable serologically for extreme frequencies of three genes: A_2, Rh negative (cde), and Gm–.

The Congoids have the most elaborate blood-group pattern in the world. They rank next to Caucasoids in A_2 and Rh negative (cde), are high in cDe, P, and haptoglobin Hp^1, and very low in Duffy positive. But they make up for this last deficiency in having up to 80 percent of a third Duffy allele which is neither positive nor negative but which makes no antigen now detectable. It is called the "silent" Duffy allele, Fy. They also have a number of other private genes attached to the MNSU system, including Hunter, Henshaw, and V; a special Rh gene, e^s, in the combination Dce^s; and a gamma globulin variant Gm^{ab}. Pygmies differ from Negroes in topping the Congoid list in $A_{1,2}$, B, and N, and in having the lowest frequencies of haptoglobin Hp^1.

In a general way Bushmen resemble Congoids, and they are closer serologically to Pygmies than to Negroes, but the similarity is not an identity. The Bushmen exceed the Negroes in group O, and in cDe, the "African" Rh gene, and have far less haptoglobin Hp^1. Until we know their frequencies for other systems, including P and Lewis, no final comparison between Bushmen and Congoids can be made. The Hottentots, not listed on Table 12, are like the Bushmen in some respects and closer to the Negroes in others. They also show a few peculiarities of their own.

The Mongoloids of Eastern Asia vary in the ABO series, ranging from the Chinese and Japanese, high in A_1 and B, to the Siberians, who, like the American Indians, are high in O. These Mongoloids in general are high in the Asiatic Rh gene CDe and in Duffy positive. The position of the American Indians is simple and monotonous, but distinctive. If we disregard the elevated frequency of A_1 in the northern plains of North America, apparently an artifact of recent smallpox, we find them high in O, cDE, Duffy positive, and hemoglobin Hp^1, and almost the sole possessors of Diego.

Southeast Asians and Indonesians are clinal in a number of blood groups between the northern Mongoloids and the Australoids, and are notable only in the Lewis positive factor, which has no known relationship to disease. The Australian aborigines, Melanesians, Micronesians, and Polynesians are alike enough in most blood-group traits to warrant being considered as a unit. In general they are high in the Mongoloid gene CDe, in N, NS, Duffy positive, and Haptoglobin Hp^1. The Australian aborigines part company from the others in regard to Lewis, which the Aborigines lack completely.

In sum, Movius's Line proves to be as real a barrier in the racial distribution of blood groups as in other aspects of race and culture. The Caucasoids, Congoids, and Capoids form one team; the Mongoloids and Australoids another. On either side of the line, the greatest blood-group complexity is seen in the wet tropics of the Old World, where diseases are concentrated, and the simplest patterns are found on the peripheries, particularly in Australia, Oceania, and the New World, where people once settled previously uninhabited spaces.

Our general interpretation of these blood-group distributions conforms quite well to a much more technical, mathematical study made by two professional geneticists with the help of a computer.

L. L. Cavalli-Sforza and his associates measured what they call the "number of gene substitutions" in a comparison of five blood-group systems—A_1A_2BO, Rh, MNS, Diego, and Duffy, in fifteen populations, as shown in Figure 7.[4] Some of the findings of other genetic characteristics discussed in Chapter 8, such as earwax types, fingerprints, and PTC tasting follow more or less the same pattern. We now have a fair idea of the genetic relationships of the races of the world, which were also determined in depth of time, by still other means, in *The Origin of Races*. But the populations studied so far in this book are those which were already in place before the extensive migrations and colonizations that have taken place since 1492. The latter have greatly complicated the racial geography of the world, as we shall explain briefly in the next chapter.

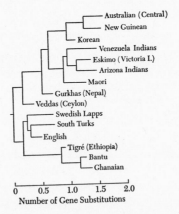

Fig. 7.— Racial Relationships Based on Blood Group Frequencies.
(after L. L. Cavalli-Sforza and A. W. F. Edwards, 1964)

[4] L. L. Cavalli-Sforza, I. Barrai, and A. W. F. Edwards: "Analysis of Human Evolution under Random Genetic Drift," CSHS, Vol. 29 (1964), pp. 9–200.

10

The Racial History of Man Since 1492

❦❦❦

Columbus Sailed

W E   H A V E   S E T the initial date of the current imbalance and disturbance among the races of man at A.D. 1492 because it is a date well known to Americans and Europeans, and because what happened in the first two centuries after the remarkable voyage of the Genoese navigator set the pattern for much of the present racial distribution in the world.

Were an Arab to choose such a date, it might be A.D. 622, the date of the Hijra, Muhammad's flight from Mekka to Medina, which touched off the Arab invasions. A Mongol might prefer A.D. 1206, the year of Genghis Khan's birth. Although Arabs and Mongols alike moved with lightning speed and spectacular military success, neither caused a fraction of the racial dislocation in the world that arose after Columbus's odd combination of truth and error.

Columbus doggedly believed that the earth was round. This idea was not original to him, only unpopular. He also accepted Posidonius's (135–50 B.C.) mistaken estimate of the circumference of the earth, 18,000 miles. Had Columbus but known of, and accepted, the true circumference of the world, which Eratosthenes (274–194 B.C.) had calculated over a century before Posidonius's mistake, he might not have thought that the shortest way to the fabulous Indies lay across the stormy Atlantic. Yet sooner or later, because of the improvements in navigation made in the school of Prince Henry the Navigator at Sagres in Portugal, someone else would have discovered America and come home to report its existence.[1]

By 1495 Columbus, who died believing that he really had discovered the East Indies, had founded a small Spanish settlement at Santo Domingo on the island of Hispaniola in what is now the Dominican Republic—a country which is presently only 28 percent white; yet the Indians that he found there have long since disappeared. The other third of the island is occupied by Haiti, the only nation outside of Africa that can be called 100 percent Negro, if, following North American usage, we include that country's 5 percent of "mulattoes." What happened in Hispaniola after Columbus is an extreme example of the displacement of populations that has taken place in many parts of the world during the last five and a half centuries, or roughly twenty generations.

The conquerors, exploiters, and settlers in the new continents and islands had in mind seven principal aims. They wished to establish trading posts in rich, civilized cities, as at Goa and Calcutta; to establish victualing stations along the routes of navigation, as at Cape Town; to convert the heathen; to strip the native peoples and their lands of precious minerals, by confiscating idols and ornaments, and by mining; to establish plantations with local or imported labor, or with both; to rid their own countries of convicts and potential indentured servants; and to provide havens and utopias for persecuted religious political minorities. Whether their object was to plunder and run, to baptize, to plant cotton, or to worship God in new places after their own fashion, in each case one result was the same. A permanent political establishment had to be created to maintain continuity and order. Viable colonies were established, some of which have grown into modern nations even more powerful than those from which the colonists had come.

These colonies met with the greatest eventual success where the climate was suitable for Europeans, where the colonists brought along their own women and children, where the native peoples were food-gatherers or simple slash-and-burn agriculturalists, and where these natives were susceptible to imported diseases. Where the climate was too hot and humid for Europeans they introduced

[1] Forbes: *Man the Maker* (New York: Henry Schuman; 1950). B. Penrose: *Travel and Discovery in the Renaissance* (Cambridge, Mass.: Harvard University Press; 1952). Coon: *The Story of Man*, 2nd ed. (New York: Alfred A. Knopf; 1962), Chapters 9 and 10.

Negroes, and both races brought malaria. Where the air was too thin, the winters too cold, or the desert too barren for profitable exploitation, the colonizers left the natives relatively undisturbed. Where the indigenous peoples practiced intensive and advanced agriculture, were skilled in the arts, crafts, and trade, possessed advanced, literate urban civilizations of their own, and were densely settled on the land and inured to epidemic diseases, the Europeans first established companies of traders and then colonial governments, most of which have since disappeared or been dissolved.

Since 1492 special regional segments of two human subspecies have been principally concerned with these overseas operations. They are the Western Europeans and the Negroes. To a lesser extent Hindus and Moslems of Greater India, and Chinese and Japanese, have been involved. Pygmies have for the most part been left undisturbed in their damp and shady retreats, and neither Papuans nor Melanesians have been massively invaded or displaced. The chief victims of these movements have been Bushmen and Hottentots, American Indians, Polynesians, and Australian aborigines.

Fig. 8.—The Principal Directions of Massive Gene Flow Since 1492.

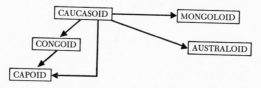

The principal directions of massive gene flow since 1492 are indicated by Figure 8, in which the Congoid lozenge is limited to Negroes and the Mongoloid to American Indians. During the last century the Chinese have, of course, been seeping into Southeast Asia, Indonesia, Tibet, and Manchuria in great numbers, but these areas were largely if not entirely Mongoloid in the first place. Hindus and Muslims from Greater India have migrated to South and East Africa, Fiji, Trinidad, and the Guianas, but from our point of view they are mostly if not entirely Caucasoid themselves.

During the twenty generations, more or less, which have been born since the initial settlement of Santo Domingo by the Spaniards, members of primary races that had not met each other for millenia, or at least since the end of the Pleistocene, have hybridized with each other. By careful observation of the results of these primary mixtures, geneticists are able to study the effects of the laws of heredity on man, and physical anthropologists interested in racial history try to determine the origins of a number of racially intermediate peoples which had previously puzzled them. Students of interracial relations concerned with what is going on in the world today will find ample evidence to support the view that human nature has not changed, at least in that category of behavior.

Latin America[2]

IN 1493, hot on the heels of Columbus's discovery, Pope Alexander VI, himself a Spaniard, divided between Spain and Portugal the overseas territories yet to be sighted and claimed. The dividing line was supposed to run north and south 100 leagues west of the Azores, which would give Portugal only a small piece of the South American mainland around Pernambuco. King John II of Portugal, who had a stronger navy than Spain's was in a position to protest, and at the treaty of Tordesillas, signed a year later, the line was moved to a point 370 leagues west of the Azores, or somewhere in the neighborhood of 46° West longitude. This gave Portugal the eastern third of what is now Brazil.

In 1492 Ferdinand and Isabella finally expelled the last of the Moors and Jews from Spain, except for those who chose to become hasty converts to Catholicism. Still, life was insecure, particularly for the ex-Jews, many of whom, not wishing to face the Inquisition, found it both expedient and adventurous to move to the New World, where their descendants are numbered among the old and aristocratic Spanish families, as, for example the Medinas of Chile.

With the departure of the infidels, northern Spaniards and northern Portuguese expanded into Andalusia and southern Portugal, which had been partially depopulated. There they founded latifundia, or large landed estates, establishing a pattern of settlement and a way of life which they transplanted to the New World and which included, in southern Portugal, the labor of African slaves. The zeal of the Spaniards in particular for evangelism, still warm from their triumph over Islam, was easily reheated in the presence of human sacrifice and cannibalism. Also the Iberian family structure condoned the extramarital activities of

2 The literature on the settlement and history of Latin America is massive. For present purposes we recommend the following titles. James: *Latin America.* G. M. Foster: *Culture and Conquest: America's Spanish Heritage,* VFPA, No. 27 (1960). J. A. Crow: *The Epic of Latin America* (New York: Doubleday; 1946).

husbands, thus facilitating the rapid rise of a mestizo population. Because the mestizos acted as go-betweens in relations with the Indians, the more of them that were begotten, the better.

According to what seem to be reasonable estimates, there were, in 1492, 4,500,000 Indians in Mexico, 800,000 in Central America, and 6,785,000 in South America. Most of the latter were concentrated in the highlands from Colombia to Chile. The Inca Empire alone contained at least 4,000,000 of them. The estimate for Brazil is about 1,000,000, more than ten times the present Indian population of that country. In the Andes, the Indians have at least doubled their numbers since Pizarro.

Within the first fifty years of colonization some 150,000 Spaniards of all social classes and occupations had spread over their part of Latin America. Although the first settlers came from all over Spain, the largest contingent were Andalusians and Estremadurans, but later the lead passed to the Castilians and Basques. In the Spanish colonies, later to become republics, the European element in the population long remained largely Spanish, except in Chile, where many Germans settled in the region between Valparaiso and Puerto Montt. There they largely replaced the Araucanian Indians, who, after about 1850, had at last been conquered, not by force or arms but by alcohol. Between Puerto Montt and the Strait of Magellan Chile is almost uninhabited. Magellanes Province, the richest in the country, contains a large increment of British, Dalmatians, Scandinavians, Poles, and other peoples from Northern and Eastern Europe who do not mind the rigorous climate of that region.

At the beginning of colonization the Portuguese, who numbered only a million at home, were unable to send out many colonists, and although King Manuel made more than two hundred crimes punishable by exile, in 1531 he was able to send only 400 settlers to Brazil, where a handful of enterprising pioneers, mostly converts from Judaism, had preceded them. Even as late as 1585 there were only 43,000 Europeans and 14,000 Negroes in Brazil. The greatest increase in the population of Brazil, one which is still going on, began in the nineteenth century when Italians, Germans, Poles, Russians, Spaniards, Japanese, and Lebanese began pouring in. Between 1900 and 1957 alone, over 4 million of these non-Portuguese immigrants arrived.

Before the abolition of slavery in 1888, more than 4 million Negroes were brought into Brazil, from four different parts of Africa. Hausas, Fulas, and Mandingos were brought from the Sudan; Yorubas, Ashantis, Fons, and others from the West Coast;

and Bantus from Angola and Mozambique. Thus Brazil got some of the most warlike and most technically skilled people in Africa.

The racial outcome of this colonization, establishment of estates, racial mixture, environmental selection, and social selection that has taken place in Latin America since the Iberians first arrived is shown, as accurately as possible, in Table 13. Here we

TABLE 13

RACIAL DISTRIBUTION IN LATIN AMERICA*

					Percent	
Population in Thousands		*European*	*Indian*	*Mestizo*	Negro + *Mulatto*	*Others*
	1957					
Mexico	31,426	15%	29%	55%	under 1%	
Guatemala	3,349	5	60	35	under 1	
Honduras	1,711	2	10	86	2	
El Salvador	2,268	11	11	78	—	
Nicaragua	1,302	17	5	69	9	
Costa Rica	1,014	80	under 1	17	2	
Panama	934	11	10	65[1]	13	
Colombia	13,227	20	7	68	5	
Venezuela	6,130	20	7	65	8	
Ecuador	3,777	15	60	22	3	
Peru	9,923	15	46	38	—	1%
Bolivia	3,235	15	53	32	—	
Chile	7,005	30	5	65	—	
Brazil	61,268	62	1	26[1]	11	
Paraguay	1,638	under 1	3	97	—	
Uruguay	2,801	90	—	3	—	
Argentina	19,678	97	—	3[2]	—	

* Based mostly on P. E. James's *Latin America* (1957)
1 Includes some Negro mixture
2 Excludes Chilotes working in Argentina, who retain Chilean citizenship

see that the Indians still range from 46 percent to 60 percent in the mountainous countries of Guatemala, Ecuador, Peru, and Bolivia. Mestizos are in the majority in all other countries of Spanish tradition except Costa Rica, Uruguay, and Argentina. Along with southern Brazil, these are the most completely European parts of Latin America, and also the parts which were most sparsely inhabited by Indians in the precolonial period and at the same time climatically the most suited to settlement by Europeans.

To the casual traveler, Chile also looks largely European because many blond Germans and Scandinavians are in evidence around Santiago, and many Yugoslavs and other lightly pigmented people are seen in Punta Arenas, and because some of the Indians with whom the Spaniards mixed were quite light-skinned. This is particularly true in the case of the Chilotes, an enterprising breed of men who come from the island of Chiloé. This cool, moist island was originally inhabited by Chono Indians, related to the Alakalufs. Settlers from northwestern Spain absorbed the Chonos, and later on Araucanian Indians from the mainland joined the mixture. The Chonos were probably light-skinned and cold-adapted, like the Alakalufs, and the Araucanians are short and very stocky.

The Chilotes grow potatoes and, like the Irish before their potato famine, have had a population explosion. They are short, barrel-chested, muscular, black-haired, and red-cheeked little men, exuding enormous energy, and impervious to the rigors of the antipodeal climate. Because of their light skin color, most of them would not be taken for mestizos by a casual observer. On both sides of the Andes, from about the fortieth degree of south latitude to Cape Horn, they do most of the out-of-door work, from sailing small ships to herding cattle and sheep, and working around oil wells. Most of the black-haired people seen among the blonds in Punta Arenas are Chilotes.

The Chilotes would be an excellent subject for a thorough study of racial mixture, one that is still to be made. In fact, the only such study of Spanish-Indian mixture available is that of G. D. Williams on the Maya of Yucatán.[3] In 1927 Williams measured 880 Maya men and 694 Maya women in Yucatán, taking many measurements and descriptive observations on each, as well as determining their ABO blood-group types. Because the Indians had been mixing with the Spaniards for over 400 years without keeping genealogical records, his only recourse was to sort them into subgroups on the basis of fourteen observations, including skin color, hair color, hair form, eye color, and beard development. He then seriated the five subgroups so determined for fifty-two measurements and indices.

He found that the means of their measurements followed significantly progressive lines of differentiation between the Indian and Spanish extremes in all measurements and indices in which the two original stocks had differed substantially. He then compared the ABO blood-type frequencies in the five subseries and discovered that the frequency of type O ranged in regular progression from 95 percent in the most Indian-looking subgroup to 54.2 percent in the most European-looking one. The ranges for type A ran from 2.5 percent to 25 percent; for B from 2.5 percent to 12.5 percent; and for AB from 0 to 8.3 percent.

Thus, even as long ago as 1927, when serology was first being used in racial studies, it confirmed Williams's conclusion that in a

[3] G. D. Williams: "Maya-Spanish Crosses in Yucatan," PMP, Vol. 13, No. 1 (1931), pp. 1–256.

long, uninterrupted history of local racial mixture, the components of the two stocks tended to retain their genetic associations, without dominance and without unusual variability. There was little evidence of selective mating, except on the plantations, where light-skinned males tended to marry light-skinned women. In the villages, where conventional mating patterns were followed, little or no preference was shown.

The history of the third major racial element in Latin America, that of the Negroes, is a record of early arrival, special geographical distribution, and, in some places, absorption. For example, in the middle of the sixteenth century in Mexico, Negroes outnumbered Spaniards, against whom they rebelled on three occasions. Today the Negroes are almost wholly submerged in the mestizo population.[4]

From Colombia to Brazil, Negroes were brought mostly to the hot, humid coastal regions to work on sugar plantations, and later in the cultivation of sisal and tobacco. Later they accompanied Portuguese prospectors into Minas Gerais and Mato Grosso, where some of their descendants are to be found today in the coffee plantations and cattle ranches.[5] So thoroughly have Negroes mixed with both Indians and Europeans that the Brazilian census-takers find it hard to divide the population into racial categories; they consider that what they call mulattoes outnumber the Negroes by at least two and one half to one. Geneticists have elucidated the census-takers' difficulty. In one mixed population, that of the so-called Nordestinos of São Paulo State, D. F. Roberts and R. W. Hiorns have calculated that the parental population was 25 percent West African, 9 percent Indian, and 65 percent Portuguese.[6] What they were labelled in the census we do not know.

Bermuda, the Bahamas, the West Indies, British Honduras, and the Guianas

NO COUNTRY on the Latin American mainland, not even Brazil or Panama, is primarily Negroid, or any more Negroid than the United States. With the exceptions of Cuba and Puerto Rico, the Atlantic islands from Bermuda to Tobago, and British Hon-

4 O. Pi-Sunyer: "Historical Background of the Negro in Mexico," JNH, Vol. 42, No. 4 (1957), pp. 237–46.
5 G. Freyre: *The Masters and the Slaves* (New York: Alfred A. Knopf; 1946).
6 D. F. Roberts and R. W. Hiorns: "Methods of Analysis of a Hybrid Population," HB, Vol. 37, No. 1 (1965), pp. 38–43.

duras, are primarily inhabited by Negroes and "mulattoes," a term which, after more than 400 years of undocumented racial mixture, is clearly an oversimplification of a complex genetic situation.

TABLE 14

RACIAL DISTRIBUTION IN BERMUDA, THE BAHAMAS, THE WEST INDIES, BRITISH HONDURAS, AND THE GUIANAS*

	Population in Thousands 1957	White	Negro	American Indian	East Indian	Others
			Percent			
Bermuda	43	40%	60%			
Bahamas	111	15	85			
Cuba	6,410	73	26[1]			
Haiti	3,390	0	100			1%[2]
Dominican Republic	2,613	15	85			
Puerto Rico	2,350	75	25			
Jamaica	1,687	23	77			
Lesser Antilles	1,541	1–23	77–99	under 1%		
Trinidad & Tobago	894	29	45		26%	
British Honduras	96	under 1	79	21[3]		
British Guiana	598	3	35[4]	4	46	12[5]
Dutch Guiana	340	2	47[6]	3	48	
French Guiana	35	5	91	4		

* Compiled from P. E. James's *Latin America* (1957) and other sources
[1] Includes 14% called "mestizos" by the Cuban census
[2] Chinese
[3] Maya Indians. Black Caribs are listed under Negroes.
[4] and [6] Includes Bush Negroes.
[5] Mixed people otherwise unclassified

In Trinidad and British Guiana the racial situation is further complicated by the presence of large numbers of people brought from India to work in the sugar plantations. In Dutch Guiana there are both Hindus and Indonesians. In the hinterland of the Guianas also live whole villages of so-called Bush Negroes, the descendants of runaway slaves.

In the other islands of the West Indies, where the racial situation is simpler than on Trinidad and in the Guianas, several detailed studies have been made of the populations of various islands, including some that are predominantly white and others that are predominantly black. In Puerto Rico, where the population is largely of Spanish descent, F. P. Thieme found that a rigid class structure prevents general mixture and that skin color is the most important physical characteristic considered in determining the choice of marital partners.[7] In Jamaica, where the ratio between the races is almost exactly the opposite of that in Puerto Rico, a class system based primarily on skin color also divides the population.[8]

In Martinique the situation is not quite the same.[9] Out of 250,000 inhabitants, the island harbors only 1,760 permanent residents who are unmixed descendants of the old French families —this is .73 percent of the population. These "Creoles," as they are called, own 80 percent of the plantations, and practice a rigidly endogamous mating system. In 1740 their ancestors constituted 20 percent of the island's inhabitants. With the arrival of a new influx of slaves from Africa, the Creoles had become so outnumbered that effective gene flow from them into the colored population slowed down to a trickle and has so remained ever since.

Among the colored population two general groups can be distinguished: an urban bourgeoisie, whose family pattern to a large extent mirrors that of the Creoles, and the vast majority of the rural Blacks. Among the latter, in 1954, 50 percent of the children born were registered as illegitimate, and 59 percent of the women bearing children were unwed. The family group of these people centers around the mother, married or unmarried, and sexual partners come and go to such an extent that, from a genetic standpoint, a state of panmixia is approached.[1]

Studying the colored population as a whole, J. Benoist calculated, on the basis of the frequencies of five blood-group alleles and PTC tasting, that the European ancestry of these islanders is between 15 percent and 25 percent. In measurements and indices he found that for the most part they are intermediate between the European French and the West Africans, and that their variability as a whole is no greater than in other populations of the world, mixed and unmixed. But some individual characteristics were more variable than others. The seven most variable out of seventeen were, in this order: nose height, the nasal index, nose breadth, face height, mouth breadth, and the distance between the inner corners of the eyes. The range in descriptive characters such as

---

[7] F. P. Thieme: *The Puerto Rican Population: A Study in Human Biology,* APMA-M (1959).

[8] C. B. Davenport and M. Steggerda: *Race Crossing in Jamaica,* CIP, No. 395, 1929.

[9] J. Benoist: "Les Martiniquais: Anthropologie d'une population métissé," BSAP, Vol. 4 (1963), pp. 241–432.

[1] The literature on African ethnography contains no precedent for such a disorganized type of family, which is believed to be a retention of the breakdown of family life on plantations under conditions of slavery.

skin color and hair form, however, encompasses those of both parental stocks.

Without attempting to subdivide his series on class lines, Benoist calculated coefficients of correlation between the different characters he had studied, both metrical and descriptive, and found twenty-three statistically significant relationships, as shown on Table 15.

TABLE 15

CORRELATIONS BETWEEN DESCRIPTIVE AND METRICAL CHARACTERS IN THE COLORED POPULATION OF MARTINIQUE

Descriptive	r	Metrical	r
Hair form	+.530	Nose breadth	+.416
Upper-lip form	+.372	Nasal index	−.355
Eye color	+.350	Mouth breadth	−.282
Hair color	+.335	Biocular diameter*	−.260
Lower-lip form	+.257	Rel. ht. of pubic symphysis	−.251
Beard development	+.253	Ear index	−.239
		Rel. arm length	−.168
		Rel. trunk ht.	−.159

NASAL INDEX AND OTHERS

Descriptive	r	Metrical	r
Hair form	−.361	Mouth breadth	−.445
Upper-lip form	−.349	Interocular diam.	−.257
Nasal profile	−.318	Biocular diam.	−.233
Eye color	−.188	Head length	+.204
Lower-lip form			

* The biocular diameter is the distance between the outer corners of the eye openings; the interocular, that between the inner corners.

Skin color showed itself to be the most sensitive of the descriptive characters in terms of racial affinities as a whole, being significantly related to six other descriptive characters and to eight metrical ones. The next most sensitive character was the nasal index, significantly related to five descriptive characters beside skin color, and to four other metrical ones. By means of this elaborate statistical study, Benoist found that, in general, African traits go together, and so do European traits.

These correlations can form a basis for the establishment of social classes within populations of mixed European and Negro ancestry where such classes happen to segregate themselves, not only in the West Indies, but also, to a large extent, in the United States.

In Chapter 7 we have already seen, from G. Olivier's work on the Tamils, that the same principles apply in comparable inter-racial contacts between Caucasoid and partly Australoid popula-tions in southern India, where light skins and narrow noses are also social symbols. Benoist's work, therefore, is not merely a study of Martinique, but a model for the general study of racial mixture in many other parts of the world.

The Russians in Siberia and North America

WHILE the Spaniards and Portuguese were beginning to settle their part of the New World, the Russians had already embarked on their eastward movement across Siberia, which led them on to Alaska and down to California, where the van of the gold seekers found them precariously established before 1849.[2]

After the Russians had broken the power of the Tatars, who had contained them on the east, the Muscovite state late in the fifteenth century sent out a few expeditions beyond the Urals. During the next three centuries these intermittent movements swelled to a steady flow. By 1697 Siberia held about 150,000 Russians and only 125,000 natives, and by 1763 Russian settle-ments had arisen on the Pacific coast. They were on Kodiak Island in 1894 and built Fort Ross in San Francisco Bay in 1812. These transpacific movements were accomplished with a minimum of personnel. When the United States bought Alaska in 1867, only 400 Russians lived in the entire territory, and their maximum at any one time had been 700. The Russian population at Fort Ross was even smaller. Except that the Russians mixed with the Aleuts, the North American adventure is of purely historical interest.

It would be interesting to learn what has happened to the Russians anatomically and physiologically in Siberia, but we have no data. We know only that the present population of Siberia is about 30 million, or 15 percent of that of the Soviet Union, and these 30 million are overwhelmingly of European descent. Today the natives seem as little in evidence as Indians and Eskimo in comparable climatic zones of the United States and Canada.

2 L. P. Potapov: "The Discovery and Occupation of Siberia," in M. G. Levin and L. P. Potapov, eds.: *The Peoples of Siberia* (Chicago: University of Chicago Press; 1964), pp. 105–34.

The Racial Composition of the People of the United States

T H E   H I S T O R Y of the post-Columbian settlement of the United States being the bailiwick of professional historians, we may know less about it than that mythical person, the informed layman, to whom many excellent books on the subject have long been available.[3] Our special interest is to trace the evidence of who came to our country whence and when; where the newcomers settled; to what extent the various ethnic groups maintained their identities and for how long; to what extent they may have been selected by social and environmental forces before they left and after they arrived; and who mixed with whom.

The present population of the United States is composed principally of the descendants of three ethnic and racial elements: Europeans, Negroes, and American Indians, in order of numerical importance. Eskimo have been added in Alaska, and Polynesians, Japanese, and Chinese in Hawaii, and there are other Japanese and Chinese on the mainland.

In the settlement of the United States the immigrants were not chosen at ramdom. Whole congregations migrated with their pastors to New England, and settled in sheltered coves and river mouths. Three centuries later, agents of New England textile mills recruited cheap labor from Sicilian villages, and most of the Albanians who came to work in shoe factories were members of the Orthodox minority from Korça. Middle-class artisans and skilled craftsmen predominated in early New England, and English aristocrats could be seen in the stately mansions of Virginia. The Sicilian laborers were humble and vigorous peasants, whereas among those who more recently have sought refuge from Hitler's police, there were some of our most gifted scholars and scientists.

Selection in migration operated from the beginning. In the early days of colonial settlement it was only natural that citizens of seafaring nations on the Atlantic shore of Europe should be the first to arrive in numbers. Of these nations, Spain and Portugal had business elsewhere. No glittering gold, silver, or heaps of

[3] For present purposes we recommend, among others: S. E. Morison: *The Oxford History of the American People* (New York: The Oxford University Press; 1965). O. Handlin: *Boston's Immigrants, 1790–1860* (Cambridge, Mass.: Harvard University Press; 1941). M. L. Hansen: *The Atlantic Migration, 1607–1860* (Cambridge, Mass.: Harvard University Press; 1941). M. Grant: *The Conquest of a Continent* (New York: Charles Scribner's Sons; 1933). Our recommendation does not extend to any opinions or special pleadings presented in these books.

emeralds met the northern explorers' eyes. The densely forested shores of North America were cold and forbidding and the Indians hostile. The British, French, and Dutch were the obvious candidates.

The settlement of the United States is usually divided into four periods: 1620 to 1790; 1790 to 1860; 1860 to 1924; and from 1923 to the ever-advancing present. The first date commemorates the landing of the Pilgrims, despite Jamestown's priority; the next two years are those of elaborate censuses; and 1924 is the date of the immigration law which limited the annual quota from any one country to 2 percent of its representation in 1890. During the first period the settlers came primarily from England and secondarily from Scotland and Scottish communities in Northern Ireland. Neither the Dutch in the Hudson Valley nor the Swedes and Finns in the lower Delaware were ever numerous. In general the English stayed near the coast, and the Scots, as might be expected, forged ahead into higher and more perilous terrain.

Most of this early immigration occurred within the first few decades of the first period. During this time land travel remained slow and overseas contact intermittent. By 1790 the citizens of each colony had the time and isolation needed to create their own local culture, tradition, and pride, and a feeling approaching that of nationhood.

In the census of 1790 the names of the heads of families are listed by counties and townships. In Massachusetts, one of the most solidly English states, names appear which are still listed in the 1965 telephone books of the same communities.[4] There were then 989 families of Smiths, 340 of Whites, and 187 of Adamses. The Putnams numbered 80; the Eliots, variously spelled, 62; the Emersons 58. Among the top Boston Brahmin families of later periods, only 27 Forbeses, 16 Lowells, 9 Cabots, and one Saltonstall appear. The Gaelic contingent included 150 names beginning with Mc, 60 Kelleys, 8 Murphys, 6 O'Briens, and 3 Sullivans. In other states the proportions varied but the ingredients were, in most cases, the same.

The second period was dominated by the arrival of many Germans, Scandinavians, and Irish, along with more English. Because the English people themselves were a mixture of Celts, Germans, and Scandinavians, English history was only repeating itself in America. The genes remained the same.

4 S. N. D. North (Director, Bureau of the Census): *Heads of Families at the First Census of the United States Taken in the Year 1790, Massachusetts* (Washington, D.C.: Government Printing Office; 1908).

After 1860 the pattern changed. Slavs, Russian and Polish Jews, both northern and southern Italians, Peloponnesian Greeks, and Lebanese began to join the stream, which grew into a torrent between 1890 and 1924, when it was suddenly dammed. Since then the most notable additions to our population have been refugees from one tyranny or another, and every tyranny across the Atlantic benefits the American people.

A survey of where the various national groups settled illustrates an ancient human tendency for people to migrate, if they can, to places where climates and work opportunities are familiar, just as ancient hunters followed the wanderings of their favorite game animals, be they wild horses or reindeer. After having settled, many of the immigrant groups formed local enclaves, maintaining some kind of contact with their parental communities and continuing to speak their native language, at least in the home, for several generations. German can still be heard on tidy farms in Pennsylvania and Wisconsin, Swedish in Minnesota, Basque on the open range in Nevada, Armenian on the vine-covered hills about Fresno, Portuguese wherever there are boats to sail, and Cockney on the streets of Philadelphia. America has been less a melting pot than a smorgasbord.

During the last two centuries, Americans of British descent, being the easiest to identify in Colonial records, have grown 3½ inches taller than their Revolutionary ancestors, and proportionately heavier. By 1930 the rate of increase had begun to level off. G. T. Bowles surmised, to use his own word, that equilibrium might be reached between 1970 and 1980, at a mean stature for adult males of about six feet, or a little taller.[5] That is as tall as any population measured to date. Bowles's apical decade, which will be a boon to shoe manufacturers, is nearly upon us.

Other Americans have also increased in stature, and some of those who have arrived most recently have grown taller the most rapidly. American soldiers of World War II of Italian, Portuguese, or other Mediterranean origin, had a mean stature then of 5 feet 6½ inches (169 centimeters), which is three inches taller than adult males are in their ancestral countries, and only 2½ inches shorter than Scandinavian-Americans.[6] In Europe the means for Scandinavian and Mediterranean countries differ by more than twice that figure.

[5] G. T. Bowles: *New Types of Old Americans at Harvard* (Cambridge, Mass.: Harvard University Press; 1932).

[6] A. M. Brues: "Regional Differences in the physical characteristics of an American population," AJPA, Vol. 4, No. 4 (1946), pp. 463–82.

Changes are also taking place in the cephalic index, but at a slower pace. Most Americans whose ancestors came from countries inhabited by brachycephals are showing a tendency toward mesocephaly or dolichocephaly. Their cephalic index means may drop dramatically in a single generation among those who have abandoned cradling, like Albanians, Armenians, and Lebanese, or more gradually among Poles, Czechs, and Hungarians, whose heads are growing longer in pace with their bodies. Among the latter it is also possible that the selective forces noted in Poland by T. Bielicki and Z. Welon[7] are being relaxed or reversed in the New World.

So far our attention has been focused on the so-called white population of the United States, which in the 1960 census comprised 87.5 percent of the whole. Negroes were then listed as comprising 10.4 percent; Japanese, Chinese, and "all others" comprised 2.1 percent. In the next few pages we shall use the terms "white" and "Negro" in their conventional meanings purely for the sake of convenience, because that is the way our data is organized. The definition of "Negro" varies from state to state; the proportion of non-African ancestry possessed by any one Negro ranges from a potential zero to over 75 percent; and the proportion of American white people of partially Negro origin is unknown.

Between 1790 and 1920 the percentage in the population of Negroes, defined as above, declined steadily each decade from 19.53 percent to 9.96 percent,[8] owing principally to European immigration. Meanwhile the absolute figures for the Negro population had increased fourteen-fold. Following the curtailment of immigration in 1924, the percentage of Negroes began to rise, reaching 10.4 percent in 1960. Now it is undoubtedly higher.

The decline of immigration coincided with the decrease in cotton cultivation in the Southern states, and Negroes began and continued to move out. In 1960 New York had the most Negroes and Vermont the fewest. Once more the Negroes are becoming a part of the entire United States and of general rather than regional importance.

We physical anthropologists would like to know the following five things about the American Negroes. (1) How do they compare physically with the West African Negroes? (2) How much American "white blood" have they acquired? (3) What proportion of

7 See page 65 (Chapter 3).
8 M. Gover: "Increase of the Negro Population of the United States," HB, Vol. I, No. 3 (1929), pp. 263–73.

them are mixed, with whites, Indians, or both? (4) How much white ancestry need a colored person have in order to be taken for white and, if he so chooses, to join the white community as a white person? (5) How much "Negro blood" do white Americans have as a result of these instances of passing? Some of these questions are easier to answer than others. Some can hardly be answered at all, because Negroes have been in America since the founding of Jamestown, and white men did not often leave records of their extramarital sexual activities. Once mixture had taken place, the European genes had more than a fair chance of spreading widely, for as in Martinique, plantation life led to an approximation of panmixia. As most interracial unions involved a white father and a Negro mother, some of the genes carried on the X chromosome may have favored the African side of the mixture, but we do not yet know exactly what these genes are.

The answer to the first question is that American Negroes are taller than the West Africans by two or three inches and American Negro males are slightly shorter than white Americans, whereas Negro women are taller than white women. Among American Negroes, heads are longer and broader than among Africans. In comparison with the Africans, American Negroes have longer and broader faces, and longer and narrower noses. Many of the American Negroes are lighter-skinned.[9]

As for the second question, B. Glass and C. C. Li estimated in 1953, on the basis of ABO and Rhesus blood groups and of PTC tasting, that the American Negroes are of about 30 percent European origin.[1] In the same year and on other and ampler grounds, C. Stern set the ratio at 20 percent,[2] and in 1955 D. F. Roberts came up with the same figure.[3] These three estimates covered the American Negroes as a whole. In 1963 P. L. Workman and his associates, limiting their studies to the Negroes of Evans and Bullock Counties, Georgia, a particularly concentrated Negro area, and using fifteen genetic polymorphisms, found the European component there to be only 10.4 percent.[4] In 1955 Glass also

[9] Herskovits: *The Anthropometry of the American Negro* (New York: Columbia University Press; 1930).

[1] B. Glass and C. C. Li: "The Dynamics of Racial Intermixture—an Analysis Based on the American Negro," AJHG, Vol. 5, No. 1 (1953), pp. 1–20.

[2] C. Stern: "Model Estimates of White and Near-White Segregants in the American Negro," AGSM, Vol. 4 (1953), pp. 281–98.

[3] D. F. Roberts: "The Dynamics of Racial Intermixture in the American Negro—Some Anthropological Considerations," AJHG, Vol. 7, No. 4 (1955), pp. 361–7.

[4] P. L. Workman, B. S. Blumberg, and A. J. Cooper: "Selection, Gene Migration, and Polymorphic Stability in a U. S. White and Negro Population," AJSG, Vol. 15, No. 4 (1963), pp. 429–37.

concluded that the American Negro population contains no recognizable American Indian ancestry.[5]

No one knows the answer to the third question because blood-group analysis cannot determine the racial origins of every individual, particularly in the case of European-Negro hybrids. In collecting his data at Howard University and in Harlem, however, M. J. Herskovits asked each of his subjects to estimate the racial components of his ancestry. Only 22 percent thought themselves to be full-blooded Africans. Of the remaining 78 percent, 6.3 percent thought they were part Indian with white admixture. Of the 71.7 percent who considered themselves part white, 20.9 percent thought they were also part Indian. Of the same 71.7 percent, 31.7 percent believed they were more Negro than white; 25.2 percent believed they were about evenly mixed; and 14.8 percent said they were more white than Negro.

Herskovits then divided his series on the basis of these answers into subseries according to putative proportions of Negro, white, and Indian ancestry, reseriated for all characters, including skin color. His results agreed with those of Benoist, who studied his Martinique sample by a different method. In most criteria the subseries aligned themselves in a consistent gradation from fully Negro to almost white, but the alleged Indian component could not be detected by this method any more than it could by means of blood-group studies.

The fourth question—how much "white blood" does a colored person need to pass for white—is difficult to answer because the act of passing is shrouded in secrecy. Yet persons who pass successfully probably come from relatively prosperous families; successful Negro men tend to marry women fairer than themselves.

Mrs. C. B. Day once conducted a careful and elaborate study of 346 Negro-white families by combining genealogical and anthropological data.[6] Some of the families studied by her have produced men prominent in our national life, like the late Walter White and the late W. E. B. Dubois. Mrs. Day had no chance to deal with first-generation (F_1) crosses except in the case of deceased ancestors; all her subjects were the products of several generations of mixture and some of them measured their racial components in thirty-seconds.

5 B. Glass: "On the Unlikelihood of Significant Admixture of Genes from the North American Indians in the Present Composition of the Negroes of the United States," AJHG, Vol. 7, No. 3 (1955), pp. 368–85.

6 C. B. Day: *A Study of Some Negro-White Families in the United States*, HAS, Vol. 10, Part 2 (1932).

Among other things, she found that in a few instances an individual who is half Negro after several generations of mixture might possibly pass, whereas a person who is three fourths white has a good chance of passing. According to C. Stern, about 25 percent of the latter could do so.[7] In her elite sample Mrs. Day found that the people who knew their ancestries over at least four generations claimed in many instances to be part Indian.

The last question is the hardest of all because anyone who passes, under the eagle-eyed scrutiny of American white people, is probably largely European genetically, as indicated by the fact that the so-called African blood type *cDe* is no commoner among white Americans than in many European populations. Glass and Li consider the genetic impact on the American population of passing, no matter how few or how many have achieved it, to have been negligible.[8]

As far as mixture between Negroes and Indians is concerned, there is possibly more Negro in the American Indians of the eastern states than vice versa. Berry has tracked down at least 200 communities in the Eastern United States consisting of triracial hybrids of mixed Indian, Negro, and white ancestry.[9] Many of these groups are classified as Indians by the government. Others have occupied anomalous positions in segregated states. When these trihybrids seek work in cities, they are likely to be absorbed into the colored population.

In the 1960 census, more than 523,000 persons are listed as Indians, as compared with 44,000 in 1860. The latest figure includes some of the triracial enclaves just mentioned, and most of the others are also mixed. The most numerous tribe today is that of the Navajos, some 80,000. In 1860 they numbered only 12,000. In their case, growth has been achieved not by mixture but by adopting a new economy, stock-breeding in place of hunting. This suggests that long ago in the Old World similar small groups of hunters may have grown into large and powerful tribes when they became pastoral nomads.

In only one state, Hawaii, are the whites in a minority, and then only if we fail to count some 125,000 servicemen who will presumably return to the mainland. Caucasoid Americans constitute about 15 percent of the permanent population; the Japanese, with about 35 percent, are the most numerous element. Pure and mixed Hawaiians make up about 13 percent, and the remaining 37 per-

[7] Stern: op. cit.
[8] Glass and Li: op. cit.
[9] B. Berry: *Almost White* (New York: The Macmillan Co.; 1963).

cent are Filipinos, Chinese, and various mixtures of the different immigrant groups.[1]

About one third of the children born in the last decade are said to be of mixed parentage, and the mixture is in many cases complex. According to blood-group studies, persons who call themselves "Hawaiians" are of 8.5 percent Caucasoid and 13.7 percent Chinese ancestry, whereas those designated as "Chinese Hawaiians" are 13.7 percent Caucasoid.[2]

On the basis of L. C. Dunn's analysis of a series of Caucasoid Hawaiians and Chinese Hawaiians measured in 1916 and 1920, we are led to believe that this situation already existed a half century ago.[3] In each group studied, the F_1 generation failed to show the uniformity expected in metrical and descriptive traits, which indicated that the parents themselves were mixed. Dunn further found that whereas the mixed individuals were intermediate between their parental stocks in most respects, the Caucasoid Hawaiians leaned toward the European prototype in the form of the nasal root but not of the tip of the nose, and that the Chinese Hawaiians had an excess of epicanthic folds. Despite the emphasis on racial mixture in the state of Hawaii, we must not forget that two thirds of its citizens are not mixed at all, being Americans of European, Japanese, Chinese, Filipino, or other ancestry.

The Canadians

THE ETHNIC HISTORY of Canada is closely tied to that of the United States in the sense that many people have moved back and forth across the border, but it differs from ours in that Canada has achieved even less ethnic unity among white people.

In 1583 Newfoundland was settled by the British, and the French established themselves in Quebec in 1608. These two principal European elements have coexisted ever since without merging. In 1961 more than 30 percent of the 18 million Canadians—that is, some 5¼ million people—were descended almost entirely from 10,000 Frenchmen who settled in the St. Lawrence

[1] R. Adams: *Interracial Marriage in Hawaii* (New York: The Macmillan Co.; 1937), and recent census reports.
[2] N. E. Morton and C. S. Chung: "Genetic Effects of Interracial Crosses," ANYAS (1965), in press.
[3] L. C. Dunn: *An Anthropometric Study of Hawaiians of Pure and Mixed Blood*, PMP, Vol. 11, No. 3 (1928).

Valley and the Maritime Provinces during the seventeenth century. In 1755 the British, including in their armed forces many New Englanders, expelled the French from the Maritime Provinces, which they repopulated with New Englanders, Scots, and a few Germans. The Scots concentrated on Cape Breton Island, where more Gaelic is spoken today than in Scotland.

Later some of the French returned, and a few hundred were exiled to Louisiana. Their descendants, the Acadians, now number over 600,000. Today French Canadians form an almost solid block in the province of Quebec and neighboring parts of Ontario and New Brunswick. In 1953, 3¾ million out of the 5¼ million in the province of Quebec spoke only French, and, with encouragement from France, their nationalism is rising. From the anthropological point of view, the French Canadians are a very interesting people for serious biological study, which they have not yet received.

Among the English-speaking Canadians are the descendants of over 40,000 Americans who migrated there at the time of the Revolution. Many of the New Englanders went to the Maritime Provinces. The New Yorkers, however, favored Lower Ontario, where they were joined by a few Southerners and their house slaves. Between the Revolution and 1812, the number of Americans emigrating to Canada exceeded that of Europeans immigrating to the United States. As a result most English-speaking Canadians have an American accent, with a few Scottish modifications.

Between 1846 and 1854, a half million British immigrated to Canada, including many Irish, but after 1860 many Canadians moved to the United States, and have continued to do so. In 1900 one fifth of the persons of Canadian birth lived south of the border. While immigrants from Central and Eastern Europe were pouring into the United States, they also went to Canada. Many of them, particularly Russians, have isolated themselves linguistically and culturally.

Owing to the understandable preoccupation of Canadian anthropologists with Indians and Eskimo, they have paid little attention to themselves. Although we know no more of the racial characteristics of the English-speaking Canadians than we do of those of the French Canadians, the implications about the English-speaking ones are clearer because most of the English-speaking Canadians and most of the Americans are a single people.

The Australians and New Zealanders

IN 1878 a few shiploads of British convicts, among whom were some 500 Irishmen who had been caught rebelling against the British Crown, landed in Sydney Harbor. From that moment until 1945, Australia and Tasmania continued to be settled from the British Isles. Since 1945 Italians, Dutchmen, Poles, and other continental Europeans have immigrated to Australia, where they now make up 10 percent of the white population.

No systematic work has been done on the physical anthropology of the white Australians. However, A. A. Abbie, the leading student of race in Australia, has observed no outstanding difference between them and their kin in the home islands.[4] He notes that children have grown about 3½ inches taller since World War I, and that the present mean adult male stature is 5 feet 7½ inches (171.5 centimeters), about the same as for most parts of the British Isles but shorter than in northern England and Scotland.

The formal settlement of New Zealand did not begin until 1840, although various white sealers, deserters from sailing vessels, and other adventurers had been there. Of the present 2½ million inhabitants, 91.8 percent are European, and 98 percent of the latter are British. The rest are Maoris, mixed Maoris, and Polynesians from other islands. Only the Maoris have been studied by physical anthropologists.

In Australia we know a little about the 30,000 half-castes, who are gaining in numbers on the 40,000 full-blooded aborigines.[5] As in America, mixed Australians have a "passing" problem, but it is a different one. In America a Caucasoid-looking colored person has already participated in the white man's culture. His or her chief barrier is the chance of being recognized as colored. In Australia the barrier is cultural, for an immense psychological gap exists between Paleolithic tribal life and the daily existence of

4 Abbie: "Physical Characters," in *The Australian Encyclopedia*, Vol. 7 (1958), pp. 106–8.
5 N. B. Tindale: "Growth of a People: Formation and Development of a Hybrid Aboriginal and White Stock on the Islands of Bass Strait, Tasmania, 1815–1949." RQVM-NS, No. 2 (1953), pp. 1–64. Gates: "The Genetics of the Australian Aborigines," AGMG, Vol. 9 (1960), pp. 1–50; "Studies in Race Crossing. IX. Crosses of Australians with Caucasians, Chinese, and other races," AMGH, Vol. 9, pp. 165–84; *Race Crossing* (Rome: Edizione dell'Istituto Gregorio Mendel), no date, but probably 1960.

even an itinerant white drover.[6] Once the cultural hurdle is surmounted, the biological barrier is lower because aborigines come closer to the European's physical range than Negroes do. Whereas only one in four colored Americans who are one fourth Negro may look white enough to pass, most of the Australians who are one fourth aborigine do. The skin color of aborigines seems to depend on fewer genes than that of the Negros—possibly only on two genes, one of which is shared with brunette whites. There is no noticeable difference in hair form between the two races. Like many Britons, the aborigines have fully developed beards, and their hair grays early in life. Their body build resembles that of lean Europeans. The chief differences between the two races that meet the eye lie in certain facial features, such as heavy browridges, deep nasal notches, sunken eye sockets, snubbed noses, and large, healthy teeth. Not one of these is unknown in the British population. Because these facial features are more evolutionary than racial, they tend to be reduced in hybrids.

It is a paradox that while blood groups and other genetic characters show the Aborigines to be more distantly related to Europeans than Negroes are, the Aborigines are closer to Europeans in the criteria that the layman recognizes. For this reason, several thousand "half-castes" have become white Australians during the last 180 years, and more will cross the invisible line in the future.

Africa, the Graveyard of Colonies

A F R I C A has been colonized by Europeans and neighboring Western Asians not just since 1492, but since the time of the Phoenicians, some of whom even sailed around it. But it has never been colonized permanently. Greek temples decorate the skyline in Cyrenaica, and some of the largest and least damaged Roman buildings within easy reach of the tourist stand like gaunt birds on the desert near Kasserine Pass, of unhappy memory. In the Dades Valley of Morocco, a French fort shelters the family of a Berber chief, who does not understand the plumbing. And 1⅕ million Frenchmen left Algeria after more than a hundred years of French rule without leaving enough mixed offspring to fill a schoolhouse. The only

[6] Tindale: "Survey of the Half-Caste Problem in South Australia," PRGS-SAB (1940–1), pp. 66–161.

viable colony of any size left in Africa is the Republic of South Africa, to which we now turn our attention.

The Boers and the Coloreds

T H E Republic of South Africa consists of two former Boer republics, Orange Free State and Transvaal, and two erstwhile British colonies, Cape Province and Natal. It also controls the former German Southwest Africa, but not Basutoland, Swaziland, or Bechuanaland, which the British retain. In 1960, the population of South Africa was a little over 16 million, of whom 3 million are listed as white, 11 million as Bantu, 1½ million as Colored (a local term to be explained presently), and 477,000 as Asian. The former owners of the land, the Bushmen and Hottentots, were not mentioned.

Only two elements in the South African population concern us here: the 1.8 million Afrikaans-speaking whites, and the 1.5 million Colored. Except for the Bushmen and Hottentots, these two elements are the oldest in South Africa. They arose from the same events in history and are mutually related. In 1652 the Dutch East Indies Company stationed Jan van Riebeeck and sixty company servants at Cape Town to grow vegetables and to buy beef from the Hottentots, in order to victual the company's ships. Several small parties of young women were sent out from Dutch orphanages to wed these and other bachelors, and some other Dutch settlers followed them. In 1689 about two hundred French Huguenots arrived, and later a small group of Plattdeutsch-speaking Germans, without women. In 1707 the Dutch East Indies Company forbade further migration and, as far as the European community was concerned, a genetic isolate was established, with a serious shortage of women.

When, in 1815, the British seized the Cape, they found it inhabited by 15,000 Boers and 20,000 slaves, not counting other Boers and slaves who had already trekked northward. Both sets of slaves were the mixed descendants of Muslim prisoners from India, Malays, natives of Madagascar, Negroes from West Africa, and undoubtedly some Bushmen and Hottentots, all blended with the genes of their Dutch masters.

In about six generations, since 1815, the Boers have grown to 1.8 million, and the descendants of the slaves, who became Coloreds in 1835 when the British freed them, now number 1.5

million. Obviously, genetic isolation cannot have been maintained during this entire period. A conservative figure of half a million who may have passed from Colored to Boer has been mentioned.[7]

As far as we know, the Boers have not been examined by physical anthropologists, but some of the Coloreds have. One group in particular, the so-called Rehobother Bastaards, long ago received the meticulous attention of the late Eugen Fischer, whose work on them has become a classic in the field of racial mixture.[8] In Afrikaans, *Bastaard* is a word that anyone can pronounce in polite company without drawing a blush. It simply means someone who is proud to be part Dutch. When Fischer studied the Rehobothers, early in this century, they constituted a group of some 3,000 persons living in ninety houses surrounding a large and well-kept church, in and near Rehoboth, a small town in what was then German Southwest Africa. They were reasonably prosperous farmers and cattle-breeders.

The community was founded in the late eighteenth century by about forty Boers and their Hottentot wives, and although a few other white men have since joined the group—including one named MacNab—they have intermarried among themselves. They are not the only such community in South Africa, but the most famous. The men are as tall as European Dutchmen, with legs relatively longer than those of either Dutch or Hottentots. In other measurements of the body, head, and face, they are more or less intermediate between the Dutch and the Hottentots, and not particularly variable. Half of the women have the fat thighs and buttocks of Hottentots, and about 20 percent of both sexes have Bushman ears. In the anatomy of their soft parts the Rehobothers show a wide range. About half have the unexposed skin color of a white man, and none are darker than medium brown, which is as dark at Hottentots become. Yet these people tan deeply. Their hair covers the world's range from straight to peppercorn, and varies in color from black to light brown, with an incidence of about 50 percent of black hair. Of the children, 43 percent are blond, but their hair darkens later. Eighty-two percent of the men have dark eyes; 14 percent have mixed eyes, and 4 percent have blue or gray eyes. Beards appear late on the men, but by the age of fifty many of them have a growth as great as that of Europeans. Judging by Fischer's photographs, and by others taken later, some

[7] S. G. Millin: *The People of South Africa* (New York: Alfred A. Knopf; 1954).

[8] E. Fischer: *Die Rehobother Bastards und das Bastardierungsproblem beim Menschen* (Jena: Gustav Fischer; 1913).

of the Rehobothers could pass for Boers, and vice versa, and a few other Rehobothers are indistinguishable from Hottentots.

If in 1709 the British government had forbidden further immigration to the North American colonies; if a European power with an alien language and culture had defeated our colonial ancestors and sent in its own colonists who did not mix; and if on top of all that, whole tribes of warlike, cattle-keeping people of another race had invaded and swamped one side of our country, those of us who are "Old Americans" might find ourselves in a position more or less analogous to that of the Boers, and some of us would be more analogous than others. In sum, the racial situation in Africa, including South Africa, is an artifact of history. The continent resists European penetration because it has long been partly European.

No epilogue on the philosophy of racial history seems to be needed at this point. We think that the lesson is loud and clear.

11

The Future of the Races
of Man

🧬🧬🧬

Every Man a Genius, and the Centaur's Return

EVERY TWO or three years *The New York Times* Sunday Magazine publishes a prognostication by some leading anthropologist on what our descendants will look like at some distant date. It usually includes a picture of a man with a bulging cranium, little jaws, and four toes. Science-fiction writers are less conservative, and so are we.

But it needs no science-fiction writer to predict what *can* happen. Herman Muller, Joshua Lederberg, J. B. S. Haldane, and other renowned scientists, some of them Nobel laureates, have made this clear.[1] Dr. Muller wants to establish sperm banks in which the semen of men of genius can be kept in deep freeze, to be thawed out from time to time to impregnate gifted females. Actually artificial insemination of married women unable to conceive by their own husband's efforts has been going on quietly for some time, and the freezing of sperm, to be thawed out alive, was achieved several decades ago, with cells from frogs, by Hudson Hoagland and Gregory Pincus, the inventor of the pill that bears his name. There is nothing impracticable about Dr. Muller's idea.

[1] This subject was discussed at length and with much fun at a CIBA Foundation conference in London late in 1962, as reported in G. Wolstenholme, ed.: *Man and his Future* (London, J. & A. Churchill; 1963). See also A. W. Galston: "From the Biologists' Laboratory: Clues to Immortality, NO, April 12, 1965, p. 22.

Joshua Lederberg has made several rather startling proposals, which may be perfectly feasible. One is to increase the number of neurons in the human brain by injecting fetal brains with growth hormone, before the number of neurons has became fixed. Another is to use a virus to carry novel DNA messages into human reproductive cells and thus permanently change the person's genes. Lederberg has already done this with microorganisms. Or DNA could be extracted from the somatic cells of a genius by simple biopsy.

A little more remote is the possibility of cutting up living chromosomes with tiny knives called nanaknives, or with lasers, and recombining them. This innovation requires advanced technical skill and a better knowledge than we now have of the genetic map of the human chromosomes. The late J. B. S. Haldane, somewhat facetiously, suggested in 1962 that intergeneric crosses might be made by combining pieces of chromosomes, even hybridizing human beings with seals to make frogmen.

The trouble with all these plans, however clever and far-reaching, is that people will have to consent to them. The churches, synagogues, and mosques of the world are unlikely to yield to these Frankensteinian dalliances with the forces of nature. Some of the Communists might follow Lederberg's scheme, but some of them have only just begun to work in modern genetics. This may slow down the Russians and the mainland Chinese, at least in the immediate future. But the Japanese, who are excellent geneticists, biochemists, and microscope makers, and disciplined enough to have led the world in birth control, might jump the gun and set their branch of the Mongoloid subspecies ahead of the rest of us.

One advance, however, which may find little or no opposition will be in geriatrics. People live longer and longer every generation. Yet few if any outlive their 115th year. With a few notable exceptions, nonagenarians and centenarians are not very productive citizens. The second goal of geriatrics, more useful than merely prolonging life, is to control and defeat the process of aging. If we can preserve our tissues and physiological processes at some optimum age, say at thirty-five, and then keep on learning to the maximum extent of our inherited mental capacities, man will have found the fountain of youth at last, and live on in beauty and wisdom until one by one we are killed off by accidents irreparable by organ transplants, and death will be rare. It is our prediction that the prolongation of life and the conquest of senile decay are actual prospects which might be achieved before the public would accept schemes that tamper with chromosomes and fetal gray matter.

If these geriatric triumphs arrive soon enough to affect persons now living who are, for example, over fifty, these individuals will continue to react unfavorably to genetic innovations. Men able to live indefinitely do not want to yield control of the world to a new and much brighter generation. If the conquest of senility is delayed until after they are dead, the future Mullers, Lederbergs, and Haldanes may have their way.

So far we have mentioned some of the currently known possibilities that might affect mankind as a whole in the future, but how about race? As we write, race is becoming more and more unmentionable. For the next decade or two if not longer, we predict that racial studies will continue to decline. We also predict that in some ways racial differences will become accentuated because geriatrists and geneticists are for the most part Europeans, Americans, Japanese, and Chinese. Will these wizards try as hard to prolong the useful lives of members of races other than their own, except for the American Negroes, or to raise their intellectual capacities? Anthropologists might opt for the preservation and wit-sharpening of elderly Australian aborigines and Bushmen, to serve as permanent informants to future generations of students, but anthropologists have little to say about policy.

The Negroes, meanwhile, have another innovation to look forward to. Recent research on the actions of two hormones secreted by the pineal body make it possible that before long people will be able to change their skin color whenever they like, by simple injections. A colored woman could thus turn white with less effort than it takes to have her hair straightened, waved, and set. This would be particularly effective for those with narrow features and dark skins.

Once the chromosome-slicing geneticists and the DNA men have eventually been allowed to perform their magic, racial differences can be made to disappear, not only in anatomy and physiology but also in the bitterly fought-over field of intelligence. Everyone who wants it can have an IQ of exactly 199.95. People as bright as that will be able to take steps to lower the birthrate, stabilize the world's population, abolish pesticides, restore the earth's natural landscapes, give everyone congenial jobs, and realize that the division of man into races is a wonderful gift of nature, rather than a source of animosity.

Unlike *The Sunday Times's* little men, they will be able to decide whether they want four toes or five, and those that feel devilish enough can walk on hoofs. Satyrs could cavort again in Arcadian glades, and angels soar over church steeples. Black centaurs could play polo against white centaurs, with gnomes and leprechauns cheering from the sidelines. This sounds like a comic-strip pipe dream. But is it?

Computers, Biotechnology, Education, and Common Sense

C O M P U T E R manufacturers are deeply interested in the research of brain surgeons and other experimental neurologists in order to improve their machines. Before long we may come to know exactly how much of "intelligence" is genetically determined and how much is environmentally induced. Once this knowledge is established, the question of interracial differences in the genetic capacities of individuals for learning, decision making, and certain aspects of behavior can be read directly from the brain itself. This new science will be to phrenology what atomic physics is to alchemy. Having determined the capacities of individuals, experts in this new science can easily plot their findings in terms of populations and races. Then it may be of academic interest to settle the question of the validity of IQ's and other psychometric tests. The computer makers will be happy, and the question of racial differences can be drawn from the political battlefield into the realms of engineers and educators.

As B. F. Pierce has brilliantly pointed out,[2] engineers specializing in what they call biotechnology have made elaborate studies of the utilization of natural resources in industry and in the perfection of machines to process them, but they have paid much less attention to the efficient utilization of the third and most important component, the human being, who is both producer and consumer of their product. Efficient utilization of human beings requires as exact a knowledge of their organs and functions as physicists, chemists, biologists, and engineers already have of matter and of machines. An essential part of the knowledge needed can be provided by the researchers in neurology and behavior whose work interests the computer manufacturers. Although Pierce has directed his inquiry chiefly to the efficient utilization of cultural differences, it is clear that racial differences are, inevitably and unavoidably, also involved.

At this point in human history the most advanced branches of science are drawing together and beginning to take over the role of the study of man from anthropologists and sociologists,

2 B. F. Pierce, *The Ethnic Factor in Biotechnology*, San Diego, General Dynamics/Astronautics, Life Sciences Section, 1964.

who work with cruder tools, techniques, and concepts. Their combined efforts must inevitably lead to what is now an unpopular conclusion. Rather than continuing to try to homogenize the cultures of the world by "developing" the "underdeveloped" peoples and nations—and rather than continuing to ignore racial differences just as we used to avoid mentioning cancer—unbiased, responsible, and practical scientists will plan and recommend ways to see that all members of all races and cultures can be given congenial and interesting work to do, or else be allowed to live undisturbed according to their own traditional cultural patterns as long as they like.

Great strides are now being made in the science and techniques of education, once a fallow field of academe. Modern educators are already hard at work trying to devise new didactic procedures which will use the maximum of each person's innate capacities for behavior, in an increasingly crowded and competitive world. Essential to the success of the educators would be a recognition of differences in race, and steps might then be taken to adjust the new educational techniques which are now being devised to fit the needs of different races and cultures. So far the leading textbook manufacturers of the United States have begun to show a recognition of race chiefly by a single hurried expedient, that of painting over the faces of a few children in every group illustration so that in each picture of erstwhile white children the reader will see at least one smiling black face. As the publishers well know, this device is not enough.

Some of them now realize that their responsibility both to their customers and to their stockholders is to do their share in guaranteeing that as many kinds of people as possible shall be as well adjusted to their physical environments, to available resources, to each other, and to other kinds of people, as are the few surviving bands of Australian aborigines who still live in a state of freedom, and these aborigines are as well adjusted as a bird in its nest or a clam between its shells.

The success of the educators would be a greater triumph than the conquest of death, success in toying with DNA, or another modern proposal—mass hybridization to eliminate races. They also have a greater chance of success than either of the other teams. More people are interested in educating their children than in building Frankensteins or even in remaining alive indefinitely. No sizable or consequential church nor any political party opposes education. No one wants unemployment or poverty, which are linked in the public mind with inferior educational opportunities.

Whoever wins, our prediction about the future of the races of man remains the same. We predict that if things go on as they are, the Australoids and the Capoids will eventually be absorbed by their neighbors, but it may take longer for them to disappear as unmixed races than some anthropologists think. We further predict that the Caucasoids, the Mongoloids, and the Congoids will be with us both as separate units and in clines, for a long, long time to come. There is nothing startling about these predictions, and we hope that no one will be disappointed at not being surprised.

CIRCUMPOLAR PEOPLES

Plates 1–16

Before the end of the last glacial period the circumpolar regions were almost entirely uninhabited. Then both Caucasoid and Mongoloid peoples migrated northward and eastward. As we move to the east from Lapland to Greenland, we find the Circumpolar peoples starting out Caucasoid and ending up Mongoloid, with many stages of transition.

1. A Norwegian Lapp woman.

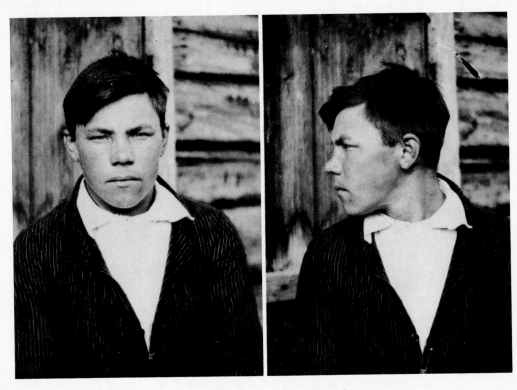

2. *a.* and *b.* A Norwegian Lapp boy.

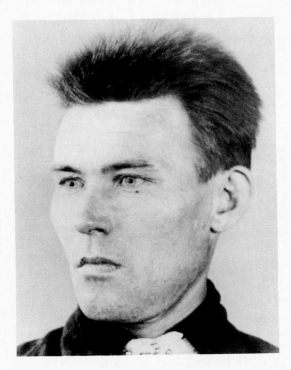

c. A Russian Lapp.

3. *a*. A Zyrian. The Zyrians are Finnish people hunting and herding reindeer in the forests of northern European Russia.

b. A Vogul. The Voguls are Ugrian-speaking peoples of the Obi River country who live principally by fishing.

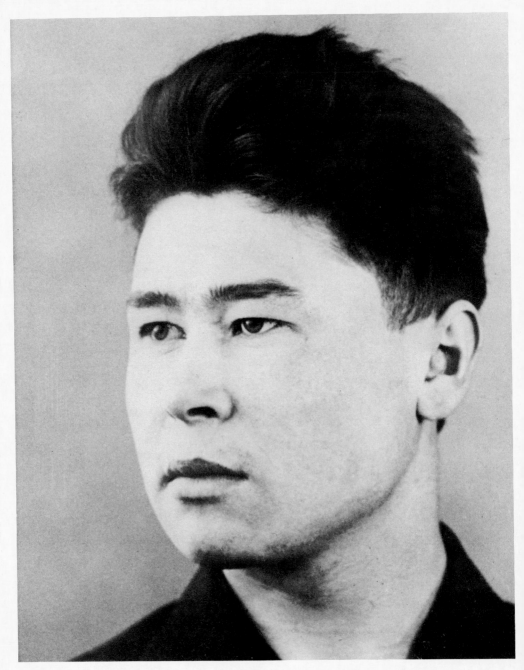

4. A Samoyed. The Samoyeds are reindeer-breeders and hunters of northwestern Siberia.

5. A Yukaghir. The Yukaghirs are Paleasiatic-speakers who once inhabited a large territory in north-central Siberia.

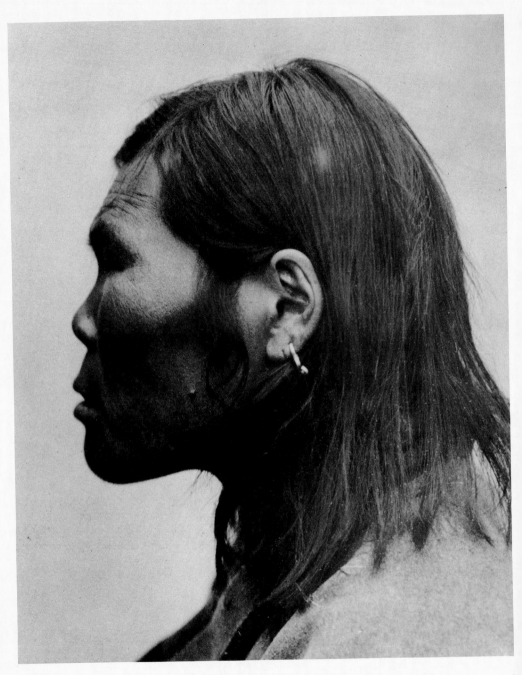

6. A Tungus man. The Tungus occupy much of the interior of eastern Siberia. Note the great face length and facial flattening.

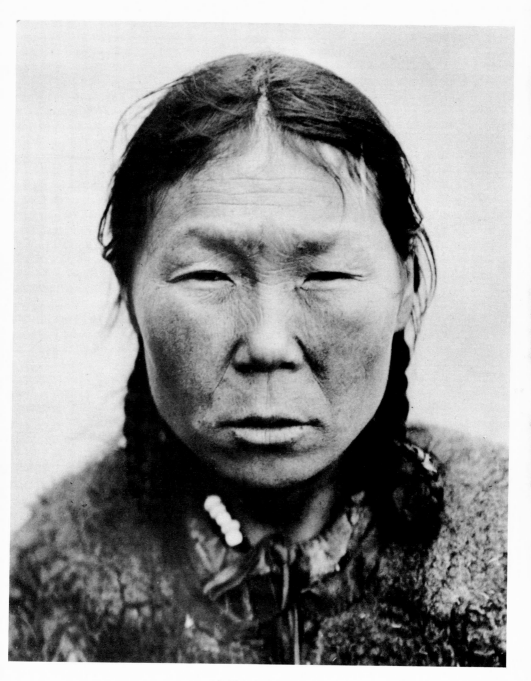

7. A Tungus woman.

8. A Chukchi man. The Chukchi are the northeasternmost
Paleasiatic-speaking people, living on the shore of Bering Strait
and inland.

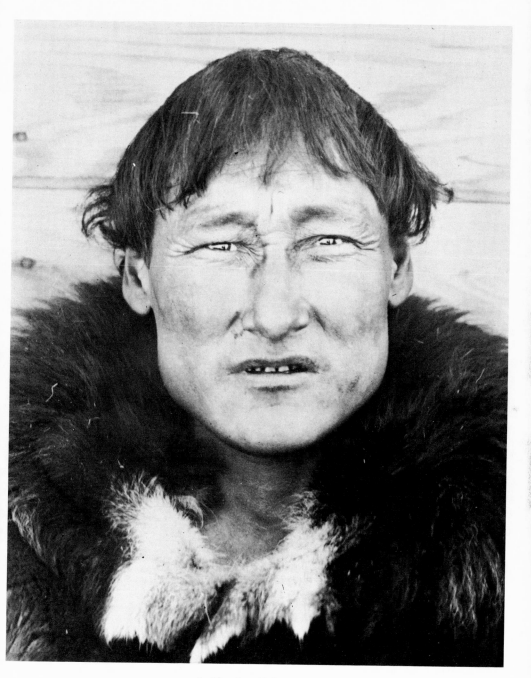

9. A Siberian Eskimo man.

10. Two Canadian Eskimos.

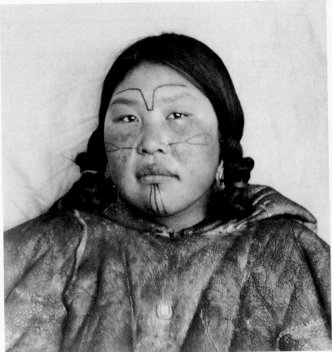

11. *a*. and *b*. An Eskimo woman of East Greenland.

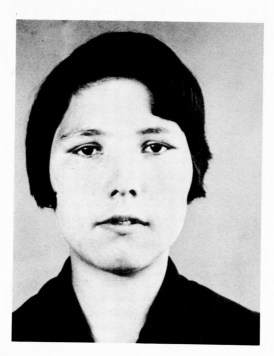

c. A Siberian woman with a Ukrainian father and an Eskimo mother. She looks completely European.

12. An Orok man. The Oroks (also called Udes) are Tungusic-speaking hunters on Sakhalin Island.

13. A Gilyak. The Gilyaks are Paleasiatic-speakers living at the mouth of the Amur River and on Sakhalin Island. Like the Ainu they are heavily bearded, but lack the Ainus' extreme development of body hair.

14. *a*. An Ainu man of Hokkaido. Note the European-like facial features and curly head and beard hair.

b. An Ainu woman. A simulated mustache has been tattooed on her face.

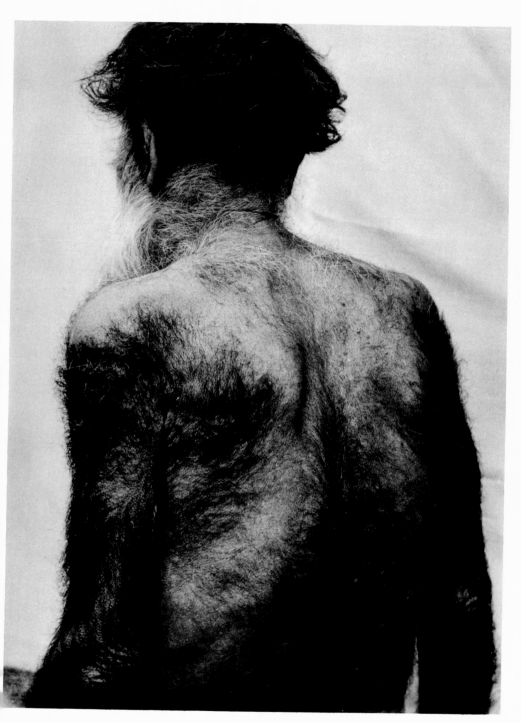

15. An Ainu man's back, showing heavy body hair.

16. A modern Ainu, shaven and shorn.

AMERICAN INDIANS

Plates 17–29

The ancestors of the American Indians entered the New World from Asia before the end of the last glaciation, between 30,000 and 13,000 years ago, and well before the Eskimo. They differ from most Asiatic Mongoloids in that some of them have more European-like facial features. Despite certain local variations they are more homogeneous in appearance than the inhabitants of any other continental land mass.

17. A Connecticut Indian.

18. A Mandan chief. Natives of North Dakota, the Mandans are now rare, scattered, and mixed. George Catlin painted some of them as blond.

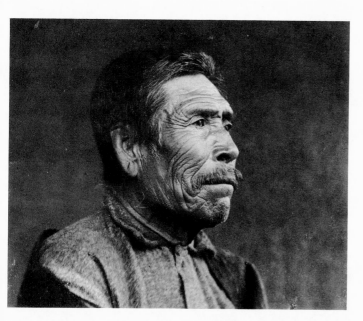

19. *a.* A chief of the Kwakiutl Indians of Vancouver Island.

b. A Hupa Indian of California.

20. *a*. and *b*. Two Maya Indian Women of Yucatán, showing different facial profiles.

21. *a.* A Maya-Spanish Mestizo of Yucatán.

b. A Mestizo of the Guatemala Lowlands. His father was apparently pure Spanish.

c. A Guatemalan Trihybrid: Spanish, Indian, and Negro.

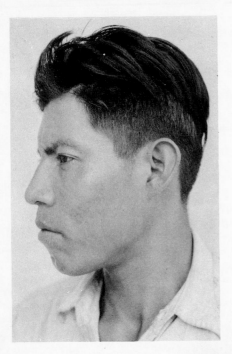

22. *a.* A Yupa Indian of the western Venezuela Highlands.

b. A Quechua Indian from the Peruvian Highlands.

23. *a*. and *b*. Two Wai-Wai Indians from the border between British Guiana and Brazil. These men show clearly the two principal types of facial features common among American Indians.

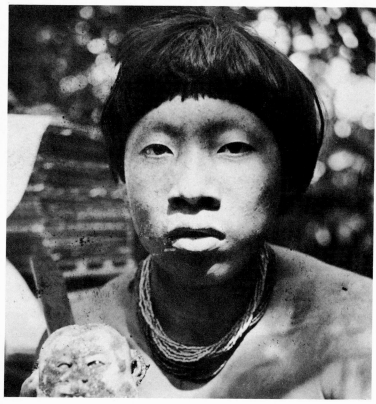

24. *a*. Two Arawak men from British Guiana. The Arawaks once also occupied the West Indies, before the invasion of the Caribs.

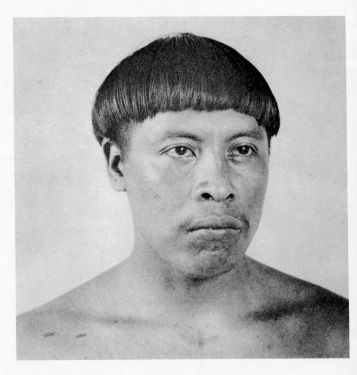

b. A Bakairi Indian from the Xingú, Brazil.

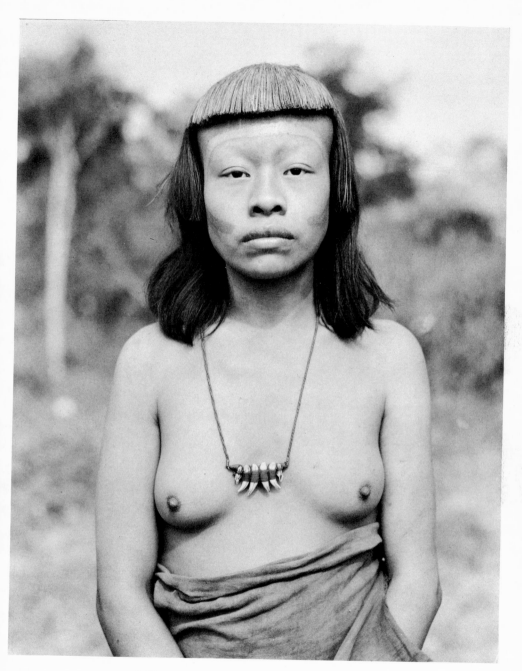

25. A Bororo woman from the Mato Grosso, Brazil.

26. *a.* An Ona man, probably the last full-blooded survivor.

b. An Ona woman.

c. A Yaghan man.

27. The twilight of a people: three Alakalufs in their hut.

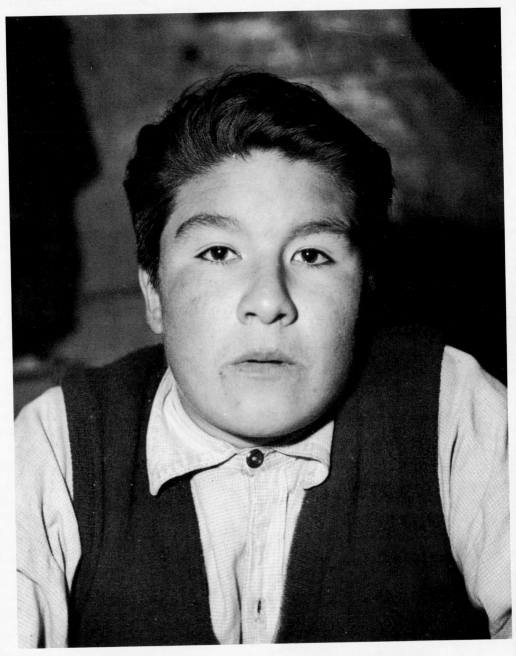

28. A young Chilote. The Chilotes are a numerous and vigorous people found throughout southernmost South America. They come from the island of Chiloé and are a mixture of early colonial Spaniards with Chono and Araucanian Indians.

29. A man of mixed Spanish and Patagonian Indian ancestry. He bears a striking likeness to the late Pierre Teilhard de Chardin, S.J.

MONGOLOIDS OF EAST ASIA, SOUTHEAST ASIA, AND INDONESIA

Plates 30–53

China was the ancient home of the Mongoloids. Toward the end of the last glaciation some of them were migrating northward into previously uninhabited terrain, while others were pushing southward into Southeast Asia and its fringing islands, from Formosa to Sumatra. In these places they encountered native Australoids, surrounding some, absorbing others, and driving still others eastward along the island chain as far as Australia.

30. A Korean.

31. A North Chinese.

32. *a*. A Fukienese. The Fukienese live in west-central China and western Formosa.

b. A Hakka. The Hakkas are coastal Chinese some of whom live in boats. Others inhabit the fringes of the mountains in western Formosa.

33. A Japanese nobleman of aristocratic facial type.

34. *a*. A Japanese student.

b. A Japanese farmer from the central mountains of Honshu.

35. A Kalmuck woman. The Kalmucks are Mongols who stayed in Russia after the Mongol invasions. Some now live in Philadelphia, Pa., and Medford, N.J.

36. *a.* A Mongol.

b. A Kirghiz from the Pamirs.

37. A Tibetan nobleman, the Dalai Lama's secretary.

38. A Tibetan lama with curly hair.

39. *a.* A Lepcha of Sikkim.

b. A Bhutanese nun.

40. A Nepalese woman, wife of a Khasi tribal chief.

41. *a*. A Khasi woman from the Khasi Hills of of Assam.

b. A Garo from the Garo Hills to the west of the Khasi territory.

42. An Abor from the Northeast Frontier Administration.

43. *a.* A Bhutanese man.

b. Three Nagas from north-easternmost India and adjacent portions of Burma. The Nagas resemble American Indians in appearance.

44. *a*. A Shan woman from Upper Burma.

b. A Miao woman from Laos.

45. *a.* and *b.* A Burmese from Rangoon.

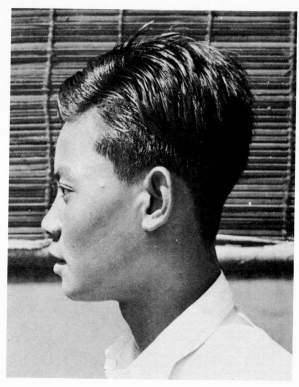

46. A Cambodian woman.

47. An Annamite from Vietnam.

48. A Yumbri from the forests of northern Laos, one of the few remaining "People of the Yellow Leaves."

49. *a*. An Atayal woman from
northern Formosa. Note the
Ainu-like features and tattooing.

b. A group of Ami girls from southeastern Formosa.

50. A Filipino from Luzon.

51. A Punan from northern Borneo. The Punans are nomadic hunters.

52. *a*. A Kelabit from Sarawak.   *b*. A Malay of Sarawak.

c. Three Iban women of Sarawak.

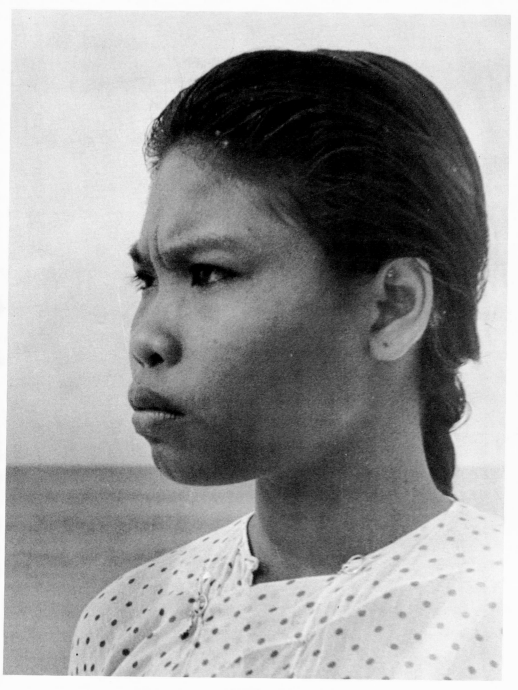

53. A girl from the Nicobar Islands, off the western tip of Sumatra.

THE AUSTRALOIDS

Plates 54–76

The Australoids evolved in Southeast Asia and Indonesia. When the Mongoloids began to expand southward some of the Australoids, who had become—or then became—dwarfs, formed enclaves in forested mountain refuges and inaccessible offshore islands. Others mixed with the invaders, while still others pushed westward to New Guinea and Australia. Later some partly Australoid peoples migrated westward into India, bringing Southeast Asian agriculture.

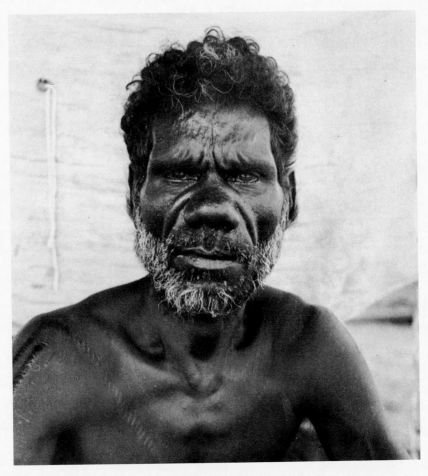

54. A Tiwi—an Australian aborigine from Melville Island, north of Darwin.

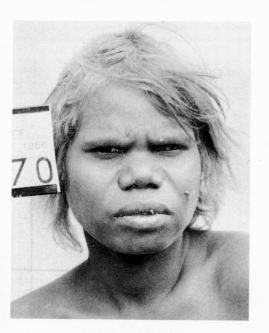
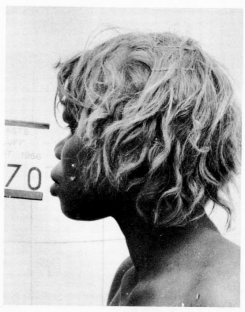

55. *a.* and *b.* A blond aboriginal girl from the desert of central
Australia, aged 18.

c. A half-caste girl from near Fowler's Bay, South Australia.
Many half-castes are indistinguishable from Europeans.

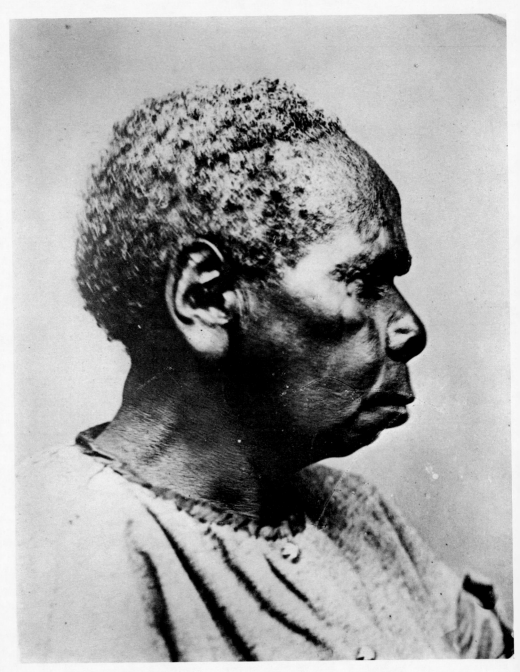

56. A Tasmanian woman named Wapperty, one of the last survivors.

57. *a.* Three Papuans from the Central Highlands of New Guinea.

b. A Pygmy from the New Guinea Highlands.

58. A Melanesian woman of New Caledonia.

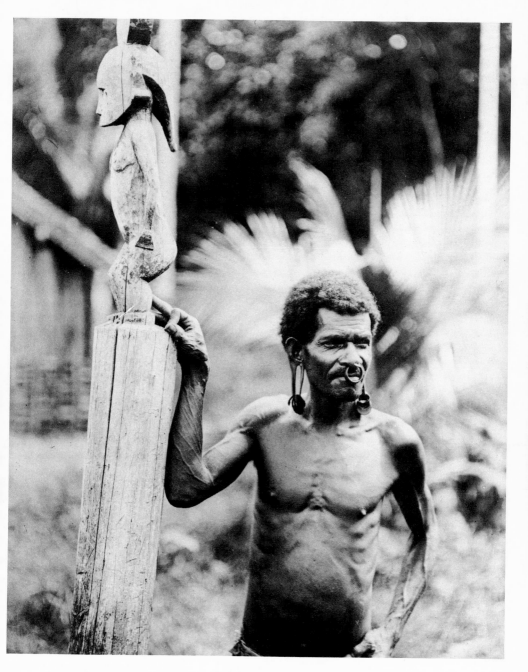

59. A Solomon Islander.

60. A Fijian.

61. A Negrito woman of Luzon.

62. A Negrito woman of Mindanao.

63. Semangs hunting with the blowpipe. The Semangs are Negritos of the Malay Peninsula.

64. Önges of Little Andaman Island.

65. A steatopygous Andamanese mother.

66. A Munda woman. Chota Nagpur Hills, India.

67. Four Asuras of the same region. The Asuras are tribal people
who smelt iron.

68. An Asura girl.

69. An Oraon. The Oraons are Dravidian-speaking tribal people
of north-central India.

70. An "Untouchable" woman employed in a government rest
house, Chota Nagpur Hills.

71. Micronesia—a Marshall Islander.

72. Micronesians of Yap.

73. A Samoan chief.

74. A Samoan lady.

75. A Maori woman, New Zealand.

76. A Hawaiian woman of Hawaiian, English, and Chinese ancestry.

THE CAUCASOIDS, FROM
IRELAND TO INDIA

Plates 77–102

The Caucasoids evolved in Europe, West Asia, and possibly India. According to specialists in blood-group studies, the Lapps and the Basques form two genetic extremes of the Caucasoid race, although both are physically variable. The regional differences between the Caucasoids of Europe and Asia show Mongoloid influences in Central Asia, and possible Australoid remnants in southern Arabia.

77. A Basque, with the facial features usually attributed to these people.

78. *a.*, *b.*, *c.* Three other Basques, showing a wide range of facial features.

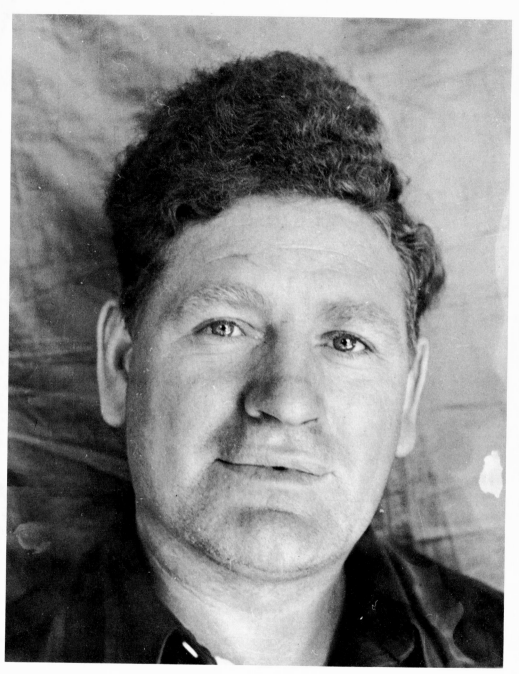

79. An Irishman from County Cork.

80. *a*. A Fleming from Belgium.

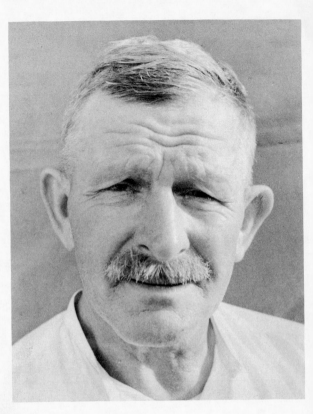

b. A Swede from Göteborg.

81. A Hutzul from the Carpathians. The Hutzuls are Ruthenian-
speaking mountaineers whose country is divided between Poland and the U.S.S.R.

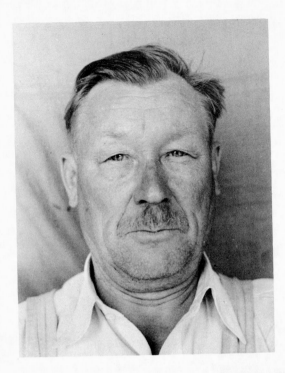

82. *a*. A Finn.

b. An American girl of
Finnish parentage.

83. A White Russian of what Russian anthropologists call the "Ural" racial type.

84. *a.* A Ukrainian.

b. A Hungarian.

85. *a*. A Spanish lady.

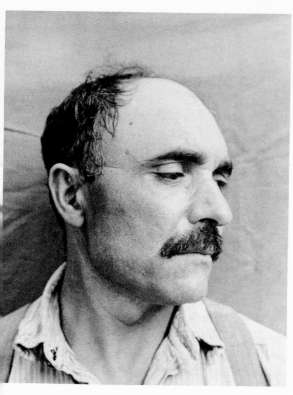

b. An Italian from the region of Naples.

86. *a*. A North Albanian mountaineer.

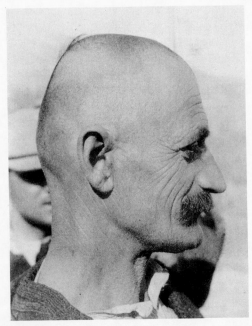

b. Another, showing occipital flattening caused by cradling.

87. A Bulgarian of a facial type also common in the West Asian highlands.

88. *a*. and *b*. Two Turks.

89. *a*. A Syrian from Damascus.

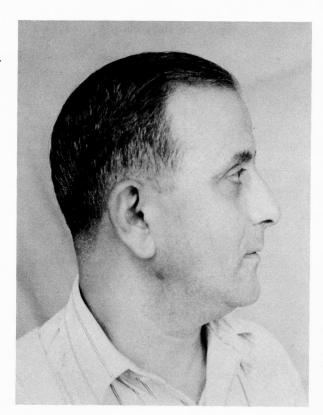

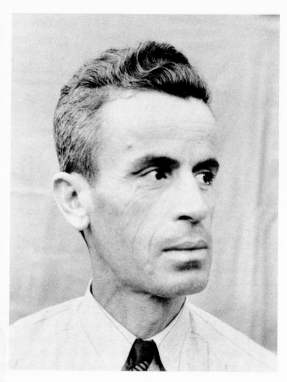

b. A Druse.

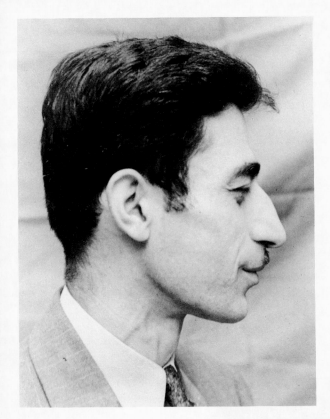

90. *a*. An Armenian from the region of Lake Van. Note occipital flattening.

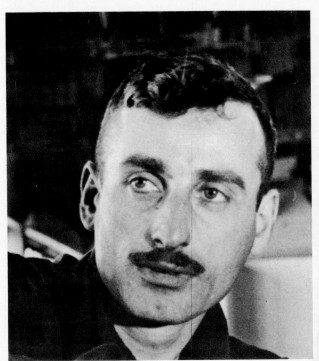

b. A Georgian.

91. *a.* A Persian of Mazandaran
on the Caspian shore.

b. A Kurd.

92. *a*. A Tajik from northern Afghanistan.

b. A Pathan.

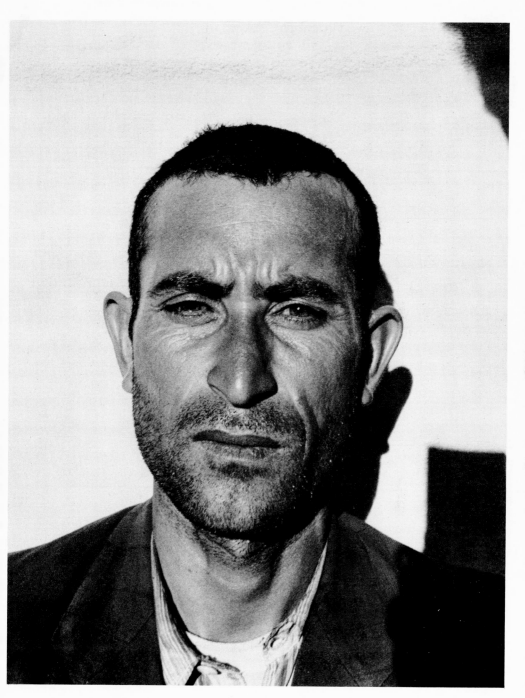

93. A Turkoman.

94. A Rwala Bedawi, Saudi Arabia.

95. *a*. A family of Sulubba, tinkers and guides in the Arabian desert.

b. Soldiers of the Imam—
Yemeni Highlanders.

96. *a*. A man from Dhofar, southern Arabia.

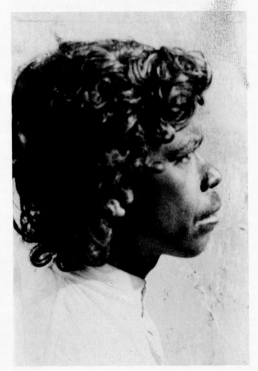

b. A Hadhramaut Arab with Australoid features.

c. A Hadhramaut Arab with Negrito-like features.

97. A Kafiri of Nordic racial type. The Kafiris live in the inaccessible mountains of eastern Afghanistan and adjacent parts of West Pakistan.

98. A Nepalese Brahmin.

99. A farmer of Rajasthan.

100. A Sikh.

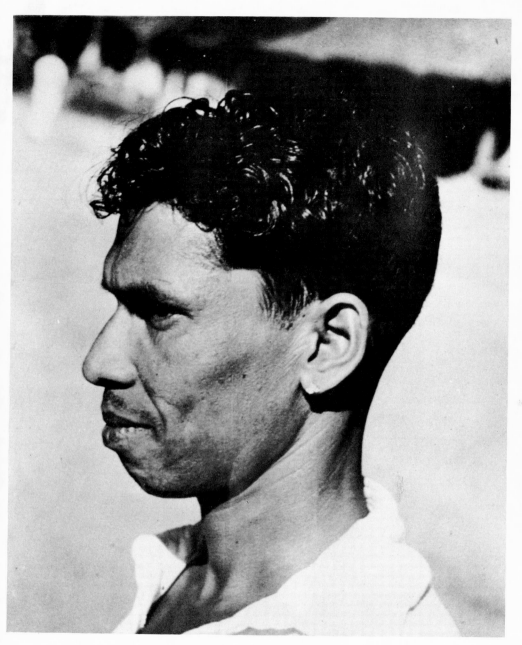

101. A Malayali, a Dravidian of Kerala.

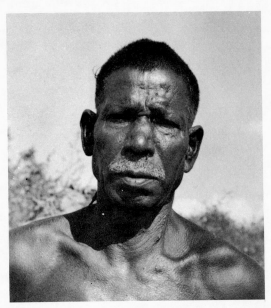

102. *a*. A Birhor—member of a tribe of monkey-hunters of the Chota Nagpur Hills.

b. A Vedda of Ceylon.

THE AFRICANS

Plates 103–125

Africa is the home of the Bushmen. The origin of the Pygmies and Negroes is unknown. As early as 13,000 years ago, Caucasoids invaded North Africa from Europe and Western Asia. Some of the invaders crossed the Sahara and mixed with the peoples they found beyond it. It is quite evident from these pictures as it is from genetic studies that the African Negroes have long been partly Caucasoid.

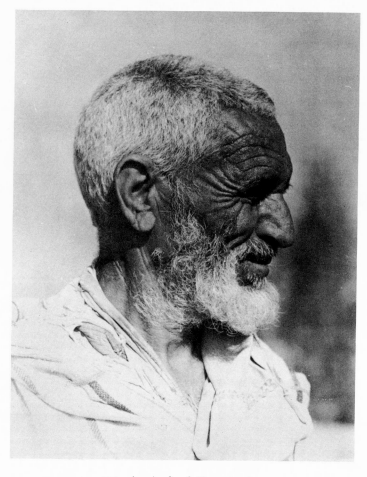

103. An Arab of Mauretania.

104. A Rifian woman of Morocco with a broad face reminiscent of the Mesolithic inhabitants of North Africa.

105. The Paramount Chief of the Ait Atta, a numerous Berber
people of the Middle Atlas, Morocco.

106. A Soussi from southern Morocco.

107. *a*. A Tuareg of the expected lean and aquiline type.

b. and *c*. Two other Tuaregs who look like ordinary Berbers.

108. The Sheikh of a village in the northern Sudan, Wadi Halfa region.

109. *a*. A South African Bushman.

b. A Duwwud woman, southern Libya.

c. A Berber with Bushman-like features, Taroudant.

d. A Boer-Hottentot hybrid.

110. A Bushman hunter.

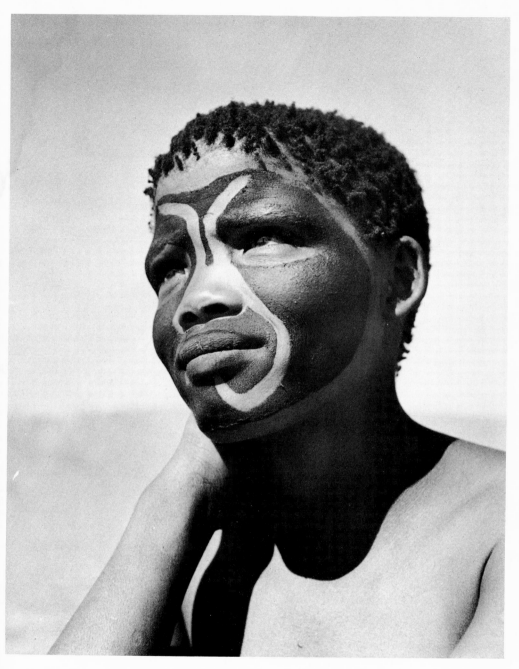

111. A Bushman girl.

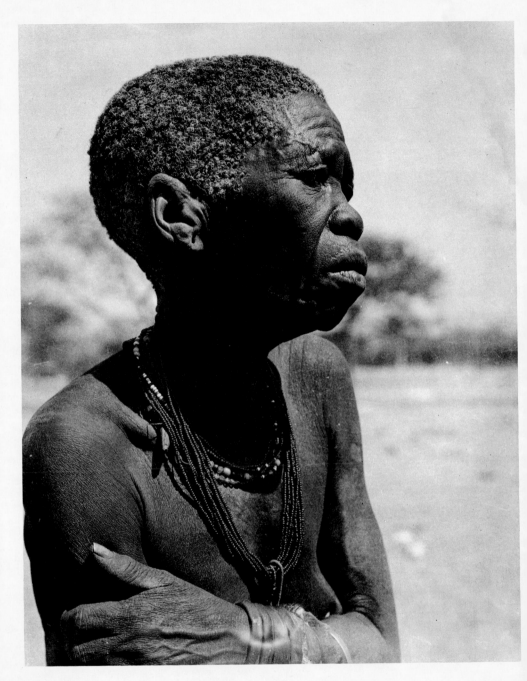

112. An elderly Bushman woman.

113. A Hottentot woman.

114. *a*. A Korana Hottentot woman.

b. A Haratin woman of the Dades Valley, southern Morocco, showing Hottentot-like features.

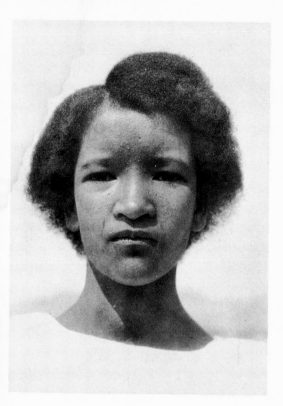

115. *a.* and *b.* Two young Rehobother women—Boer-Hottentot mixture—one of whom could pass for Dutch.

116. An Ituri Pygmy.

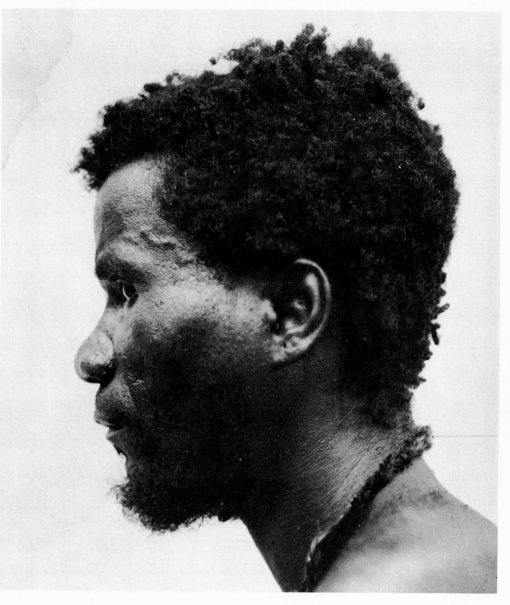

117. A Pygmy from the Central Congo, showing the coarse skin
typical of the Lake Kivu potters.

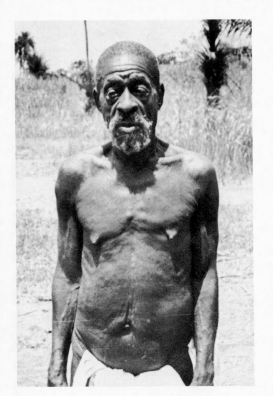

118. *a.* and *b.* Ilombé, Chief of the Bambenga Pygmies, extremely unusual because of his Caucasoid features.

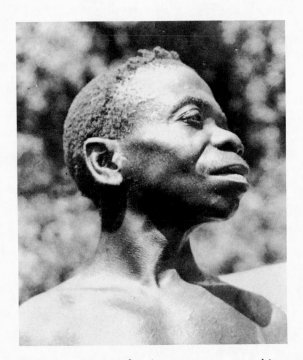

c. An Ituri Pygmy showing extreme prognathism.

119. *a.* and *b.* Two Senegalese.

120. A lady of Accra, Ghana.

121. Aggrey Awori of Uganda, B.A. Harvard, 1965, an outstanding athlete and student. Compare the muscles of his arms with
those of the Bushman hunter shown in Plate 110.

122. *a.* An Amhara man, northern Ethiopia.

b. An Amhara woman.

c. A Galla woman.

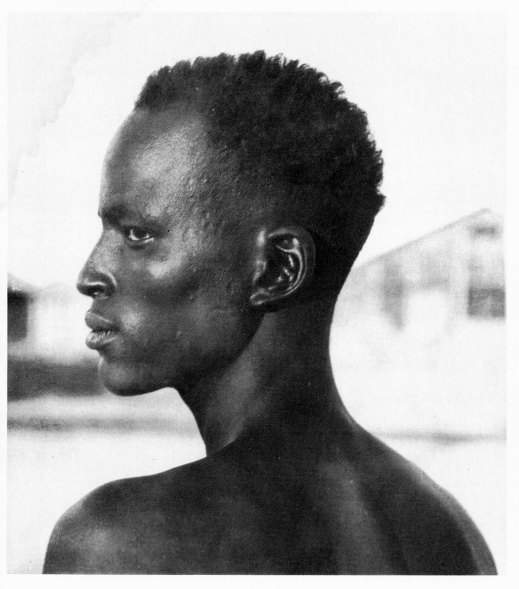

123. A Somali.

124. A Shilluk, with European features.

125. A young Zulu woman.

MADAGASCAR

Plates 126–128

Madagascar was settled during the first millennium A.D. by Indonesians coming possibly from Borneo, who also brought in Bantu Negroes from the coast of East Africa. Persian and Arab traders also settled there. Because the Indonesians are part Australoid and the Bantu part Bushman, the peoples of Madagascar may be a mixture of all five human subspecies.

126. A Merina woman from the central highlands. She is predominantly Indonesian.

127. A Sakalava man from the western part of Madagascar, showing a general mixture.

128. A Mahafaly woman from southern Madagascar. She is predominantly African in appearance.

GLOSSARY

ABBEVILLIAN   The earlier of two successive hand-axe industries west of Movius's Line, formerly known as the Chellean.

ACHONDROPLASTIC   A form of dwarfing in which the extremities are shortened and thickened.

ACHEULEAN   The second of the two hand-axe industries mentioned above.

AEPYORNIS   An extinct giant bird of Madagascar.

ALLEN'S RULE   A zoological observation that the extremities of warm-blooded animals of a single species tend to be longer and thinner in warm regions than in cold ones.

ALVEOLAR   Pertaining to the tooth-bearing part of the upper jaw.

ANAGENESIS   The evolution of one species out of another by succession: phyletic evolution.

ANASTOMOSIS   A connecting link between two arteries which ensures blood flow to the vascular territories of both if one is cut.

ANGSTROM   A metrical unit equaling one ten-billionth of a meter, used in measuring the wavelengths of light.

ANTIGEN   A substance in the blood which stimulates the production of an antibody.

APOCRINE (gland)   A kind of sweat gland that produces a creamy substance.

ATERIAN   A North African flint industry characterized by bifacial pressure flaking and tanged points.

AURIGNACIAN   A European Upper Paleolithic flint industry.

AUSTRALOID   One of the five living subspecies of man, including the native peoples of Australia, New Guinea, and Melanesia; the Negroid dwarfs of Indonesia and Southeast Asia; and certain aboriginal tribes of India.

AUSTRALOPITHECINES   Erect, bipedal hominids related to man that preceded human beings in Africa and possibly elsewhere.

BASION   The point at the forward lip of the *foramen magnum* of the cranium, on the sagittal line.

BERGMANN'S RULE   A zoological observation that the bodies of warm-blooded animals of a single species tend to be larger in cold regions than in warm regions.

BRACHYCEPHALIC   Round- or short-headed.

BREGMA   The point at or near the top of the skull where the parietal and frontal sutures meet.

BURIN   A graver or narrow chisel, particularly of flint.

CAPOID   One of the five living subspecies of man, including the Bushmen and Hottentots.

CAUCASOID   One of the five living subspecies of man, including most Europeans, West Asians, North Africans, inhabitants of India, and overseas settlers from these regions.

CELT   A stone axe or adze.

CLACTONIAN   A Lower Paleolithic flint industry of Europe.

CLINE, CLINAL   A graual progression in the dimensions, form, or color of an anatomical feature from one geographical region to another.

CONGOID   One of the five living subspecies of man, including the Negroes and Pygmies of Africa and overseas descendants of the former.

CORTEX   The outer layer of an organ or structure, as in hair.

DERMATOGLYPHICS   The study of the ridges of the skin in the palms and fingers of the hand and the soles and toes of the feet, particularly of fingerprints.

DNA   Deoxyribonucleic acid.

DOLICHOCEPHALY   The condition of being long-headed.

ECTOMORPHY   One of the three somatotype components of W. H. Sheldon characterized by a lean, elongated body build.

ENDOGAMOUS   Marrying within a specified social unit.

ENDOMORPHY   One of the three somatotype components of W. H. Sheldon characterized by a predominance of visceral development and fat.

EPICANTHIC   Of an eyefold which covers the inner corner of the upper eyelid.

ERGOSTEROL   An alcohol, $C_{28}H_{43}OH$, which is converted indirectly by ultraviolet radiation into Vitamin D_2, particularly in the skin.

ERYTHEMA   A reddening of the skin caused by capillary congestion; a severe sunburn.

EXOGAMOUS   Marrying outside a specified social unit.

FEMUR   The thighbone.

FIBULA   The thinner and outer of the two lower legbones.

FUSI   In a hair, air spaces between the cells of the medulla.

GENUS   The sixth of seven levels in the Linnaean taxonomy, e.g. *Homo*.

GERIATRICS   The branch of medical science concerned with the problems and diseases of old age.

GLOBULIN   Any of several proteins found in the blood plasma.

GLOGER'S RULE   A zoological observation that the fur or feathers of warm-blooded animals of a single species tend to be black or red in moist regions and grayish or yellowish in dry regions.

HAPTOGLOBINS   Proteins that bind together particles of disintegrated hemoglobin from aged and broken-down red blood cells.

HEMOGLOBIN   A substance inside the red blood cells which consists of two parts, the heme or iron-containing portion and the globin, which is made up of chains of amino acids.

HETEROZYGOUS   Possessing genes for more than one allele at a specified gene locus.

HOMOGAMY   The marriage of like with like.

HOMO SAPIENS   The living species of man and some of our fossil ancestors.

HOMOZYGOTE   An individual possessing genes for only one allele at a specified gene locus.

HUMERUS   The upper armbone.

HYPERGAMY   Marrying into a higher social class or caste.

INTERSTADIAL   A cool interval between two maxima of a single glaciation.

KERATIN   Fibrous protein found in the outer layer of the skin, also in hair, nails, horn, and hoofs.

LASER   An abbreviation for Light Amplification for Stimulated Emission of Radiation. Laser light, which is extremely concentrated and a homogenous band of wavelengths, has many uses, including bloodless surgery.

LUMBAR   The region of the back between the rib cage and the pelvis; e.g., the lumbar vertebrae.

MACROMOLECULE   A very large molecule.

MAGDALENIAN   An Upper Paleolithic industry of Europe.

MAGOSIAN   A Mesolithic industry of East Africa.

MALAR   The *os zygomaticum*, or cheekbone.

MANDIBLE   The lower jaw.

MASSETER   One of a pair of muscles which take part in the raising and grinding motions of the lower jaw.

MEDULLA   In the case of hair, the central canal.

MELANIN   Pigment granules.

MESOCEPHALY   A head form intermediate between dolichocephaly and brachycephaly.

MESOMORPHY   One of the three somatotype components of W. H. Sheldon characterized by a stocky body build emphasizing bone and muscle.

MICROLITH   A small flint implement struck from a small blade core.

MONGOLOID   One of the five subspecies of living man, including principally the peoples of East and Southeast Asia, most of Indonesia, and the American Indians.

MORPHOLOGY, MORPHOLOGICAL   The study of the form and structure of living animals and plants.

MOUSTERIAN   A Middle Paleolithic flake industry of Europe, Africa, and West Asia.

MOVIUS'S LINE   A line in Asia dividing hand-axe industries in the West from chopper- chopping-tool industries in the East.

NANAKNIVES   Knives putatively capable of cutting chromosomes.

OCCIPUT, OCCIPITAL BONE   The hindmost bone of the cranium.

OMENTAL FAT   Visceral fat.

PALEOLITHIC   The Stone Age industries of the Pleistocene and their time span.

PEDOMORPHIC   Infantile or childlike in the adult form.

PHENOTYPE, PHENOTYPICAL   What you are: the product of heredity and environment.

PHYLUM   A group of languages more remotely related than those of a superfamily, language group, or family.

PLATYSMA   A broad, thin sheet of muscle covering much of the face in primitive mammals; from parts of it are derived the muscles of facial expression in man.

PLEIOTROPY   Of a gene, the ability to produce more than one effect.

PLEISTOCENE   The earlier and longer of the two epochs of the Quaternary period, ending about ten thousand years ago.

PLUVIALS   Rainy intervals during the Pleistocene. In Africa they are believed to have corresponded more or less to intervals of glaciation in northerly regions.

POLYANDROUS   Pertaining to a system of mating in which a woman may have two or more husbands.

POLYGYNOUS   Pertaining to a system of mating in which a man may have two or more wives.

POLYMORPHISM   In genetics, a situation in which more than one allele exists on a gene locus among individuals in a population.

PROGNATHISM, PROGNATHOUS   A protrusion of the jaws.

PSALIODONT   Of the incisor teeth, projecting forward in both jaws.

PTC   Phenylthiocarbamide, a bitter substance that some people can taste and others cannot.

RACE   A general term referring to genetically distinct divisions of a species.

RISS   The third of the four Alpine glaciations of the Pleistocene.

SAHUL SHELF   A region of shallow water off the northwest coast of Australia which reaches New Guinea; it was dry land during parts of the Pleistocene.

SANGOAN   A modified Acheulean culture of Central Africa in which the hand axe became a pick.

SAVANNA   Tropical or semitropical grassland dotted with trees.

SCLERA   The fibrous outer capsule of the eye, including the cornea.

SEDENTES   People who stay home while others emigrate.

SELVA   Tropical rain forest.

SHOVEL INCISORS   Incisor teeth that are concave on the inside.

SICKLING, SICKLE CELL   A heritable deformation of the red corpuscles which inhibits oxygen transfer but is believed to produce immunity to some forms of malaria.

SOMATOTYPE   Body build as defined by W. H. Sheldon.

SPECIES   The seventh of the seven levels in the Linnaean taxonomy, and the basic unit of the Linnaean system; e.g., *Homo sapiens*.

STEATOPYGIA   The condition of having large deposits of fat on the buttocks.

STRATUM CORNEUM   The outer layer of the epidermis.

STRATUM GRANULOSUM   A layer of granular cells in the epidermis lying just above the *stratum germanitivum*.

SUNDA SHELF   A body of shallow water lying between parts of Indonesia and Southeast Asia. During intervals of the Pleistocene this area was above water.

TAXONOMY, TAXONOMIC   The science of classifying animals and plants; systematics.

TIBIA   The shinbone.

TORUS   A bony ridge; e.g., the mandibular torus, a ridge on the inside of either branch of the lower jaw.

TRANSFERRINS   Substances in the blood that carry iron to various parts of the body.

TRANSHUMANTS   Semi-nomads who grow crops during part of the year.

TYMPANIC   Pertaining to the eardrum; e.g., the tympanic plate, which lies beneath the ear hole.

VILLAFRANCHIAN   The earliest part of the Pleistocene.

VENAE COMITES   Veins that run parallel to each other on either side of certain arteries and may be joined by connecting blood vessels called anastomoses, q.v.

WALLACE'S LINE   A line between Bali and Lombok, and points north and east, which divides the Oriental fauna from that of Wallacea— the Australian fauna.

WÜRM   The fourth and last of the Alpine glaciations of the Pleistocene epoch.

ZYGOMATIC   A paired bone of the face which forms part of the lower and outer borders of the eye socket and parts of its floor. It articulates particularly with the sphenoid, temporal, and maxillary bones.

Bibliography

Abbie, A. A.: "Physical Characters," in *The Australian Encyclopedia*, Vol. 7, pp. 106–8. Kingsgrove: The Halstead Press; 1958.
——: "Metrical Characters of a Central Australian Tribe." *Oceania*, Vol. 27, No. 3 (1957), pp. 220–43.
—— and Adey, W. R.: "Pigmentation in a Central Australian Tribe with Special Reference to Fair-headedness." *AJPA*, Vol. 11, No. 3 (1953), pp. 339–60.
Abdushelishvili, M. G.: *Antropologiia Drevnevo i Sovremennevo Naseleniia Gruzii. IEM-ANG* (1964).
Adams, R.: *Interracial Marriage in Hawaii*. New York: The Macmillan Co.; 1937.
Adé, B.: "Le Nanisme Raciale." *ASAG*, Vol. 19, No. 1 (1954), pp. 1–8.
Adler, S.: "Remarks on the Host Range of Some Malarial Parasites," in E. Goldschmidt, ed.: *The Genetics of Migrant and Isolate Populations*, pp. 114–17. Baltimore: Williams and Wilkins; 1963.
Adolph, E. F., et al.: *Physiology of Man in the Desert*. New York: Interscience Publishers; 1947.
Afet, Mlle: "Recherches Anthropologiques sur 59,728 Turcs des Deux Sexes." *ASAG*, Vol. 9 (1941), pp. 79–192.
Allchin, F. R.: *Neolithic Cattle Keepers of Southern India*. Cambridge: Cambridge University Press; 1963.
Allen, J. A.: "The Influence of Physical Conditions in the Genesis of Species." *RR*, Vol. 1 (1877), pp. 108–40.
Ammar, A. M.: *The Peoples of Sharqiya*, 2 vols. PSRGE, 1944.
Anderson, J. E.: "The Skeletons from Tehuacan, Mexico: A Preliminary Report." Paper read at 33rd AAPA Conference, Mexico, D. F., June 21–25, 1964.
Anderson, R. T.: "Lapp Racial Classifications as Scientific Myths." *APUA*, Vol. 11, No. 1 (1962), pp. 15–31.
Andrews, J. M. IV: "Evolutionary Trends in Body Build (Thailand)." *PMP*, Vol. 20 (1943), pp. 102–21.
Angel, J. Lawrence: "The Human Skeletal Remains from Hotu Cave, Iran." *PAPS*, Vol. 96, No. 3 (June 1952), pp. 258–69.

Armelagos, G. J., Ewing, G. H., Greene, D. L.: "Fossil Man Discoveries from Wadi Halfa, Sudan." ms, 1964.

Azevêdo, E., Krieger, H., and Morton, N. E.: "Smallpox and the ABO Blood Groups in Brazil." *AJHG*, Vol. 16, No. 4 (1964), pp. 451–4.

Azevêdo, E., Krieger, H., Mi, M.M., and Morton, N. E.: "PTC Taste Sensitivity and Endemic Goiter in Brazil." *AJHG*, Vol. 17, No. 1 (1965), pp. 87–90.

Baker, P. T.: "American Negro–White Differences in Thermal Insulative Aspects of Body Fat." *HB*, Vol. 31, No. 4 (1958), pp. 316–24.

Bandi, H–G., ed.: *The Art of the Stone Age*. New York: Crown Publishers; 1961.

Bannerjee, A. R.: "Hair," in T. N. Madan and G. Sarana, eds.: *Indian Anthropology*, pp. 37–49.

Barnicot, N. A.: "Human Pigmentation." *Man*, No. 144 (1957), pp. 1–7.

Bates, Marston: "Man as an Agent in the Spread of Organisms," in W. L. Thomas, Jr., ed.: *Man's Role in Changing the Face of the Earth*. Chicago: University of Chicago Press; 1956, pp. 788–804.

Becker, B., and Morton, W. R.: "Taste Sensitivity to Phenylthiourea in Glaucoma." *Science*, Vol. 144, No. 1624 (1964), pp. 1347–8.

Benoist, J.: "Les Martiniquais: Anthropologie d'une Population Métissée." *BSAP*, Vol. 4 (1963), pp. 241–432.

Berg, L. S.: *Natural Regions of the U.S.S.R.* New York: The Macmillan Co.; 1950.

Berghe, L. van den: "Le Kwashiorkor expérimental du Porc et le Facteur L." *FSAC*, Vol. 2, No. 1 (1956), p. 13.

Bergmann, C.: Über die Verhältnisse der Wärmeökonomie der Thiere zu ihrer Grösse." *GS*, No. 3 (1947), pp. 595–708.

Bernatzik, H. A.: *Die Geister der gelben Blätter*. Munich: Bruckmann; 1938.

Bernshtam, A.: "On the Origin of the Kirghiz People," in H. N. Michael, ed.: *Studies in Siberian Ethnogenesis*. AINA, No. 2 (1962), pp. 119–28.

Berry, B.: *Almost White*. New York: The Macmillan Co.; 1963.

Biasutti, R.: *Razze e Popoli della Terra*, 2d ed. Torino: VTET; 1959, 4 vols.

——: "Crania Aegyptica." *AAE*, Vol. 35 (1905), pp. 322–62.

Bielicki, T., and Welon, Z.: "The Operations of Natural Selection on Human Head Form in an East European Population." *Homo*, Vol. 14, No. 1 (1964), pp. 22–30

Billy, G.: "Race Alpine et Type Alpin." Paper read at the 7th International Congress of Anthropological and Ethnological Sciences, Moscow, August 3–10, 1964.

Birbeck, M. S. C., and Barnicot, N. A.: "Electron Microscope Studies on Pigment Formation in Human Hair Follicles," in M. Gordon, ed.: *Pigment Cell Biology*, pp. 549–61. New York: Academic Press; 1959.

Bird, G. W. G., Ikin, E. W., Mourant, A. E., and Lehmann, H.: "The Blood Groups and Hemoglobin of the Malayalis," in T. N. Madan and G. Sarana, eds.: *Indian Anthropology—Essays in Memory of D. N. Majumdar*, pp. 221–6. Bombay: India Publishing House; 1962.

Birdsell, J. B.: "The Racial Origins of the Extinct Tasmanians." *RQVM*, Vol. 2, No. 3 (1949); also *YPA* (1950), pp. 143–60.

Black, D.: *A Study of Kansu and Honan Aeneolithic Skulls and Specimens from Later Kansu Prehistoric Sites in Comparison with North China and Other Recent Crania*. Part 1. *On Measurement and Identification*. PS-D, Vol. 6, Fasc. 1 (1928), Peiping, December 1928.

Bloch, R.: Review of Mayani, Z.: *Les Étrusques Commencent à Parler*. *Antiquity*, Vol. 37, No. 147 (1963), p. 238.

Blum, H. F.: "Light and the Melanin Pigment of Human Skin." *NYAS-Sp*, Vol. 4 (1948), pp. 388–98.

Bordes, F.: "Mousterian Cultures in France." *Science*, Vol. 134, No. 3482 (1961), pp. 803–10.

Borisovsky, P. I.: "Archaeological Discoveries in Vietnam." *HASR*, Vol. 4 (1962), pp. 98–101.
———: "Exploration of ancient sites of the Stone Age in the Democratic Republic of Vietnam." *Soviet Archaeology*, Vol. 2 (1962), pp. 17–25.
Bostanci, E.: "An Examination of a Neanderthal-type Fossil Skull Found in the Chalcidique Peninsula." *Belleten*, Vol. 28, No. 3 (1964), pp. 373–81.
Bouckaert, J. P.: "Étude de métabolisme de base de certains groupes d'indigènes au Congo belge." *CIAN* (1949), pp. 241–2. Cited in G. A. Heuse: *Biologie du Noir*. Brussels: Les Editions Problèmes d'Afrique Centrale; 1957.
Bowles, G. T.: "Linguistic and Racial Aspects of the Munda Problem," *PMP*, Vol. 20 (1943), pp. 81–101.
———: *New Types of Old Americans at Harvard*. Cambridge, Mass.: Harvard University Press; 1932.
Boyd, W. C.: "Genetics and the Human Race," *Science*, Vol. 140, No. 3571 (1963), pp. 1057–65.
Boyer, S. H., Rucknagel, D. L., Weatherall, D. J., and Watson-Williams, E. J.: "Further Evidence for Linkage between the Beta and Delta Loci Governing Human Hemoglobin and the Population Dynamics of Linked Genes." *AJHG*, Vol. 15, No. 4 (1963), pp. 438–48.
Brace, C. L.: "The Fate of the 'Classic' Neanderthals: A Consideration of Hominid Catastrophism." *CA*, Vol. 5, No. 1 (1964), pp. 3–43.
———: "On the Race Concept." *CA*, Vol. 5, No. 4 (1964), pp. 313–20, including comments by six other persons, and the author's reply.
Briggs, L. C.: *The Living Races of the Sahara*. PMP, Vol. 28, No. 2 (1958).
———: *The Stone Age Races of Northwest Africa*. BASP, No. 18 (1955).
Bröste, K., and Jørgensen, J. P.: *Prehistoric Man in Denmark*, 2 vols. Copenhagen: Einar Munksgaard; 1956.
Brown, F. J., and Roucek, J. S.: *Our Racial and National Minorities*. New York: Prentice-Hall; 1937.
Brown, F. M.: "The Microscopy of Mammalian Hair for Anthropologists." *PAPS*, Vol. 85, No. 3 (1942), pp. 250–74.
———: "Regional Differences in the physical characteristics of an American population." *AJPA*, Vol. 4, No. 4 (1946), pp. 463–82.
Brues, A. M.: "The Spearman and the Archer." AA, Vol. 61, No. 3 (1959), pp. 457–69.
———: "Regional Differences in the physical characteristics of an American population." AJPA, Vol. 4, (1946), pp. 463–82.
Bruk, C. I., and Apenchenko, B. S., eds.: *Atlas Narodov Miri*. Moscow: Institut Etnografii i m. N. N. Mikhlukho-Maklaia, Akad. Nauk SSSR; 1964.
Buck, P. H.: "Maori Somatology." *PSJ*, Vol. 31, No. 121 (1922), pp. 37–44, 145–53; No. 124 (1822), pp. 159–70; No. 128 (1923), pp. 189–99.
Buckwalter, J. A., Wohlwend, E. D., Colter, D. C., and Tidrick, R. T.: "Natural Selection Associated with the ABO Blood Group." *Science*, Vol. 123, No. 3202 (1956), pp. 840–1.
Bulmer, S. and R.: "The Prehistory of the Australian New Guinea Highlands." AA, Vol. 66, No. 4, Part 2 (1964), pp. 39–76.
Bunak, V. V.: "Anthropological Composition of the Population of the Caucasus," in V. V. Bunak, G. F. Debetz, and M. G. Levin: *Contributions to the Physical Anthropology of the Soviet Union*. RTS–PM, Vol. 1, No. 2 (1960), pp. 1–23.
———, Debetz, G. F., and Levin, M. G.: *Contributions to the Physical Anthropology of the Soviet Union*. RTS–PM, Vol. 1, No. 2 (1960).
Bushnell, G., and McBurney, C.: "New World Origins Seen from the Old World." *Antiquity*, Vol. 33, No. 130 (1959), pp. 93–101.

Candela, P. B.: "The Introduction of Blood Group B into Europe." *HB*, Vol. 14, No. 3 (1942), pp. 413–44.

Capell, Arthur: "Oceanic Linguistics Today." *CA*, Vol. 3, No. 4 (1962), pp. 371–428.

Castro e Almeida, M. E. de: "Contribução para o estudo dos caracteres descritivos dos nativos 'Tongas' et 'Tonguinhas' da Ihla de São Tomé." *CIAO*, Vol. 5 (1958), pp. 41–54.

Cavalli-Sforza, L. L., Barrai, I., and Edwards, A. W. F.: "Analysis of Human Evolution under Random Genetic Drift." *CSHS*, Vol. 29 (1964), pp. 9–200.

Chafe, W. L.: "Another Look at Siouan and Iroquoian." *AA*, Vol. 66, No. 4, Part 1 (1964), pp. 852–62.

Chang, Kwang-chih: "Prehistoric and Early Historic Culture Horizons and Traditions in South China." *CA*, Vol. 5, No. 5 (1964), pp. 359, 368–75.
——: *The Archaeology of Ancient China.* New Haven: Yale University Press; 1963.

Chard, C. S.: "New World Origins: A Reappraisal." *Antiquity*, Vol. 33, No. 129 (1959), pp. 44–9.

Charlesworth, J. K.: *The Quarternary Era*, Vol. 1 and 2. London: Edward Arnold; 1957.

Chatterjee, B. K., and Kumar, G. D.: *Comparative Study and Racial Analysis of the Human Remains of Indus Valley Civilization with Particular Reference to Harappa.* Calcutta: B. K. Chatterjee; 1963.
——: "Somatometric and Somatoscopic Observations and their Affinities of the Manuans of Travancore-Cochin." *JASC*, Vol. 28, No. 2 (1957), pp. 1–18.
——: "Racial Affinities of Travancore and Cochin States." *Anthropologist*, Vol. 3, No. 1–2 (1956), pp. 1–22.

Chen, K. P., Damon, A., and Elliot, O.: "Body Form, Composition, and Some Physiological Functions of the Chinese on Taiwan." *ANYAS*, Vol. 10, Part III (1963), pp. 760–77.

Chêng Te-K'un: *Archaeology in China.* Vol. 1. *Prehistoric China*, 1959; Vol. 2. *Shang China*, 1960; and Vol. 3, *Chou China*, 1963. Cambridge: W. Heffer & Sons.

Chia Lan-po, in W. W., No. 4–5 (Peiping, 1962), pp. 25–6.
—— and Woo Ju-Kang: "Fossil Human Skull Base of Late Paleolithic Stage from Chilinshan, Leipin District, Kwangsi, China." *VP*, Vol. 3, No. 1 (1959), pp. 37–9.

Chin You-Di: "Thailand." *AP*, Vol. 5, No. 1 (1962), pp. 54–7.

Chung, C. S., Witkop, C. J., and Henry, J. L.: "A Genetic Study of Dental Caries with Special Reference to PTC Taste Sensibility." *AJHG*, Vol. 16, No. 2 (1962), pp. 231–45.

Cipriani, L.: "Un interesante Pueblo del Sahara: Los Dauada." *RGA*, Vol. 2, No. 2 (1934), pp. 141–52.

Clark, J. D., and Bakker, E. M. van Zinderen: "Prehistoric Culture and Pleistocene Vegetation at the Kalambo Falls, Northern Rhodesia." *Nature*, Vol. 201, No. 4923 (1964), pp. 971–5.

Clarke, C. A.: "Blood Groups and Disease," in A. G. Steinberg, ed.: *Progress in Medical Genetics*, Vol. 1, pp. 81–119. New York: Grune and Stratton; 1961.

Cline, W. B.: "Anthropometric Notes on the Natives of Siwah Oasis." *Varia Africana V, HAS*, Vol. 10 (1932), pp. 3–19.

Cohen, A. S., Boyd, W. C., Goldwasser, S., Cathcart, E. S., and Heisler, M.: "Correlation between Rheumatic Diseases and Rh Blood Groups." *Nature*, Vol. 200, No. 4912 (1963), p. 1215.

Cohen, M.: "Hamito-Semitic," in Meillet and Cohen: *Les Langues du monde*, pp. 82–181.

Cole, Sonia: *The Prehistory of East Africa*, p. 115. New York: Penguin Books; 1954.

Collinder, B.: *The Lapps*, pp. 67–8. Princeton: Princeton University Press; 1949.

Comas, J.: *Manual of Physical Anthropology.* Springfield, Ill.: Charles C. Thomas; 1960.
Coon, C. S.: "The Taxonomy of Human Variation." *PNYAS.* In press (1965).
——: "Growth and Development of Social Groups," in Wolstenholme, G., ed.: *Man and His Future,* pp. 120–31. London: J. & A. Churchill; 1963.
——: "The Rock Art of Africa." *Science,* Vol. 42, No. 3600 (1963), pp. 1642–5.
——: *The Origin of Races.* New York: Alfred A. Knopf; 1962.
——: *The Story of Man,* 2nd ed. New York: Alfred A. Knopf; 1962.
——: "An Anthropogeographic Excursion Around the World." HB, Vol. 30, No. 1 (1958), pp. 29–42.
——: *Caravan.* New York: Henry Holt & Co.; 1951, 1958.
——: Review of *Prehistoric Man in Denmark* by Bröste and Jørgensen. *Antiquity,* Vol. 32, No. 127 (1958).
——: *The Mountains of Giants.* PMP, Vol. 23, No. 3 (1950).
——: "Have the Jews a Racial Identity?" in I. Graeber, ed: *Jews in a Gentile World,* pp. 20–37. New York: The Macmillan Co.; 1942.
——: *The Races of Europe.* New York: The Macmillan Co.; 1939.
——: *Tribes of the Rif.* HAS, Vol. 19 (1931).
——: "Contribution to the Study of the Ethiopians and Somalis" (unpublished).
Count, E. W.: *This Is Race.* New York: Henry Schuman; 1950.
Crichton, J. M.: "A Multiple Discriminant Analysis of Egyptian and African Negro Crania." Harvard University Senior Honors Thesis for A.B. in Anthropology, 1964. Peabody Museum Library.
Crow, J. A.: *The Epic of Latin America.* New York: Doubleday; 1946.
Cummins, H., and Midlo, C.: *Finger Prints, Palms and Soles.* New York: Dover Publications; 1961.

Dani, A. H.: "Sanghao Cave Excavation, the First Season: 1963." APak, Vol. I, No. 1 (1964), pp. 1–50.
Daniels, F.: "Man and Radiant Energy: Solar Radiation," in D. B. Dill, E. F. Adolph, and C. G. Wilber, eds.: *Handbook of Physiology, Section 4: Adaptation to the Environment,* pp. 969–88. Washington, D.C.: American Physiological Society; 1964.
Davenport, C. P., and Steggerda, M.: *Race Crossing in Jamaica.* CIP, No. 358 (1929).
Davies, O.: "The Climatic and Cultural Sequence in the late Pleistocene of the Gold Coast." PTPA, (1957), pp. 1–5.
Day, C. B.: *A Study of Some Negro-White Families in the United States.* HAS, Vol. 10, Part 2 (1932), pp. 1–126.
Debetz, G. F.: "The Origin of the Kirghiz in the Light of Physical Anthropological Findings," in H. N. Michael, ed.: *Studies in Siberian Ethnogenesis.* AINA, No. 2 (1962), pp. 129–43.
——: *Palaeontropologiia SSSR.* TIE, n.s., Vol. 4 (1948).
Deniker, J.: *The Races of Man.* New York: Charles Scribner; 1900.
Díaz Ungria, A. G. de: "El Poblamiento Indígena de Venezuela a Través de la Genética." *TESA,* 1963.
Dodt, E., Copenhaver, R. M., and Gunkel, R. D.: "Electroretinographic Measurement of the Spectral Sensitivity in Albinos, Caucasians, and Negroes." *AMAAO,* Vol. 62, No. 5 (1959), pp. 795–803.
Dostal, W.: "Die Sulubba und ihre Bedeutung für die Kulturgeschichte Arabiens." AfV, Vol. 11 (1956), pp. 15–42.
Ducros, A.: "Contribution à l'Anthropologie des Miaos (d'après les Documents du Dr. Olivier)." *BSAP,* Vol. 6, No. 3 (1964), pp. 461–76.
Duggins, O. H., and Trotter, M.: "Hair from a Kadar Woman of India." *AJPA,* Vol. 17, No. 2 (1959), pp. 95–8.
Dunn, L. C.: *An Anthropometrical Study of Hawaiians of Pure and Mixed Blood.* PMP, Vol. 11, No. 3 (1928).

—— and Dunn, S. P.: "The Jewish Community of Rome." *SA*, Vol. 196, No. 3, pp. 118–132.

Ehrenfels, U. R. von: *Kadar of Cochin.* Madras: University of Madras Press; 1952.

Eickstedt, E. von: *Rassenkunde und Rassengeschichte der Menschheit.* Stuttgart: Gustav Fischer Verlag; 1934.

Elsner, R. W.: "Skinfold Thickness in Primitive Peoples Native to Cold Climates." *ANYAS*, Vol. 110 (1963), pp. 503–14.

Eng, Lie-Injo Luan: "Haemoglobinopathies in East Asia." *AHG*, Vol. 28, Part 1 (1964), pp. 101–11.

Ennouchi, E.: "Un Néanderthalien: l'Homme du Jebel Irhoud (Maroc)." *L'Anth*, Vol. 66, No. 3–4 (1962), pp. 279–99.

Erckert, R. von: "Kopfmessungen Kaukasischer Völker." *AFA*, Vol. 18 (1889), pp. 263–81, 297–335; Vol. 19 (1890), pp. 55–84, 211–49, 331–56.

——: *Antropologicheskaiia izmereniia nekotorykh Kavkazakh narodov.* IKO, Vol. 7–8, pp. 1882–3.

Ericson, D. B., and Wollin, G.: *The Deep and the Past.* New York: Alfred A. Knopf; 1964.

Estrada, E., Meggers, B. J., and Evans, C.: "Possible Transpacific Contact on the Coast of Ecuador." *Science*, Vol. 135, No. 3501 (1962), pp. 371–2.

Ewing, J. F.: *Hyperbrachycephaly as Influenced by Cultural Conditioning.* *PMP*, Vol. 23, No. 2 (1950).

Ferembach, D.: *La Nécropole Epipaléolithique de Taforalt (Maroc oriental).* Rabat; 1962.

——: "Squelettes du Natoufien d'Israël, étude anthropologique." *L'Anth*, Vol. 65, No. 1–2 (1961), pp. 46–66.

Fiedler, W.: "Übersicht über das System der Primates," in *Primatologia*, Vol. 1, 1. 173, Fig. 47. Basel: S. Karger; 1956.

Field, H.: *An Anthropological Reconnaissance in West Pakistan, 1955. PMP*, Vol. 52 (1959).

——: *Contributions to the Anthropology of the Caucasus.* PMP, Vol. 48, No. 1 (1952).

——: "Mountain Peoples of Iraq and Iran." *AJPA*, Vol. 9, No. 4 (1951), pp. 1–3.

——: *Contributions to the Anthropology of the Soviet Union.* SMC, Vol. 110, No. 13 (1948). Pub. 3947.

——: *The Anthropology of Iraq. Part I, No. 1. The Upper Euphrates. FMAS,* Vol. 30, Part 1, No. 1 (1940). Pub. 469.

Part I, No. 2. The Lower Euphrates–Tigris Region. FMAS, Vol. 30, Part 1, No. 2 (1949). Pub. 531.

Part II, No. 1. The Northern Jazira. PMP, Vol. 46, No. 1 (1951).

Part II, No. 2. Kurdistan, and *Part II, No. 3. Conclusions. PMP,* Vol. 46, No. 2 and 3 (1952).

——: *Contributions to the Anthropology of Iran. FMAS,* Vol. 29, No. 1 (1939). Pub. 458.

Firschein, I. L.: "Population Dynamics of the Sickle-Cell Trait in the Black Caribs of British Honduras, Central America." *AJHG*, Vol. 13, No. 2 (1962), pp. 233–54.

Fischer, E.: *Die Rehebother Bastards und das Bastardierungsproblem beim Menschen.* Jena: Gustav Fischer Verlag; 1913.

Fletcher, R.: *Instinct in Man.* New York: International Universities Press; 1957.

Foltz, D. E.: "Boobs in the Woods." *SEP*, Oct. 13, 1962, p. 8.

Forbes, R. J.: *The History of Technology*, p. 597. London: Oxford University Press; 1954.

———: *Man the Maker*. New York: Henry Schuman; 1950.

Foster, G. M.: *Culture and Conquest: America's Spanish Heritage. VFPA*, No. 27 (1960).

French, C. E., Siddiqui, M. K. R., Youmans, J. B., and Schafer, A. F.: "A Nutritional Survey of the Armed Forces of Pakistan." *JNS*, No. 2 (1959), pp. 1–69.

Freyre, G.: *The Masters and the Slaves*. New York: Alfred A. Knopf; 1946.

Frobenius, L.: *Ekade Ektab, Die Felsbilder Fezzans*. Graz: Akademische Druck und Verlagsgesellschaft; 1962. First published in 1937.

———: *Madsimu Dsangara, Südafrikanische Felsbilderchronik*. Graz: Akademische Druck und Verlagsgesellschaft; 1962. First published in 1932.

Fromaget, J. and Saurin, E.: "Note Préliminaire sur les Formations Cénozoiques et plus Récentes de la Chaîne Annamite Septentrionale et du Haut Laos (Stratigraphie, Préhistoire, Anthropologie)." *BSGI*, Vol. 12, Nos. 1, 2, 3 (1925).

Fry, Edward I.: "Subcutaneous Tissue in Polynesian Children." *HB*, Vol. 32 (1960), pp. 239–48.

Fuchs, P.: *Die Völker der Südost-Sahara*, pp. 184–8. Vienna: Wilhelm Braumüller; 1961.

Galston, A. W.: "From the Biologist's Laboratory: Clues to Immortality." *NO*, April 12, 1965, p. 22.

Garay, A. L. de, Rodarte, U., and Cobon, L: "The Frequency of PTC Tasting, Hard Ear Wax, Colour Blindness, and Other Genetical Characters in Urban and Rural Mexican Populations." *HB*, Vol. 36, No. 2 (1964), pp. 134–45.

Gardner, B. B., and MacAdam, D. L.: "Colorimetric Analysis of Hair Color." *AJPA*, Vol. 19, No. 2 (1934), pp. 187–201.

Gates, R. R.: *The Totos, a Sub-Himalayan Mongoloid Tribe. MM*, No. 5 (1963).

———: "The Asurs and Birhors of Chota Nagpur," in T. N. Madan and G. Sarana, eds.: *Indian Anthropology*, pp. 163–84. Bombay: Asia Publishing House; 1962.

———: "The Melanesian Dwarf Tribe of Aiome New Guinea." *AGMG*, Vol. 10, No. 3 (1961), pp. 277–311.

———: "Race Crossing," in L. Gedda, ed.: *De Genetica Medica*, Part II, pp. 27–153. Rome: Edizioni dell'Istituto Gregorio Mendel; 1961.

———: "The Genetics of the Australian Aborigines." *AGMG*, Vol. 9 (1960), pp. 1–50.

———: *Race Crossing*. Rome: Edizione dell'Istituto Gregorio Mendel; n.d. Probably 1960.

———: "Studies in Race Crossing." *AGMG*, Vol. 9 (1960), pp. 165–84.

———: "Studies in Race Crossing. IX. Crosses of Australians with Caucasians, Chinese, and other Races." *AMGH*, Vol. 9 (1960), pp. 165–84.

———: "The African Pygmies." *AGMG*, Vol. 7 (1958), pp. 159–218.

———: *Pedigrees of Negro Families*. Philadelphia: The Blakiston Co.; 1949.

———: *Human Ancestry*. Cambridge, Mass.: Harvard University Press; 1948.

———: "A Pedigree Study of Amerindian Crosses in Canada." *JRAI*, Vol. 58 (1928), pp. 511–32.

Gay, F. P.: *Agents of Disease and Host Resistance*. Springfield, Ill.: Charles C. Thomas; 1935.

Genet-Varcin, E.: *Les Negritos de Luçon. L'Anth*, Vol. 8 (1949).

Gerhard, Peter: "Emperors' Dye of the Mixtecs." *NH*, Vol. 73, No. 1 (1964), pp. 26–31.

Getz, B.: *The Hip Joint in Lapps and its Bearing on the Problem of Congenital Dislocation. AOSS*, No. 18 (1955).

Gibb, H. A. R., and Bowen, H.: *Islamic Society and the West Islamic in the Eighteenth Century*, Vol. 1, Part I. London: Oxford University Press; 1950.

Giddings, J. L.: *The Archaeology of Cape Denbigh.* Providence, R.I.: Brown University Press; 1964.

Gimbutas, M.: "The Indo-Europeans: Archaeological Problems." *AA*, Vol. 65, No. 4 (1963), pp. 815–36.

Gjessing, R. R.: *Die Kautokeinolappen.* Oslo: *ISKF;* 1934.

Glass, B.: "On the Unlikelihood of Significant Admixture of Genes from the North American Indians in the Present Composition of the Negroes of the United States." *AJHG,* Vol. 7, No. 3 (1955), pp. 368–85.

—— and Li, C. C.: "The Dynamics of Racial Intermixture—An Analysis Based on the American Negro." *AJHG,* Vol. 5, No. 1 (1953), pp. 1–20.

Gloger, C. L.: *Das Abändern der Vögel durch Einfluss des Klimas.* Breslau, 1833.

Gloor, P.-A.: "Recherches anthropologiques en Palestine méridionale. I. Enquête sur les Arabes (série masculine)." *ASAG,* Vol. 15, No. 2 (1950), pp. 107–42.

Goodall, J., and van Lawick, H.: "My Life among Wild Chimpanzees." *NG,* Vol. 124, No. 2 (1963), pp. 272–308.

Gover, M.: "Increase of the Negro Population of the United States." *HB,* Vol. 1, No. 3 (1929), pp. 263–73.

Grace, G. W.: "The Linguistic Evidence." *CA,* Vol. 5, No. 5 (1964), pp. 361–8.

Grahmann, R.: *The Lower Paleolithic Site of Markkleeberg and Other Comparable Localities near Leipzig,* ed. by H. L. Movius, Jr. *TAPS,* n.s., Vol. 45, Part 6 (1955).

Grahn, D.: and Kratchman, J.: "Variation in Neonatal Death Rate and Birth Weight in the United States and Possible Relations to Environmental Radiation, Geology and Altitude." *AJHG,* Vol. 15, No. 4 (1963), pp. 329–52.

Grant, M.: *The Conquest of a Continent.* New York: Charles Scribner's Sons; 1933.

Greenberg, J. H.: "The Languages of Africa." *IJAL,* Vol. 29, No. 1 (January 1963).

——: "The General Classification of Central and South American Indian Languages," in A. F. C. Wallace, ed.: *Selected Papers of the Fifth International Congress of Anthropological and Ethnographical Sciences.* Philadelphia: University of Pennsylvania Press; 1960.

——: Reply to H. K. Schneider: "Confusion in African Linguistic Classification," *CA,* Vol. 5, No. 1 (1964), pp. 56–7.

Grimm, H.: "Neue Ergebnisse zur Anthropologie des Mitteldeutschen Neolithikums." Paper read at 7th International Congress for Anthropological and Ethnological Sciences, Moscow, August 3–10, 1964.

Guenther, D. W.: "Zur Altersdatierung der diluvialen Fundstelle von Krapina in Kroatien." *BDGA,* 6 Tagung, 1959, pp. 202–9.

Guha, B. S.: *Racial Affinities of the Peoples of India.* Part A of *Census of India,* 1931, Vol. 1, Part 3.

—— and Basu, P. C.: "Report on the Human Remains Excavated at Mohenjo-Daro in 1928–29," in *Further Excavations at Mohenjo-Daro,* Chap. XVIII, pp. 613–38.

Gupta, P., Basu, P. C., Datta, A.: "Human Remains from Harappa," in *Human Skeletal Remains from Harappa.* Calcutta: Anthropological Survey of India; 1962.

Gusinde, M.: *Die Twiden: Pygmäen und Pygmoide im tropischen Afrika.* Vienna and Stuttgart: Wilhelm Braumüller; 1956.

——: "The Yupa Indians in Western Venezuela." *PAPS,* Vol. 100, No. 3 (1956), pp. 197–220.

——: "Monorchie der Buschmänner als ontogenetische Spezialisation," in *Festschrift für Hans Plischke, Von Fremden Völkern und Kulturen,* pp. 175–81. Düsseldorf: Droste-Verlag; 1955.

Haag, W. G.: "The Bering Strait Land Bridge." *SA*, Vol. 206, No. 1 (1962), pp. 112–23.

Haas, M. R.: "A new linguistic relationship in North America, Algonkian and the Gulf Languages." *SWJA*, Vol. 14, No. 3 (1958), pp. 231–64.

Hagen, B.: *Die Orang Kubu auf Sumatra.* Frankfurt: Josef Baer & Co.; 1908.

Haldane, J. B. S.: "A Defense of Beanbag Genetics." *PBM*, Vol. 7, No. 3 (1964), pp. 343–59, 348.

Hall-Craggs, M., Marsden, P. D., Raper, A. B., Lehmann, H., and Beale, D: "Homozygous Sickle-cell Anemia Arising from Two Different Haemoglobin S." *BMJ*, Vol. 2 (1964), pp. 87–9.

Handlin, O.: *Boston's Immigrants, 1790–1865.* Cambridge, Mass.: Harvard University Press; 1941.

Hansen, M. L.: *The Atlantic Migration, 1607–1860.* Cambridge, Mass.: Harvard University Press; 1940.

Harrisson, T.: "New Archaeological and Ethnological Results from the Niah Caves, Sarawak." *Man*, Vol. 58, No. 1 (1959), pp. 1–8.

Hasebe, K.: *The Natives of the South Sea Archipelago* (in Japanese). *JSK*, Vol. 1 (1938), pp. 1–35.

Haynes, C. V. Jr.: "Fluted Projectile Points: Their Age and Distribution." *Science*, Vol. 145, No. 3639 (1964), pp. 1408–13.

——: "Physical Types of West African Negroes." *HB*, Vol. 9, No. 4 (1937), pp. 483–97.

Heider, K. G.: "A Pebble Tool Complex in Thailand." *AP*, Vol. 2, No. 2 (1958), pp. 63–6.

Heinzelin, J. de, and Paepe, R.: *The Geological History of the Nile Valley in Sudanese Nubia: Preliminary Results. SMU–CPN*, No. 2 (1964).

Hendrickse, R. G., Boyo, A. E., Fitzgerald, P. A., and Kuti, S. R.: "Studies on the Haemoglobin of Newborn Nigerians." *BMJ*, Vol. 1, No. 5173 (1960), p. 611.

Herskovits, M. J.: "Physical Types of West African Negroes." *HB*, Vol. 9, No. 4 (1937), pp. 483–97.

——: *The Anthropometry of the American Negro. CUCA*, Vol. 11 (1930).

Hertzberg, H. T. E., Churchill, E., Dupertuis, C. W., White, R. M., and Damon, A.: *Anthropometric Survey of Turkey, Greece and Italy.* New York: Pergamon Press; 1963.

Heuse, G. A.: *Biologie du Noir.* Brussels: Les Editions Problèmes d'Afrique Centrale; 1957.

Hiernaux, J.: "Données Génétiques sur Six Populations de la République du Congo." *ActG*, Vol. 42, No. 2 (1962), pp. 145–74.

——: "Les Caractères Physiques des Populations du Ruanda et de l'Urundi." *MIRSN*, 2nd ser., Vol. 52 (1954).

——: "Les Caractères physiques des Bashi." *MIRCB*, Vol. 23, No. 5 (1953), pp. 5–50.

Hiraizumi, Y.: "Are the MN Blood Groups Maintained by Heterosis?" *AJHG*, Vol. 16, No. 3 (1964), pp. 375–9.

Hockett, C. F.: "Sound Change." Presidential address given at the annual meeting of the Linguistic Society of America, December 28, 1964, New York.

—— and Ascher, Robert: "The Human Revolution." *CA*, Vol. 5, No. 3 (June 1964), pp. 135–70.

Hodgson, B. H.: *The Languages, Literature, and Religion of Nepal and Tibet.* London: Trubner & Co.; 1874.

Holt, S. B.: "Genetics of Dermal Ridges: Sib Pair Correlations for Total Finger Counts." *AHG*, Vol. 21, Part 4 (1957), pp. 352–62.

Hooton, E. A.: *Indians of Pecos.* New Haven: Yale University Press; 1930.

Howells, W. W.: "The Racial Elements of Melanesia." *PMP*, Vol. 20 (1943), pp. 38–49.

——: "Anthropometry of the Natives of Arnhem Land and the Australian Race Problem." *PMP*, Vol. 16, No. 1 (1937), pp. 1–97.

Hsai Nai: "Our Neolithic Ancestors." *CR*, Vol. 5, No. 5 (1956), pp. 24–8.

Hulse, F. S.: *The Human Species*, p. 319. New York: Random House; 1963.

——: "Exogamie et Heterosis." *ASAG*, Vol. 22, No. 2 (1957), pp. 103–25.

——: "Physical Types among the Japanese." *PMP*, Vol. 20 (1943), pp. 122–33.

Hunt, E. E. Jr.: "Metrical Variability and Population Size in Micronesia." *ANYAS*, 1965. In press.

——: "A view of somatology and serology in Micronesia." *AJPA*, Vol. 8, No. 2 (1950), pp. 157–83.

Iampietro, P. F., Goldman, R. F., Buskirk, E. R., and Bass, D. E.: "Responses of Negro and White Males to Cold." *JAP*, Vol. 14, No. 5 (1959), pp. 798–803.

Ishak, I. G.: "The Photopic Luminosity Curve for a Group of Fifteen Egyptian Trichromats." *JOSA*, Vol. 42 (1952), pp. 529–34.

Jackson, K. H.: "The Pictish Language," Ch. 6, and Appendix in F. T. Wainwright, ed.: *The Problem of the Picts*, pp. 129–66. New York: Philosophical Library; 1956.

Jacob, F., and Monod, J.: "Genetic regulatory mechanisms in the synthesis of proteins." *JMB*, Vol. 3 (1961), pp. 318–56.

James, P. E.: *Latin America*, 3rd ed. New York: Odyssey Press; 1959.

——: *An Outline of Geography*. Boston: Ginn & Co.; 1935.

Jansen, A. A. J.: "Skinfold Measurements from Early Childhood to Adulthood in Papuans from Western New Guinea." *ANYAS*, Vol. 110 (1963), pp. 515–31.

Jelliffe, D. B.: "The origin, fate, and significance of the umbilical hernia in Nigerian children." *TRST*, Vol. 46 (1952), pp. 428–34.

Jennings, J. D., and Norbeck, E., eds.: *Prehistoric Man in the New World*. Chicago: University of Chicago Press; 1964.

Johnstone, R. F., and Selander, R. K.: "House Sparrows: Rapid Evolution of Races in North America." *Science*, Vol. 144, No. 3618 (1964), pp. 548–50.

Jones, G. I., and Mulhall, H.: "An Examination of the Physical Types of Certain Peoples of S.E. Nigeria." *JRAI*, Vol. 79, Parts 1–2 (1949), pp. 11–19.

Jonxis, J. H. P.: "The Frequency of Haemoglobin S and Haemoglobin C carriers in Curaçao and Surinam." In Jonxis and J. F. Delafresnaye, eds.: *Abnormal Haemoglobins. Symposium Organized by the Council for International Organizations of Medical Sciences*, pp. 300–6. Oxford: Blackwell; 1959.

Kalmus, H., Garay, A. L. de, Rodarte, U., and Cobon, L.: "The Frequency of PTC Tasting, Hard Ear Wax, Colour Blindness, and Other Genetical Characters in Urban and Rural Mexican Populations." *HB*, Vol. 36, No. 2 (1964), pp. 134–45.

Kampier, R. H.: "Splenic Infarction Due to Sicklemia and Air Travel." *SoMJ*, Vol. 50 (1957), pp. 277–8.

Kanelle, A., and Sabba, A.: *Kraniometrikē Meletē tou Homo Neanderthalensis tōn Petralēnōn* (Thessalonikē: Aristoteleion Panepistēmion Thessalonikēs, Physikomathematike Schōle; 1964).

Karvé, I., and Kurulkar, G. M.: "Human Bones Discovered So Far," Preliminary Report on the Third Gujarat Prehistoric Expedition. Bombay: Times of India Press; 1945.

Keers, W.: "An Anthropological Survey of the Eastern Little Sunda Islands"; "The Negritos of the Eastern Little Sunda Islands"; and "The Proto-Malay of the Netherlands East Indies." *KVII*, No. 26 (1948).

Kelso, J.: "Fossil Man Discoveries from Wadi Halfa, Sudan." Preliminary report read at 33rd meeting of the AAPA in Mexico City, June 22–25, 1964.

Khatri, A. P.: "A Century of Prehistoric Research in India." *AP*, Vol. 6 (1962), pp. 169–85.
——: "Mahadevian: An Oldowan Pebble Culture of India." *AP*, Vol. 6 (1962), pp. 186–96.
Kherumian, R.: *Les Arméniens*. Paris: Librairie Orientaliste Paul Geuthner; 1943.
Kidder, H. H., Coon, C. S., and Briggs, L. C.: "Contribution à l'anthropologie des Kabyles." *L'Anth.*, Vol. 59, No. 1–2 (1955), pp. 62–79.
Kidder, J. E. Jr.: "Japan." *AP*, Vol. 4 (1960), pp. 21–34.
——: "Japan." *AP*, Vol. 1, No. 1–2 (1957), pp. 28–30.
Kidson, C., and Gajdusek, D. C.: "Glucose-6-phosphate dehydrogenase deficiency in Micronesia." *AJS*, Vol. 25, No. 1 (1962), pp. 61–2.
Kirk, R. L.: "Blood Group Interaction and the World Distribution of the ABO Gene p^2 and the Rh Gene r (cde)." *AJHG*, Vol. 13, No. 2 (1961), pp. 224–32.
Kitchen, K. D., Evans, W. Howell, Clarke, C. A., McConnell, R. B., and Sheppard, P. M.: "PTC taste responses and thyroid disease." *BMJ*, Vol. 1 (1959), pp. 1069–74.
Kochetkova, V. I.: "Muliaj Mozgovoi Polosti Iskopaemovo Cheloveka Kro-Magnon III." *TMOIP*, Vol. 14 (1964), pp. 111-35.
Kokkoros, P., and Kanellis, A.: "Découverte d'un Crâne d'Homme Paléolithique dans la Péninsule Chalcidique." *L'Anth.*, Vol. 64, No. 5–6 (1961), pp. 438–46.
Kretzoi, M., and Vertes, L.: "Upper Biharian (Intermindel) Pebble-Industry Occupation Site in Western Hungary." *CA*, Vol. 6, No. 1 (1965), pp. 74–87.
Krishnaswamy, V. D.: "Stone Age India." *BASI*, No. 3 (1947), pp. 11–58.
Kroeber, A. L: *Peoples of the Philippines*. New York: AMNH, Handbook No. 8 (1919).
Krut, L. H., and Singer, R.: "Steatopygia: The Fatty Acid Composition of Subcutaneous Adipose Tissue in the Hottentot." *AJPA*, Vol. 21, No. 2 (1963), pp. 181–8.
Kuno, Y.: *Human Perspiration*. Springfield, Ill.: Charles C. Thomas; 1956.
Kurtén, B., and Vasari, Y.: "On the Date of Peking Man." *SSFCB*, Vol. 23, No. 7 (1960), pp. 3–10.

Lamberg-Karloski, C. C.: "Concerning Gimbutas' 'The Indo-Europeans: Archaeological Problems.'" *AA*, Vol. 66, No. 4, Part 1 (1964), pp. 887–9.
Landsberg, H. E.: "Die Mittlere Wasserdampfverteilung auf der Erde." *MR*, Vol. 17, No. 4 (1964), pp. 102–3.
Langer, W. L.: "Europe's Initial Population Explosion." *AHR*, Vol. 69, No. 1 (1963), pp. 1–17.
Lasker, G. W.: "Migration and Physical Differentiation." *AJPA*, Vol. 4, No. 3 (1946), pp. 273–300.
Layrisse, M., Layrisse, Z., and Wilbert, J.: "Blood Group Antigen Tests of the Yupa Indians of Venezuela." *AA*, Vol. 62, No. 3 (1960), pp. 418–36.
Leakey, L. S. B.: "Age of Bed I, Olduvai Gorge, Tanganyika." *Nature*, Vol. 191, No. 4787 (1961), pp. 478–9.
Lerner, A. B.: "Hormones and Skin Color." *SA*, Vol. 205, No. 1 (1961), pp. 98–108.
Levin, M. G.: "The Anthropological Types of Siberia," in M. G. Levin and L. P. Popatov, eds.: *The Peoples of Siberia*, translated by S. P. Dunn, pp. 99–104. Chicago: University of Chicago Press; 1964.
——: *Ethnic Origins of the Peoples of Northeastern Asia*, H. N. Michael, ed. Chapter 4, pp. 192–233. AINA, No. 3 (1963).
Liptak, P.: "Materiali Po Kraniologii Khantov." *AEASH*, Vol. 1, No. 1–4 (1950), pp. 197–230.
Livingstone, F. B.: "Aspects of the Population Dynamics of the Abnormal

Hemoglobin and Glucose–6–Dehydrogenase Deficiency Genes." *AJHG*, Vol. 16, No. 4 (1964), pp. 435–50.
——: "On the Non-existence of Human Races." *CA*, Vol. 3, No. 3 (1962), pp. 279–81, including comments by T. Dobzhansky, and the author's reply.
——: "Natural Selection, Disease, and Ongoing Human Evolution, as Illustrated by the ABO Blood Groups." *HB*, Vol. 32, No. 1 (1960), pp. 17–27.
——: "Anthropological Implications of Sickle-Cell Gene Distributions in West Africa." *AA*, Vol. 60, No. 3 (1958), pp. 533–62.
Loth, E.: *Anthropologie des Parties Molles.* Warsaw: Fondation Mianowski; and Paris: Masson et Cie; 1931.
Lowe, C. van R.: *The Vaal River Chronology. SAAB*, Vol. 7, No. 28 (1952), p. 103.
Luckeish, M.: *Applications of Germicidal, Erythemal, and Infrared Energy.* New York: D. Van Nostrand; 1946.

McCown, T. D.: "Natufian Crania from Mt. Carmel." Ph.D. Thesis, University of California, Berkeley, 1940.
—— and Keith, Sir Arthur: *The Stone Age of Mount Carmel*, Vol. 2. Oxford: Clarendon Press; 1939.
Macdonald, G.: *On the Respiratory Functions of the Nose.* London: Alexander Watt; 1889.
Macfarlane, W. V., Morris, R. J., and Howard, B.: "Water Economy of Tropical Merino Sheep." *Nature*, Vol. 178, No. 4528 (1956), pp. 304–5.
McKennan, R. A.: "The Physical Anthropology of Two Alaskan Athapaskan Groups." *AJPA*, Vol. 22, No. 1 (1964), pp. 43–52.
Madan, T. N., and Sarana, G., eds.: *Indian Anthropology.* Bombay: Asia Publishing House; 1962.
Majumdar, D. N.: *Races and Cultures of India*, 2nd ed. Lucknow: Universal Publishers; 1950.
Man, E. H.: "On the Aboriginal Inhabitants of the Andaman Islands." *JRAI*, Vol. 12 (1883), Appendix C.
Mansuy, H.: "Contribution à l'étude de la préhistoire de l'Indochine," Parts 5, 6, 7. *BSGI*, Vol. 12, Nos. 1, 2, 3 (1925).
Maringer, J.: "Some Stone Tools of Early Hoabinhian Type from Central Japan." *Man*, Vol. 57, No. 1 (1957), pp. 1–4.
——: "Die Industrie von Iwajuku I (Japan), und ihre kulturelle Einordnung." *Anthropos*, Vol. 52 (1957), pp. 721–31.
——: "Einige faustkeilartige Geräte von Gongenyama (Japan) und die Frage des japanischen Paläolithikums." *Anthropos*, Vol. 51 (1956), pp. 175–93.
Marquer, P.: "Contribution à l'étude anthropologique du peuple basque et au problème de ses origines raciales." *BMSA*, Vol. 4, No. 1 (1963), pp. 1–240.
Martin, R.: *Lehrbuch der Anthropologie*, 2nd. ed., et seq. Jena: Gustav Fischer Verlag; 1928. 3rd ed. Stuttgart: Gustav Fischer Verlag; 1957.
——: *Die Inlandstämme der Malayischen Halbinsel.* Jena: Gustav Fischer Verlag; 1905.
Matsunaga, E.: "The Dimorphism in human normal cerumen." *AHG*, Vol. 25, No. 4 (1962), pp. 277–86.
——: "Polymorphism in Ear Wax Types and its Anthropological Significance." *ZZ*, Vol. 67, No. 722 (1959), pp. 171–84.
Mayani, Z.: *Les Étrusques Commencent à Parler.* Paris: Arthaud; 1961.
Meehand, J. P.: "Body Heat Production and Surface Temperatures in Response to a Cold Stimulus." *JAP*, Vol. 7, No. 3 (1954), pp. 537–41.
Meggers, B. J., Estrada, E., and Evans, Clifford: "Possible Transpacific Contact on the Coast of Ecuador." *Science*, Vol. 135, No. 3501 (1962), pp. 371–2.
Meillet, A., and Cohen, M.: *Les Langues du Monde*, 2nd ed. Paris: CNRS; 1952.

Mendes Corrêa, A. A.: *Timor Português*. *MSAE*, Vol. 1 (1944).

Millin, S. G.: *The People of South Africa*. New York: Alfred A. Knopf; 1954.

Mitra, A. K.: "The Riang of Tripura." *BDAI*, Vol. 5, No. 2 (1956), pp. 21–120.

——: "Physical Anthropology of the Muslims of Bengal." *BDAI*, Vol. 1, No. 2 (1952), pp. 79–104.

Monge, C.: *Acclimatization in the Andes*. Baltimore: Johns Hopkins Press; 1948.

Monod, T.: "Late Tertiary of Pleistocene in the Sahara," *VFPA*, No. 36 (1963), pp. 117–229.

Montagna, W., and Yun, J. S.: "The Skin of Primates. XV. The Skin of the Chimpanzee (*Pan satyrus*)." *AJPA*, Vol. 21, No. 2 (1963), pp. 189–97.

Morgenthaler, P. W.: "Quelques remarques au sujet de l'inclinaison et de la rétroversion du tibia." *BSS*, Vol. 31 (1954–5), pp. 45–59.

Morison, S. E.: *The Oxford History of the American People*. New York: Oxford University Press; 1965.

Mourant, A. E.: "Gruppi Krovi Narodov Severnoi Evropi i Azii." *TMOIP*, Vol. 14 (1964). pp. 46–53.

——: "Notes on Blood Groups in India," in T. N. Madan and G. Sarana, eds.: *Indian Anthropology*.

——: *The Distribution of the Human Blood Groups*. Springfield, Ill.: Charles C. Thomas; 1954. After M. A. Etcheverry, 1947.

——, Kopec, A. C., and Domaniewska-Sobczak, K.: *The ABO Blood Groups*. Oxford: Blackwell Scientific Publications; 1958.

Movius, H. L. Jr.: "New Paleolithic Sites near Ting Ts'un on the Fen River, Shansi Province, North China." *Quaternaria*, Vol. 3 (1956), pp. 13–26.

——: "Old World Prehistory: Paleolithic," in A. L. Kroeger et al.: *Anthropology Today*, pp. 163–92. Chicago: University of Chicago Press; 1953.

——: *Early Man and Pleistocene Stratigraphy in Southeast Asia. PMP*, Vol. 19, No. 3 (1944).

——: "The Stone Age of Burma." *TAPS*, n.s. Vol. 32, Part 3 (1943).

Mulvaney, D. J.: "The Pleistocene Colonization of Australia." *Antiquity*, Vol. 38, No. 152 (1964), pp. 263–7.

Murdock, G. P.: "Genetic Classification of the Austronesian Languages: A Key to Oceanic Culture History." *Ethnology*, Vol. 2, No. 2 (1964), pp. 117–26. ("An expository review" of I. Dyen's *The Lexicostatistical Classification of the Austronesian Languages*. New Haven, 1963.)

——: *Africa*. New York: McGraw-Hill Book Co.; 1959.

Murray, F. G.: "Pigmentation, Sunlight, and Nutritional Disease." *AA*, Vol. 35, No. 3 (1934), pp. 438–45.

Nance, Walter E.: "Genetic Control of Hemoglobin Synthesis." *Science*, Vol. 141, No. 3576 (1963), pp. 123–9.

Neel, J. V.: "Mutations in the Human Population," in W. J. Burdette, ed.: *Methodology in Human Genetics*, pp. 203–24. San Francisco, Calif.: Holden-Day; 1962.

—— and Post, R. H.: "Transitory 'Positive' Selection for Colorblindness?" *EQ*, Vol. 10, No. 1 (1963), pp. 33–5.

——, Salzano, F. M., Junqueira, P. C., Keiter, F., and Maybury-Lewis, D.: "Studies on the Xavante Indians of the Brazilian Mato Grosso." *AJHG*, Vol. 16, No. 1 (March 1964), pp. 52–140.

Negus, V. E.: "Humidification of the Air Passages." *AOL*, Supplement 100 (1952), pp. 74–83.

Neumann, G. K.: "Archaeology and Race in the American Indian." *YPA*, Vol. 8 (1952), pp. 213–55.

Newcombe, H. B.: "Risk of Fetal Death to Mothers of Different ABO and Rh Blood Types." *AJHG*, Vol. 15, No. 4 (1963), pp. 449–64.

Newman, M. T.: "Mankind and the Heights." *NH*, Vol. 67, No. 1 (1958), pp. 9–19.

——: "The Blond Mandan: A Critical Review of an Old Problem." *SJA*, Vol. 6, No. 3 (1950), pp. 255–72.

Newman, R. W.: "Skinfold Measurements in Young American Males." *AB*, Vol. 28, No. 2 (1956), pp. 154–64.
——: "The Relation of Climate and Body Composition in Young American Males." *AJPA*, Vol. 13 (1955), pp. 386–7.
Nöldeke, T.: "Semitic Languages," in *Encyclopedia Britannica*, 12th and 13th editions (1922–26), Vol. 24, pp. 617–30.
North, S. D. (Director, Bureau of the Census): *Heads of Families at the First Census of the United States Taken in the Year 1790, Massachusetts*. Washington, D.C.: Government Printing Office; 1908.

Oakley, Kenneth P.: *The Problem of Man's Antiquity*. BBNH–Geology, Vol. 9, No. 5 (1964).
Oba, T., and Chard, C. S.: "New Dates for Early Pottery in Japan." *AP*, Vol. 6 (1962), pp. 75–6.
Okladnikov, A. P.: "Ancient Populations of Siberia and Its Cultures." *RTPM*, Vol. 1, No. 1 (1959).
Oliver, D. L., and Howells, W. W.: "Micro-Evolution: Cultural Elements in Physical Variation." *AA*, Vol. 59, No. 6 (1957), pp. 965–78.
Oliver, R., and Fage, J. D.: *A Short History of Africa*. Baltimore: Penguin Books; 1962.
Olivier, G.: *Anthropologie des Tamouls du Sud de l'Inde*. Paris: École Française d'Extrème-Orient; 1961.
——: *Les Populations du Cambodge*. Paris: Masson et Cie.; 1956.
Oppenheim-Lautrach, S.: "Metrische und deskriptive Merkmale des menschlichen und tierischen Auges." *TB*, Vol. 22 (1947), *Oculus* 1, pp. 54–153.
Oschinsky, L.: "The Supposed 'Melanesian Affinities' of Ancient New World Mongoloids." Paper read at 33rd AAPA Congress, Mexico, D.F., 1964.
——: "A Critique of *The Origin of Races* by C. S. Coon." *Anthropologica*, Vol. 5, No. 1 (1963), pp. 111–16.
——: "Facial Flatness and Cheekbone Morphology in Arctic Mongoloids." *Anthropologica*, n.s., Vol. 4, No. 2 (1962), pp. 349–77.
——: "Races of Burma." *AJPA*, Vol. 15, No. 3 (1957), pp. 440–1.
——: *The Racial Affinities of the Baganda and Other Bantu Tribes of British East Africa*. Cambridge: W. Heffer & Sons; 1954. See Appendix D. for contributions by C. S. Coon.
Oshanin, L. V., and Zezenkova, V. Ia.: *Voprosi Etnogeneza Narodov Srednei Azii v Svete Dannikh Antropologii*. Tashkent: *IIA-ANUS*; 1953.
Osman Hill, W. C.: "The Soft Anatomy of a North American Indian." *AJPA*, Vol. 21, No. 3 (1963), pp. 245–70.

Peacock, P. R.: "Quantitative Data in Skin Reactions to Ultra Violet Rays." *Lancet*, Vol. 2 (1925), pp. 367–72.
Penrose, B.: *Travel and Discovery in the Renaissance*. Cambridge, Mass.: Harvard University Press; 1952.
Pierce, B. F.: *The Ethnic Factor in Biotechnology*. San Diego: General Dynamics/Astronomics, Life Sciences Section; 1964.
Pi-Sunyer, O.: "Historical Background on the Negro in Mexico." *JNH*, Vol. 42, No. 4 (1957), pp. 237–46.
Post, R. H.: "Population Differences in Vision Acuity: A Review, with Speculative Notes on Selection Relaxation." *EQ*, Vol. 9, No. 4 (1962), pp. 189–212.
——: "Population Differences in Red and Green Color Vision Deficiency: A Review and a Query on Selection Relaxation." *EQ*, Vol. 9, No. 3 (1962), pp. 131–46; Vol. 12, No. 1 (1965), pp. 28–9.
Potapov, L. P.: "Historical-Ethnographic Survey of the Russian Population of Siberia in the Prerevolutionary Period," in M. G. Levin, and L. P. Potapov, eds.: *The Peoples of Siberia*, pp. 105–34. Chicago: University of Chicago Press; 1964.

Powell, J. W.: "Indian Linguistic Families North of Mexico." BAE, 7th Annual Report for 1891 (1892), pp. 1–142.
Proetz, A. W.: *Applied Physiology of the Nose.* St. Louis: Annals Publishing Co.; 1954.
Puccioni, N.: "Berberi e Arabi nell'Africa Mediterranea," in R. Biasutti: *Razze e Populi della Terra,* Vol. 3, pp. 109–47.

Race, R. R., and Sanger, R.: *Blood Groups in Man.* Oxford: Blackwell Scientific Publications; 1954.
Reed, T. E., Gershowitz, H., Soni, A., and Napier, A.: "A Search for Natural Selection in Six Blood Group Systems and ABH Secretion." AJHG, Vol. 16, No. 2 (1964), pp. 161–79.
Ripley, W. Z.: *The Races of Europe.* New York: Appleton; 1899.
Risley, H. H.: *Census of India.* Calcutta: Government of India; 1908.
Roberts, D. F.: "Contribuzione alla etnologia dei pre-niloti." RA, Vol. 44 (1957), pp. 319–24.
——: "The Dynamics of Racial Intermixture in the American Negro—Some Anthropological Considerations." AJHG, Vol. 7, No. 4 (1955), pp. 361–7.
—— and Bainbridge, D. D.: "Nilotic Physique." AJPA, Vol. 21, No. 3 (1956), pp. 341–66.
—— and Hiorns, R. W.: "Methods of Analysis of a Hybrid Population." HB, Vol. 37, No. 1 (1965), pp. 38–43.
Rucknagel, D. L., and Neel, J. V.: "The Hemoglobinopathies," in A. G. Steinberg, ed.: *Progress in Medical Genetics,* Vol. 1, pp. 158–260. New York: Grune and Stratton; 1961.

Said, P., and Issawi, B.: *Preliminary Results of a Geological Expedition to Lower Nubia and to Kurkur and Dungal Oases, Egypt.* SMU-CPN, No. 1 (1964).
Sakakibara, T.: *Kraniologie der Otoshibe-Aino,* Sonderabdruck von *Crania Ainoica.* Sapporo, 1940.
Sankalia, H. D.: "Middle Stone Age Culture in India and Pakistan." *Science,* Vol. 146, No. 3642 (1964), pp. 365–75.
Sapir, E.: "Central and North American Indian Languages." *Encyclopedia Britannica,* 14th ed. (1929), Vol. 5, pp. 138–41.
Sarasin, R. and F.: *Die Weddas von Ceylon.* Wiesbaden: C. W. Kreidel's Verlag; 1893.
Sarkar, S. S., ed.: *A Physical Survey of the Kadar of Kerala,* Memoir No. 6. Calcutta: Dept. of Anthropology, Govt. of India; 1959.
——: *The Aboriginal Races of India.* Calcutta: Bookland; 1954.
Sauter, M. R.: "Recherches anthropologiques en Palestine méridionale." ASAG, Vol. 15, No. 2 (1950).
——: "Les Races brachycephales du Proche-Orient, des origines à nos jours." ASAG, Vol. 11, No. 1 (1945), pp. 68–131.
—— and Könz, A.: "L'humérus des Pygmées de l'Ituri (Congo-Belge)." BSS, Vol. 31 (1954–5), pp. 5–6.
Schebesta, P., and Lebzelter, V.: "Anthropological Measurements on Semangs and Sakais in Malaya." *Anthropologie,* Vol. 6 (1928).
Schlaginhaufen, O.: "Die Variabilität, geographische Verteilung, und Stellung der Körpergrösse der Eingeborenen Neuirlands." GH, Vol. 1 (1953), pp. 18–28.
——: "Zur Anthropologie der Admiralty-Inseln in Melanesien." BSGA, Vol. 26 (1950), pp. 12–23.
Schreiner, K. E.: *Zur Osteologie der Lappen,* 2 vols. Oslo: ISKF; 1935.
Schultz, A. H.: "Age Changes, Sex Differences, and Variability in the Classification of Primates," in S. L. Washburn, ed.: *Classification and Human Evolution,* pp. 85–115. Chicago: Aldine Publishing Co.; 1963.
——: "Characters common to higher primates and characters specific for man." QRB, Vol. 11 (1936), pp. 259–83, 425–55.

Schwidetzky, I.: *Die neue Rassenkunde.* Stuttgart: Gustav Fischer Verlag; 1962.
——: "Neuere Entwicklungen in der Rassenkunde des Menschen," in I. Schwidetzky, ed.: *Die neue Rassenkunde.*
——: "Turaniden-Studien." *AWLM*, No. 9 (1950), pp. 235–91.
Scott, P.: "An Isonoetic Map of Tasmania." *GR*, Vol. 47, No. 3 (1957), pp. 311–29.
Sebeok, T.: "Languages of the World: Sino-Tibetan Fascicle One." *AL*. Vol. 6, No. 3 (1964), pp. 1–13.
Seligman, C. G. and B. Z.: *The Veddas.* Cambridge: Cambridge University Press; 1911.
Selmer-Olsen, R.: *An Odontometrical Study on the Norwegian Lapps.* Oslo: *SNVA*; 1949.
Seltzer, C. C.: "The Jew, his racial status: an anthropological appraisal." *HMAB*, April 1939, pp. 3–11.
——: *The Racial Characteristics of Syrians and Armenians.* PMP, Vol. 13, No. 3 (1936).
Serizawa, C., and Ikawa, F.: "The Oldest Archaeological Materials from Japan." *AP*, Vol., 2, No. 2 (1958), pp. 1–39.
Shanklin, W. M.: "Anthropology of the Alouite, Mitwali, and the Bekaa males." *MS*, 1946.
——: "Anthropology of Transjordan Bedouin with a discussion of their racial affinities." *AJPA*, Vol. 4, No. 3 (1946), pp. 323–76.
——: "Anthropometry of Syrian Males." *JRAI*, Vol. 68 (1938), pp. 379–414.
——: "Anthropology of the Akeydat and the Maualay Bedouin," *AJPA*, Vol. 21 (1936), pp. 217–52.
——: "The Anthropology of the Rwala Bedouins." *JRAI*, Vol. 45 (1935), pp. 375–90.
——: "The Anthropology of Transjordan Arabs." *PNB*, No. 3–4 (1935), pp. 3–12.
—— and Izzeddin, N., *Anthropology of the Near East Female. AJPA*, Vol. 22, No. 3 (1937), pp. 381–415.
Shapiro, H. L.: "Physical Differentiation in Polynesia." *PMP*, Vol. 20 (1943), pp. 3–8.
——: "The Physical Relationships of the Easter Islanders." *BPMB*, Vol. 160 (1940), pp. 24–30.
——: *Migration and Environment.* New York: Oxford University Press; 1939.
——: *The Heritage of the Bounty.* New York: Simon & Schuster; 1936.
——: "The Physical Characters of the Society Islanders." *MBM*, Vol. 11, No. 4 (1930), pp. 275–311.
—— and Buck, P. H.: "The physical characters of the Cook Islanders." *MBM*, Vol. 12, No. 1 (1936), pp. 1–35.
—— and Suggs, R. C.: "New Dates for Polynesian Prehistory." *Man*, Vol. 59, No. 1 (1959), pp. 12–13.
Shirakogarov, S. M.: *Anthropometry of Eastern China and Kwantung Province. RAS-NCB*, Extra Vol., No. 4 (1925).
——: *Anthropometry of Northern China. RAS-NCB*, Extra Vol., No. 2 (1923).
Shulter, Richard Jr.: "Peopling of the Pacific in the Light of Radiocarbon Dating." *AP*, Vol. 5, No. 2 (1961), pp. 207–12.
Sieveking, A.: "The Paleolithic Industry of Kota Tampan, Perak, Northwestern Malaya." *AP*, Vol. 2, No. 2 (1958), pp. 91–102.
Singer, R., Budtz-Olsen, O. E., Brain, P., and Saugrain, J.: "Physical Features, Sickling and Serology of the Malagasy of Madagascar." *AJPA*, Vol. 15, No. 1 (1957), pp. 91–124.
—— and Weiner, J. S.: "Biological Aspects of Some Indigenous African Populations." *SWJA*, Vol. 19, No. 2 (1963), pp. 168–76.

Sjövold, T.: *The Iron Age Settlement of Arctic Norway*. Trömso, Oslo: Norwegian Universities Press; 1964.

Škerlj, B., Brožek, J., and Hunt, E. E.: "Subcutaneous Fat and Age Changes in Body Build and Body Form in Women." *AJPA*, Vol. 11 (1953), pp. 577–600.

Smith, P. E. L.: "Radiocarbon Dating of a Late Paleolithic Culture." *Science*, Vol. 145, No. 3634 (1964), I–1291 and I–1292, p. 811

Soejono, R. P.: "Preliminary Notes on New Finds of Lower-Paleolithic Implements from Indonesia." *AP*, Vol. 5, No. 2 (1961), pp. 217–32.

Solheim, W. G. II.: "Pottery and the Malayo-Polynesians." *CA*, Vol. 5, No. 5 (1964), pp. 360, 376–84.

——: "Vietnam." *AP*, Vol. 6, No. 1–2 (1963), pp. 23–31.

Sonneville-Bordes, D. de: "Upper Paleolithic Cultures in Western Europe." *Science*, Vol. 142, No. 3590 (1963), pp. 347–55.

Spuhler, J. N.: "Empirical Studies on Quantitative Human Genetics," in *The Use of Vital and Health Statistics for Genetic and Radiation Studies*. pp. 241–50. New York: United Nations; 1962.

Srivastara, R. P.: "A Quantitative Analysis of the Fingertips of the Tharus of Uttar Pradesh." *AJPA*, 1965. In press.

Stearn, E. W. and A. E.: *The Effect of Smallpox on the Destiny of the Amerindian*. Boston: Bruce Humphries; 1945.

Stern, C.: "Model Estimates of White and Near-White Segregants in the American Negro." *AJHG*, Vol. 5. No. 1 (1953), pp. 1–20.

Steward, J. H., ed.: *Handbook of the South American Indians*. SIBAE, Bull. 143 (1950).

Stewart, T. D.: "A Physical Anthropologist's View of the Peopling of the New World." *SWJA*, Vol. 16, No. 3 (1960), pp. 259–73.

Stitt, K. R.: *Skinfold Measurement; A Method of Determining Subcutaneous Fat*. Department of Foods and Nutrition, School of Home Economics, University of Alabama, 1962.

Stoudt, H. W.: "The Physical Anthropology of Ceylon." CMES, Pub. 2, 1961.

Struthers, D.: "ABO Groups of Infants and Children Dying in the East of Scotland (1949–1951)." *BJSM*, Vol. 5. No. 4 (1951), pp. 223–8.

Sullivan, L. R.: "Marquesan somatology, with comparative notes on Samoa and Tonga." *MBM*, Vol. 9, No. 2 (1923), pp. 141–249.

——: "A Contribution to Tongan Somatology." *MBM*, Vol. 8, No. 4 (1922), pp. 233–60.

——: "A Contribution to Samoan Somatology." *MBM*, Vol. 8, No. 2 (1921), pp. 79–98.

——: "Anthropometry of the Siouan Tribes." *APAM*, Vol. 23 (1920), pp. 81–174.

Summers, R., ed.: *Prehistoric Rock Art of the Federation of Rhodesia and Nyasaland*. New York: Humanities Press; 1961.

Suzuki, Hisachi: "Changes in the bodily features of the Japanese people from the protohistoric to the present time" (in Japanese), in *Papers in Memory of the hundredth anniversary of Darwin's Origin of Species*, pp. 140–6. Tokyo, 1960.

——: "Changes in the Skull Features of the Japanese People from ancient to Modern Times." *FICA*, 1956, pp. 717–24.

—— and Takai, F., "Entdeckung eines Pleistozänen Hominiden Humerus in Zentral-Japan." *AAnz*, Vol. 23, No. 2–3 (1959), pp. 224–35.

Suzuki, H. et al.: "Craniometry of the Japanese Skulls of the Final Edo Era." ZZ, Vol. 70, No. 733 (1962), 47–120.

Suzuki, M. and Sakai, T.: "Shovel-Shaped Incisors in Polynesians." *AJPA*, Vol. 22, No. 1 (1964), pp. 65–76.

Swadesh, M., in *Discussion and Criticism*: "On Aboriginal Languages of Latin America." *CA*, Vol. 4, No. 3 (1963), pp. 317–18.

Swindler, D. R.: *A Racial Study of the West Nakanai*. MMUM, 1962.

342 *Bibliography*

Talbot, P. A., and Mulhall, H.: *The Physical Anthropology of Southern Nigeria.* Cambridge: Cambridge University Press; 1962.
Tamaru: "On the Weight and Size of Human Eyes" (in Japanese). *AOMA,* Vol. 41 (1929), pp. 551–68.
Tax, Sol: "Aboriginal Languages of Latin America." *CA,* Vol. 1, No. 5–6 (1960), pp. 430–6.
Taylor, E. G. R.: "A Fourteenth Century Riddle—and its Solution." *GR,* Vol. 54, No. 4 (1964), pp. 573–6.
Thieme, F.: *The Puerto Rican Population: A Study in Human Biology APMA-M,* 1959.
Thieme, P.: "The Indo-European Language." *SA,* Vol. 199, No. 4 (1958), pp. 63–74.
Thomas, E. M.: *The Harmless People.* New York: Alfred A. Knopf; 1959.
Thomson, A., and Buxton, L. H. F.: "Man's Nasal Index in Relation to Certain Climatic Conditions." *JRAI,* Vol. 53 (1923), pp. 53–92.
Tindale, N. B.: "Growth of a People: Formation of a Hybrid Aboriginal and White Stock on the Islands of Bass Strait, Tasmania, 1815–1949." *RQVM,* No. 2 (1953), pp. 2–64.
——: "Survey of the Half-Caste Problem in South Australia." *PRGS* (S. Australian Branch), 1940–1, pp. 66–161.
—— and Birdsell, J. B.: "Tasmanoid Tribes in North Queensland." *RSAM,* Vol. 7, No. 1 (1941), pp. 1–9.
Tobias, P. V.: "Bushman Hunter-Gatherers: A Study in Human Ecology," in D. H. S. Davis, ed.: *Ecology in South Africa,* pp. 67–86. The Hague: W. Junk; 1965.
——: "Les Bochimans Auen et Narou de Ghazni." *L'Anth,* Vol. 59, No. 3–4 (1955), pp. 235–52; No. 5–6 (1955), pp. 429–61; Vol. 60, No. 1–2 (1956), pp. 22–52; No. 3–4 (1956), pp. 268–89.
——: "Physical Anthropology and Somatic Origins of the Hottentots." *Africa,* Vol. 14, No. 1 (1955), pp. 1–15.
Todd, T. W., Beecher, H., Williams, G. H., and Todd, A. W.: "The Weight and Growth of the Human Eyeball." *BH,* Vol. 12, No. 1 (1940), pp. 1–20.
Tondo, C. V., and Salzano, F. M.: "Hemoglobin Types in Caingang Indians of Brazil." *Science,* Vol. 130, No. 3443 (1960), pp. 1893–4.
Torii, R.: *Etudes Archeologiques et Ethnologiques: Les Ainous des Iles Kouriles.* JCS-IUT, Vol. 42, Art. 1 (1919).
Trager, G. L.: "Languages of the World," in *Collier's Encyclopedia,* Vol. 14, pp. 299–310. New York: Crowell-Collier; 1965.
Tretyakov, P. N.: "Volga-Oka Place Names and Some Problems of the Ethnogenesis of the Finno-Ugric Peoples of the Volga Region," in H. N. Michael, ed.: *Studies in Siberian Ethnogenesis.* AINA, No. 2 (1962), p. 197.
Trevor, J. C.: *Race Crossing in Man.* ELM, No. 36 (1953).
——: "The Physical Characteristics of the Sandawe." *JRAI,* Vol. 77, Part 1 (1946), pp. 61–78.
Tuchinda, S., Rucknagel, D. L., Minnich, V., Boonyaprakob, U., Balankura, K. and Suvatee, V.: "The Coexistence of the Genes for Hemoglobin E and Thalassemia in Thais, with Resultant Suppression of Hemoglobin E Synthesis." *AJHG,* Vol. 16, No. 3 (1964), pp. 311–35.
Twiesselmann, F.: "Expedition Anthropologique du Dr. D. J. H. Nyessen. I. L'Oasis de Kharga." *BIRSB,* Vol. 27, No. 14 (1950), pp. 1–36.
——: "Contribution à l'Étude des Pygmées de l'Afrique Occidentale." *MMRH,* Ser. 2, Fasc. 27 (1942), pp. 1–32.

Uhlenbeck, C. C.: "The Indogermanic Mother Language and Mother Tribes Complex." *AA,* Vol. 39, No. 3 (1937), pp. 385–93.
Upham, E., and Landauer, W.: "The relation of thickness of cutis and

subcutis to hair slope in human skin." *AR*, Vol. 61, No. 3 (1935), pp. 359–66:

Utinomi, H.: *Bibliography of Micronesia*, edited and revised by O. A. Bushnell. Honolulu: University of Hawaii Press; 1952.

Vallois, H. V.: "Les Bédouins Taamré du Désert de Judée: Étude Anthropologique." *L'Anth*, Vol. 63 No. 1–2 (1959), pp. 62–92.

——: "Les Badjoué du Sud Cameroun." *BMSA*, Vol. 1, No. 1–3 (1950), pp. 18–59.

——: "New Research on the Western Negrillos." *AJPA*, Vol. 26, No. 4 (1940), pp. 449–71.

—— and Marquer, P.: "La Répartition en France des Groupes Sanguins ABO." *BMSA*, Vol. 6, 9th Series, No. 1 (1964), pp. 1–200.

Van Heekeren, H. F.: *The Stone Age of Indonesia*. The Hague: Martinus Nijhoff; 1957.

Van Valen, L.: "Selection in Natural Populations: Human Fingerprints." *Nature*, Vol. 200, No. 4912 (1963), pp. 1237–8.

Vérin, P.: "Rétrospective et Problèmes de l'Archéologie à Madagascar." *AP*, Vol. 6, No. 1–2 (1962), pp. 198–218.

Vidal, F. S.: *Anthropometry of al-Hasa Oasis*. MS.

Vlekke, B. H. M.: *Nusantara*. Cambridge, Mass.: Harvard University Press; 1943.

Vogel, F., Dehnert, J., and Helmbold, W.: "Ueber Beziehungen zwischen den ABO Blutgruppen und der Säuglingsdyspepsie." *HG*, Vol. 1, No. 1 (1964), pp. 31–57.

——, Pettenhofer, H. J. V., and Helmbold, W.: "Ueber die Populationsgenetik der ABO-Blutgruppen. 2. Mitteilung: Gehäufigkeit und epidemische Erkrankungen." *ActG*, Vol. 10 (1960), pp. 267–94.

Wald, G.: "Human Vision and the Spectrum." *Science*, Vol. 101, No. 2635 (1945), pp. 653–8.

Walter, H.: "Die Bedeutung der serologischen Merkmale für die Rassenkunde," in I. Schwidetzky, ed.: *Die neue Rassenkunde*, pp. 135–232.

Wanke, A.: "Anthropological Characteristics of African Skulls," *MIPA*, No. 67 (1964), pp. 5–28.

Wastl, J.: "Beitrag zur Anthropologie der Negrito von Ost-Luzon." *Anthropos*, Vol. 52 (1957), pp. 768–812.

Weiner, J. S., Harrison, G. A., Singer, R., Harris, R., and Jopp, W.: "Skin Colour in Southern Africa." *HB*, Vol. 36, No. 3 (1964), pp. 294–307.

Weyl, N., and Possony, S. T.: *The Geography of Intellect*. Chicago: Henry Regnery; 1964. (See especially pp. 97–9.)

White, R. M.: *Anthropometric Survey of the Armed Forces of the Republic of Vietnam*. Natick, Mass.: U. S. Army; 1964.

——: *Anthropometric Survey of the Royal Thai Armed Forces*. Natick, Mass.: U. S. Army; 1964.

Wijeserka, N. D.: *The People of Ceylon*. Colombo: M. D. Gunasena; 1949.

Williams, G. D.: "Maya-Spanish Crosses in Yucatan." *PMP*, Vol. 13, No. 1 (1931).

Wilmer, W. H.: *Atlas Fundus Oculi*. New York: The Macmillan Co., 1934.

Wissler, C.: "Observations on Hawaiian Somatology." *MBM*, Vol. 9, No. 4 (1927), pp. 263–342.

Wolstenholme, G., ed.: *Man and His Future*. London: J. and A. Churchill; 1963.

Woo, T. L., and Morant, G. M.: "A Biometric Study of the 'Flatness' of the Facial Skeletal in Man." *Biometrika*, Vol. 26 (1934), pp. 196–250.

Workman, P. L., Blumberg, B. S., and Cooper, A. J.: "Selection, Gene Migration, and Polymorphic Stability in a U. S. White and Negro Population." *AJHG*, Vol. 15, No. 4 (1963), pp. 429–37.

Wormington, H. M.: *Ancient Man in North America* 4th ed., pp. 249–60. Denver Museum of Natural History, Popular Series No. 4, 1957.

Wurm, S. A.: "Australian New Guinea Highland Languages and the Distribution of their Typological Features." *AA*, Vol. 66, No. 4, Part 2 (1964), pp. 77–97.

Wurtman, R. J., Axelrod, J., and Fischer, J. E.: "Melatonin Syntheses in the Pineal Gland: Effect of Light Mediated by the Sympathetic Nervous System." *Science*, Vol. 143, No. 3612 (1964), pp. 1328–9.

Yoshimura, H., and Iida, T.: "Studies on the Reactivity of Skin Vessels to Extreme Cold. Part II. Factors Governing the Individual Difference of the reactivity, or the Resistance Against Frostbite." *JJP*, Vol. 1 (1950–51), pp. 177–85.

Young, C. M., Blondin, Jr. Tensuan, R., and Fryer, J. H.: "Body Composition Studies of 'Older' Women, Thirty to Seventy Years of Age." *ANYAS*, Vol. 110 (1963), pp. 589–607.

INDEX

Abbevillian industry, 49, 87
Abbie, A. A., 310
Abors, 203
acetylcholinsterase, 14
Acheulean industry, 49, 50, 52, 87, 88, 93, 159
Adé, Boris, 107
adzes, 160, 165
Afalou-Bou-Rhummel remains, 93–4
afer, 6
Afghanistan, 55, 60, 75, 77, 78, 131, 134, 192, 201, 204, 212
Africa, 84–125; agriculture, 89–91; archaic mammalian fauna, 85; Bushman, *see* Bushmen; Capoid sequence, 92; Caucasoid sequence, 93–5; climates, 82–6; colonization, 311–12; Congoid sequence, 92–3; cultures, 86–91; early skeletal remains, 88, 92–5; Europeans in, 311–12; geography, 85–6; Horn of, peoples of, 119–21; languages, 95–101; living peoples, 101–25; Negro-Caucasoid cline, 8, 93; Negroes, *see* African Negroes; Paleolithic tools, 86–9, 93; pluvial periods in, during Pleistocene, 85–7; Pygmies, *see* Pygmies; racial distribution, 84–5; southern Sahara, peoples of, 121–2; Sudan, peoples of, 121–2; weather maps of, 214–29; West, malaria in, 273–7; *see also* South Africa
African Negroes, 6, 7, 122–5; altitude-adapted, 17, 248; and American Negroes, physical comparison of, 305; apocrine glands, 14; blood-group frequencies, 66, 123, 280, 284, 287; body build, 12–13, 124–5; cold adaptation and, 247; ears, 12, 124; earwax, 123; eye color, 12, 123, 235, 236; eyeballs, 12, 124; facial expressions, 257; fat pattern, 124, 243; fingerprints, 123; food-gathering, 84–5; foreheads, 12; genitalia, 107; hair, 12, 123, 239; heads, 123; heat-adapted, 17, 124, 183, 214; importation of, 35, 122, 290–1, 293–4, 296, 298; invasion and absorption of, 277–8; jaws, 12; lips, 12, 123–4; malaria among,

267–8, 275; massive gene flow and, 291; muscles, 13, 124; Nilotic, 101, 125, 243, 252; nose form, 12, 123–124, 251; PTC tasting among, 264; sickle-cell trait among, 17; skin color, 12, 107, 123, 124, 214, 230, 232–4; skulls, 12, 94, 123; stature, 124–5, 254; teeth, 12, 124; umbilical hernia among, 13, 106
Afro-Asiatic languages, 56, 95–6
Agaus, 120
agriculture: in Africa, 89–91; in China, 55, 90, 132; in Europe, 54–55; in India, 197; Iron Age, 90–1; Mesolithic, 89, 207; Neolithic, 90, 94, 169, 195, 197, 207; paddy-rice, 197; slash-and-burn, 160, 195, 197, 202, 203, 290
Ainu, 172; earwax, 151, 255–6; eye color, 151; eyes, 151; fingerprints, 151; foreheads, 151; hair, 150–1, 173; nose form, 151, 153; skin color, 150–1; skulls, 135–6; sweat glands, 151; teeth, 151, 254
Ait Atta, 115, 117
Akkadian, 58
Alakalufs, 22, 129, 137, 153, 242–3, 246, 247, 295
Alaska, 129, 126, 214, 300; *see also* Eskimos
Alaskan Indians, 153
Albanians, 70, 119, 301, 304
albinos, 176, 231, 236
Aleppo, 79
Aleuts, 137, 152, 300
Alexander VI, 292
Algeria, 87, 92, 93, 116
Algonkian, 137
Algonkian-Mosan languages, 143, 145
Algonkian-Wakashan languages, 143
alleles, 18, 133, 269, 272, 279, 283, 284, 286, 298
Allen, J. A., 252
Allen's Rule, 252
Altaic languages, 140
altitude, adaptation to, 16, 17, 47, 183, 214, 248–9, 266
Amazon Valley, 11, 217
Amazonian Indians, 153, 218

A NOTE ABOUT THE AUTHOR

CARLETON STEVENS COON, Research curator of General Anthropology at the University Museum of the University of Pennsylvania since 1963, was born in Wakefield, Massachusetts, was educated at Phillips Academy, Andover, and received his A.B., A.M., and Ph.D. from Harvard University. Until his retirement, in 1963, as Curator of Ethnology and Professor of Anthropology at the University Museum, he had divided his time between field work and teaching, first at Harvard (1935–48) and then at the University of Pennsylvania (1948–63). In connection with his work he has traveled extensively in Africa, Asia, and Europe. Dr. Coon arranged the famous Hall of Man exhibit at the University Museum, and is a regular panel member on the Peabody Award-winning television program *What in the World?* which is now in its fifteenth year. He is past President of the American Association of Physical Anthropologists. Among his many books are *Caravan: The Story of the Middle East* (1951, 1958); *The Story of Man* (1954, revised edition 1962); *The Seven Caves* (1957); and *The Origin of Races* (1962). Dr. Coon has been a leading authority on race ever since his famous and highly successful book, *The Races of Europe*, was published in 1939. He has two sons and six grandchildren, and lives with his wife, the former Lisa Dougherty, in Gloucester, Massachusetts.

A NOTE ON THE TYPE

The text of this book was set in a typeface called Primer, designed by Rudolph Ruzicka for the Mergenthaler Linotype Company and first made available in 1949. Primer, a modified modern face based on Century broadface, was designed with a view to greatest legibility in the use of today's methods of composition and printing.

Primer is Ruzicka's third typeface. In 1940 he designed Fairfield, and in 1947 Fairfield Medium, both for the Mergenthaler Linotype Company.

Ruzicka was born in Bohemia in 1883 and came to the United States at the age of eleven. He attended public schools in Chicago and later the Chicago Art Institute. During his long career he has been a wood engraver, etcher, cartographer, and book designer. For many years he was associated with Daniel Berkeley Updike and produced the annual keepsakes for The Merrymount Press from 1911 until 1941.

Ruzicka has been honored by many distinguished organizations, and in 1936 he was awarded the gold medal of the American Institute of Graphic Arts. From his home in New Hampshire, Ruzicka continues to be active in the graphic arts.

Composed, printed, and bound by

THE HADDON CRAFTSMEN, SCRANTON, PA.

Typography based on designs by

W. A. DWIGGINS